'I found Mr Scott's account quite fascina
he demonstrates conclusively that it mu.
Indeed, he demonstrates that [the Dryfiek

**– Patrick Cadell, Historian, ex Keeper of t
Scottish Local History, Spring 2006 (Of Bl**

'In my opinion, this research settles the site of

– Irvine Smith QC, Advocate, Sheriff, Historian

'William Scott has indisputably solved what happened at Bannockburn and,
more importantly how. His proofs are exhaustive, detailed and correct. No
one else has come close. Historians who refuse to recognise his work remind
me of the Flat Earth Society.'

– Roger Graham, Editor

'A masterpiece of research, two decades of meticulous scientific investigation
of every inch of the battle area, all the maps and all the written sources.'

– Donald Morrison, Teacher, Expert on the Battle.

'The book (GB) is certainly a tour de force, and the most intelligent and
comprehensive account ever written.'

– Rev J Stein, Minister, Theologian, Publisher.

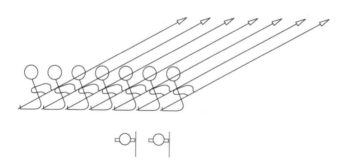

On 23rd June 1314, an army led by Edward II, King of England, arrived at the Bannock burn, a mile south of Stirling, as part of a plan to relieve the Castle which for years had been in English hands. Sir Philip de Mowbray, the governor of the Castle for King Edward, had in 1313, arranged a truce with Lord Edward Bruce, brother of the Scottish King. The terms were that if the Castle were not relieved 'within eight days of St John's day, a year hence,'[i] it would voluntarily surrender to the Scots.

Stirling Castle, perched high on its rock, was very difficult to capture. It had been in English hands for a decade. Given the task of taking it by siege, yet without siege equipment, Lord Edward Bruce was flummoxed. Mowbray, who knew that supplies within the Castle were almost used up, asked for a parley and arranged the truce, telling the lie that the Castle was well-stocked.

So Edward Bruce, who had expected to have to spend the winter starving the Castle's inhabitants into submission, went off to report the success of the truce to his brother.

'It was ill done!' shouted King Robert.

'Why so?' said his astonished brother.

'Because they will bring an army to relieve it. They will have to! Chivalry demands it! To leave it to fall by forfeit would be a grave dishonour.'

'But we will manage, Robert,' said Edward Bruce. 'We always have.'

'We have never faced the whole English army. In a pitched battle we will lose. '

'But why, brother?'

'Because they are ten times as many; they have better weapons, bigger and better horses, better armour and they have better training. Most of them have fought in Wales, France and even here. How many English knights do you think there are?'

'I have no idea.'

'Seven thousand. They will have five thousand archers and thousands more infantry. How many have we?'

'A few hundred knights, a few hundred archers and a few thousand foot.'

'Well then? How do you expect us to win against these odds?'

'Maybe they won't all come.'

---

[i] Scalacronica p52, BR p187; St John's day is 24th June.

'They won't need to. But they will all want to. A pitched battle will be the biggest thing in their lives and they know they will win. You know how they love to show off their chivalry. It is life and death to them.'

Red-faced by now, confronted by the evidence of his folly, Edward Bruce blustered: 'But brother, you will think of something.'

That was the problem we faced.

What follows is the full solution, for the first time, reconstructed in a narrative form, with the characters telling their stories: Robert Bruce, his brother, Edward, Randolph Earl of Moray, their nephew, and Sir James Douglas, Walter Stewart, Robert's son in law, Sir Alexander Seaton, and some of the ordinary men who took part.

You will know it is the full solution when you study the maps of the stages of the battle. They are unlike any others, except within the books of this research which began in 1991 and continued to the present time, half of it full time. These maps alone took over three years full time to reach this standard. What makes them unique is that they are the first fully justified maps of the area. That is, every detail in the area map is explained and justified with reference to all the other maps and the ground itself. The justification was written up like a lab experiment and occupies in the several scholarly works of this research about 150,000 words, a large volume in itself, all of which has been confirmed by many able people: Sheriffs, Advocates, Crown Prosecutors, one a QC, Theologians, Classicists, Editors, Teachers, an Ex Keeper of the Records of Scotland, as well as other historians. Even a Colonel in the SAS with a first class honours degree in Geography, a necessary subject for the solution of the problems. Other subjects necessary are mathematics, science, philosophy, psychology, cartography and hydrology. History alone was never enough —the reason no historian could solve the problems.

So we have a reconstruction based on a very accurate map of the area. One other thing we have: a collection of end notes which prove every significant move made in the narrative. These quote all the reports of the battle and, with photographs of the place itself, explain and justify everything.

This, the outcome of 23 years intensive research and the sixth book on this subject, each an advance on the others, is the easiest book of the lot, better than any history book outside this research. At least this is correct and exhaustive, everything proved in the end notes; every history book outside this research is full of mistakes and omissions.

BRUCE's GENIUS BATTLE

Reconstruction in narrative form with explanations and proofs

William Scott
BA,BSc,MEd,FIMA,FSAScot

MMXIII

First published in Great Britain on 30th October, 2013, by
Elenkus Limited,
23 Argyle Place,
Rothesay PA20 0BA,
Isle of Bute
Email: elenkus @yahoo.com; websites: www.elenkus .com and
www.elenkus.co.uk
tel: 01700505439; mobile: 07557025013

© William Wallace Cunningham Scott
All rights reserved.

ISBN 9780952191032

The right of William Wallace Cunningham Scott to be identified as the
author of this work has been asserted by him in accordance with the
Copyright, design and patent act, 1988. All rights are reserved and copies
of pages, images or statements may not be made without the author's
written permission.

By the same author

The Bannockburn Years [BY]
Bannockburn Revealed [BR]
Bannockburn Proved [BP]

The Bute Witches
A Bute Crucifixion
Honour Killing in Argyle & Bute

The Genius of Bannockburn [GB]
The Genius Summary   [GS]

Cover: image by Edmund Leighton, design by Georgina Pensri

CONTENTS

Map of Stirlingshire (part) in 1746 by Thomas Jefferys.
Little different in 1314, except for the road: there was only
One road from Falkirk to Stirling then, for the bridge that
carried the other to the NE was not built until 1516.

THE PLAN: the maps showing the 12 stages in the battle.
Coloured images necessary to explain and validate this plan:
1.The pools in the Carse p164-166; p190-192 B&W
2.The pools are a permanent feature of this ground after heavy rain:
The ZIG ZAG Rd : P166,167; p174, 183
3. Why does this Carse uniquely have pools after prolonged heavy rain?
P68; p194 B&W
4. The Brut y Tywysogyon (Peniarth Ms. 20 version tells us the battle
occurred in the pools p169; B&W p206
5. Milton Ford, where the road of 1314 crossed the Bannock burn and
Bruce killed de Bohun p171-175, 179

6. The Knoll is shown on Roy's map, c1750 and Jefferys 1746
   So the Knoll is an invariant back to 1746 and therefore 1314
  (because there is no evidence anyone moved it there between these
dates: it is about a quarter mile by an eighth and 60 feet high) p166,167,
174,175,181,184; B&W p10,190,192,193
7. The size of Livilands Bog and the line of the Pelstream in 1314
p177,178;B&W 224
8. The Amphitheatre where Bruce spoke to the army p179

ENDNOTES: All the important moves are explained and justified here

Stirlingshire (part) in 1746 by Thomas Jefferys

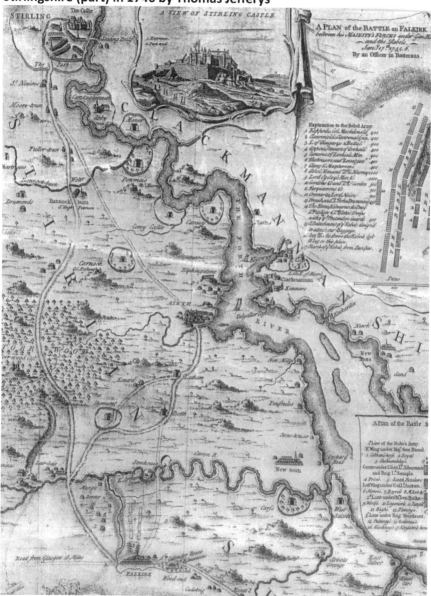

Notice: **TORWOOD, (middle left)**, Falkirk (bottom left), The Bannock burn Water, St Ninians, Stirling, River Forth. In 1314, there was no place Bannockburn and no road through Airth which dates from 1516, when the first bridge was built by Robert Spitall. Only one road from Falkirk to Stirling through Torwood in 1314, across the Bannock burn at Milton Ford, still the preferred route in 1746 and on to St Ninians.

Scotland lay like a wildcat in the dawn, scarred by a decade of suffering, starvation and strife, hunkered down in the heather on her ridges between hills like pointed ears listening, breathless, for the invader, peering southwards whence came the danger.

Generations had felt it, experienced it first hand: the thousands of marching feet, well shod. The sound of them hammering the ears like a giant millipede crossing the land in hobnail boots, relentless, invulnerable, invincible, crushing everything.

England was on the rampage.

Was not this the army that ravaged Wales, enslaved Ireland, terrified France —even the Saracen on the far side of the world? The weapons: all bristling points and steel edges. Raiment? Every colour of the rainbow from violet to red: blue, green, yellow, orange and scarlet, that most of all— a promise of blood soon to flow. Rich! Oh, so rich and so beautiful! Most of all, the men in full armour, shining so brightly in the sunshine of summer that you could be blinded by them. Like Gods they seemed: the coloured plumes on helmets waving in the breeze of their own inexorable advance, red crosses on white (the thousands!)—but these were mainly for ordinary men—the rich suited themselves, caparisoned in designs of their own choice, each finer than his neighbour. Why, even the horses (the thousands!)—groomed and gleaming, dressed up like their owners, were from another, far different, world: so large, so powerful—snorting with eagerness, nostrils steaming with exertion, muscles rippling. And so swift!

Even the horses were better cared for than we, each one worth far more than a company of Scots. It was a thing of marvellous beauty, this danger. Intended to conquer by appearance, intimidate simply by being. The threat only apparent in the steel-tipped lances with their fluttering coloured pennants and carts full of needle-sharp arrows by the million. Everyone had known the cruelty or heard of it. And behind them, twenty miles of wagons piled high with tents, beds, beer-barrels, chairs and tables, food and wine, cutlery and chalices—every last thing the finest men on earth needed to support themselves in the field: servants, cooks, tradesmen, monks, musicians, actors, poets and prostitutes.

How was the danger defeated?

That is what this is about.

I was there.

This is my story.

FORMATIONS

In February 1314, Roxburgh Castle was taken back from the enemy and a month later Edinburgh, by different forces of Scots, under Douglas and Randolph. There was much rejoicing at these advances. Yet, apart from Stirling, other castles still defied us: Berwick and Bothwell, among them.
Soon after, there was a general command to assemble at Torwood and that was when the mood changed.

By mid-summer day the English would be here in force not just to take the Castle at Stirling which would fall by default otherwise—a great dishonour—but to rout the rebels: us.

We all knew this of course. That was why our march towards Torwood was made in silence. In his heart, everyone knew how it must turn out. Taking a castle from a small garrison by a ruse was one thing; taking on the whole of England in a pitched battle, was another. Their population was ten times ours. But when you added their conquered territories: Ireland, Wales and Aquitaine, the number was fifteen or twenty. Nor was that all. Their armies were superbly equipped, trained and experienced in ways we could never match. Thousands of knights, archers, infantry—to our hundreds.

So the Scots around me in my company arrived at Torwood and began to make our billets at the side of the road, with hardly a word exchanged with those already present and none among ourselves. The gloom, the fear, was palpable. You could feel it everywhere around, in every beating heart, see it in every eye. Bump anyone, scrape a tree trunk or a branch and you became aware of yourself and felt it there most of all: in yourself. There was nothing to be said about it. Since everyone had it, what was the point? Besides, in that army, fear was something you learned to hide from your companions, if not yourself. You could get killed just for being afraid, for it affected people, was contagious and could lose a fight, a battle or a war.

Within an hour, by which time our brochs had been erected, fires started and we had settled in, some of Bruce's men were among us, greeting us with smiles and sacks of oatmeal, even some ale and a deer newly shot that very day and we began to feel better. They sat with us chatting as the bannocks hardened and the deer basted on the spit.

It was when the meal was over and we were all feeling replenished in body if not in spirit, that the King himself appeared.

Our company was sitting around half a dozen fires, quaffing ale out of whatever we had for a dish, when silence gradually descended upon us. He stood a few yards from me across the burning branches, dressed in a yellow tunic and red hose, a striking figure. And there was a reason for it. There was always a reason for things Bruce did.

He pointed to five men, one after the other: 'You, you, you, you and you. Go to that tree and sit down a yard away from it in a half circle. And I want you close together.'

Nobody moved. The order was too unusual. Bruce grabbed the first man by the arm and led him to the tree, shoved him into a sitting position with his back to us and turned to face us again, motioning to the next man, a grizzled bearded giant. 'You next,' Bruce ordered.

Again the man did not move. It was either age, infirmity or the effect of the ale on a full stomach. Again, Bruce went to him, grabbed his arm and led him to his new position. 'Now sit close, Jamie', said he.

Bruce turned again and beckoned to the third man, who, shamefacedly rose and did as he was bid. In this way the first five were soon sitting where Bruce wanted them. Then he pointed to six more: 'You next,' he ordered. 'Sit behind that first group with your knees touching the back of the man in front.'

'Whit's this fur, Sire?' called a man by another campfire.

'You'll soon see.' Again Bruce had to go to the next group, grab the first by the arm and then lead him to the tree where he was pushed down behind the front rank. 'Come on, now! The other five of you. Are you children or what?'

Reluctantly, slowly, they took up their positions. But not before Bruce had to shout again: 'Come on, now! Get a move on!' There was a sudden rage about him and it would prevail. Refusal was impossible. It was power of personality, a vast reservoir of self-confidence. What he said was going to happen, would happen, right now. That was the message.

And so it went on until the whole company was sitting on the ground on the pine needles in nearly eight half circles, the men tight-packed, each holding his knees which touched the man in front.

'At last,' said Bruce, smiling, as he went to the tree and stood in the yard still vacant at the base of it. 'Now you can hear what I have to say, as you never could before. '

There were a few muttered laughs at this. From the fourth rank I could see and hear everything but then, I realised, so could any of us.

From his height, Bruce surveyed us all, took us all in with a glance that moved around and across our company, never settling for long. He had us in his thrawl with that look, captured our hearts, our minds, our souls and soon lifted our spirits with it.

'In a few weeks time, the English will be coming up that road,' he said, pointing to it and paused. 'There will be a battle.' He paused again for effect and then his face split into a beaming smile the like of which I never saw on anyone before or since. 'We are going to win!' he said, levelly. 'I have a plan and I know we can win.' He paused again. 'Did you hear what I am saying?' he shouted: ' We are going to win! We are going to win!

'How do I know? Because it is not just a matter of winning. We are going to chase them back across their border and most will never make it.'

Again he paused and smiled. It was like a sun shining, that smile. It radiated self-confidence. 'What I need to do is to try things out and understand the fine details. That's why you're here early so that we can practise: discover what we must do ourselves to make the plan work really well.'

'Whit's the plan, Sire?' a voice called out.

'Never you mind. You'll be told just what you need to know.

'But you have just received your first lesson and so have I: in how to form up so that you can hear what I am saying. If every man has a place and knows exactly where it is, it should be easier to form up next time. What are we aiming for? Speed. Next time we talk, I don't want to have to go and grab you by the arms and lead you to the nearest tree. Take note of where you are now and get to the same place next time. Then time will not be wasted as it was today.' He paused to let us absorb this.

'There is not a moment to lose. We begin in a few minutes. I am going to lead you to the head of a slope in the woods and we are all going to get down the slope onto the carse. I think it will be best if you learn your position and adopt the same one every time we do this manoeuvre. So when I give the order, we will all stand up and the front row will lead off, followed by the second and so on. I will lead you all. The two squires will tell you what to do when you need to know. What you are mainly doing right now is to get a look at the ground on which you will travel. You must not fall, or slip, if it is wet. That is important. Other things are too, but that comes later.

'Once you are all formed up there in the Carse, we will walk forward a little and kneel down. That's all I ask of you tonight. When you get the signal, you will come back here and sleep. But tomorrow before dawn, when it is still dark, you will be roused and we will practise this move again. So take careful note of your surroundings. It will help you tomorrow. Remember, you must stay on your feet.

'Bit Sire!' said Boyd. 'How kin we move in the daurk? We'll slide or faw doon.'

'It won't be quite so dark when the time comes. But we need to practise moving in the dark. So look carefully where you put your feet.

'What we are going to study are formations. Decide which are best and what the rules are. When the time comes you will all be carrying pikes. Well, we need to know what to do to make that work properly.'

And so our training began. First with the formation in which Bruce could speak to all of us at once, which saved him going from group to group and would have been impossible. What none of us saw then was that Bruce would be able to address almost the whole army at one time. When it happened it was very surprising. What a tremendous move that was! It allowed the whole army to be inspired by his self-confidence. I have often wondered why? I think that the inspiration some men got from Bruce affected everyone standing beside them. But Bruce himself was the key.

1

LEARNING TO MOVE IN THE DARK

'Rags!' said Bruce. 'We need rags.'

It was a few days later. We were standing at the foot of a slope on the north-east side of Torwood, shivering in the cold of the morning, nursing our bruises after stumbling down in the dark, bouncing off branches, tree trunks and often each other. We were supposed to be in our companies but we couldn't see well enough to form up. Most of all we were cold and uncomfortable. And there we stood or shuffled about but nobody complained.

Bruce was up to something and we had no idea what it was.

Gradually, the light came up and we could see him, by now at the centre of the group, off to my left. His standard waved in the breeze and then he moved off without a word and the two squires moved after him. Nobody said anything. We all just set off, drawn forward. None of it made sense. But it was Bruce and everybody knew he was trying something.

It was the ninth year since he became king. After the first failure at Methven, retreat to the isles to find some Irish and Scottish cousins for their support, there had been a return and a gradual transfer of power to us, the Scots, and during his travels around the country Bruce had carried all before him. In all that time he never lost another fight or an argument. You could question him and he might answer but often, as now, he had nothing to tell us. That would come later.

Why did we put up with this?

He was the leader; there was no alternative. He had the answers, always grasped the situation in an instant and knew what to do, rarely needing to stop and think. One other quality he had that mattered:

precision of speech. He could tell us what to do in very few words and we understood them every time. So many times had he managed us that we had faith in him, were used to him. Above all, we knew that he cared about us; would use us sparingly. He might get us killed but we knew it would be a last resort, something he couldn't help. For sure, some of us would not survive the summer. I had seen him grieving over dead comrades and knew how it was with him. He blamed himself for every soul we lost. There were even times when tears came, after a death that was unexpected, unlucky or downright disastrous to us, because the man lost was especially good or warlike or just good-natured and well-liked. Nobody minded Bruce's tears: we had them too. We dried our eyes and got on with what we had to do. But, in truth, we were beyond tears by this time. Had seen too much death and destruction, were inured to it.

It didn't bother us much, the wounds, the discomfort, the dying. We were all used to it by then. The English were coming. That was what it was all about. It was all we knew. There was nothing to be done but defend the country and it was all up to Bruce. We all hated the English. Nobody in his right mind wants a usurper ordering you about, an invader stealing your lands, goods and your women folk as if he had a right to them. Either you acted the man or the worm; stood up and fought, or crawled away to hide in a hole in the ground, before your natural hour.

We marched out across the flat ground of the carseland at an even pace and then when he stopped, so did we, close up behind him. We saw him set his pike with a single dunt into the soft ground and point it forward; and we all did the same. Then he knelt down and so did we. And there we knelt for a while, in silence, everybody wondering what it was all about. Behind us other men did the same. Gradually the light came up; and still we knelt.

Finally, the practice over, Bruce stood up and faced us. There was no point in his saying anything. There were too many of us to hear. The squires went in different directions and gradually they passed the message to us all to rise, being careful with the pikes, and return to our camp in the Torwood. We stood up, flexed our muscles, stretched our legs and did so, still in our companies.

In this way, we practised the manoeuvre that Bruce wanted. Every morning early, before dawn, we would march in the darkness to the top of the slope among the trees and collect there in company after company, each man with his pike, the wee shield on the left forearm and the wee axe hanging by a string on the right wrist, as we had been told. And there we sat down in a long row that curved outwards from the starting place until our leader was tapped on the shoulder and we got up and moved off in silence. Moving in the dark, even though dawn was near, was difficult but every man had a hand on the shoulder of the man in front and that helped. After a few times, you got used to the darkness and could see just about well enough in early June. The danger was hitting somebody with the pike. So it had to be kept straight up with the other hand. You also got used to the path because you travelled the same one every time and soon knew every tree trunk along it.

In case it bumped a branch, branches that might snag the pike were all pruned beforehand. Going down the slope was the worst but the rags definitely helped. Every five yards or so, now, there was a white rag tied round a tree-trunk or a branch and you could see it quite well in the half dark of early morning, even under the top-hamper of foliage. Our eyes got used to us moving in the dark and gradually there were fewer bruises and, most of all, less noise. That was the one thing our leader impressed upon us, how important it was, just as he had shown us that first day how to assemble, close packed so that he could address all of us in a company at one time. Of course our company commanders told us this but that was an odd thing: Bruce sometimes came and addressed us in small groups by himself; just to make sure, I suppose.

'But where wull we git rags, Sire?' a man had enquired when the demand for them had been made again, seated around a campfire that night.

'I don't know. Just get them.'

'But where, Sire? Wull Ah send fur thaim tae Dumfermline? Thur's a tailor there, ye ken? He micht huv cloths.'

'Dunfermline? That would take all day. No. Scout among the tents and brochs and see who has spare shirts and underpants. They're always white, aren't they? Well, tear them up and they'll do nicely.'

The other move Bruce introduced soon after beginning his trials was a marshal[1] at the top of the slope to tell us when to start and another at the foot of the slope to make us line up along the foot of the wood using his outstretched arms to indicate the line he wanted. Even he was saying as little as possible to reduce the noise. I was in the second rank, so our rank was in a line parallel to the bottom of the slope behind the first rank and once our rank was ready, the next rank lined up behind us and then others behind that. The marshal in the Carse had to judge how far out from the wood to set his first line, an important matter. In this way, Bruce had control of who was in the front rank and they had to be the best men, everyone in light armour: helmet and breastplate of some kind or mail shirt only, for ease of movement, but in many cases there was no armour. Often there was no helmet either, so a man would wear what he usually wore: his hat, and these were of different kinds and colours, none of them bright, most of them dull, scuffed, stained, holed even, unlikely then to show up. Many did not even have hats. In this army not having things was common.

Even the very last rank had good men, for they would make sure no one in front of them turned tail and ran away. It took a wee while for our rank to get down through the wood and line up and it could have taken a long time to get the whole division down if there was only one way. But Bruce had made a lot of routes down through the wood, each with its white rags tied to branches to guide us in the dark. That's why some unfortunates went to the battle without underpants: weaklings were debagged to make rags to 'light' our paths to glory; and some who were just disliked. What I did not realise until much later was that the rear ranks were in some ways even more important than the front ranks. Neither did Bruce himself at this stage of our preparations.

'Would an enemy not see the rags?' said one man to Bruce. 'No,' he answered. 'Not in the dark when there are so many trees in full leaf. Not even in the light, for the rags stop well short of the edge of the wood. And the opposition's so far away. That's why you have to march out from the wood to get close to them.'

'How close do we get?' said another.

Bruce laughed. 'How can we fight them if we don't get close to them?'

'But how close?' persisted the questioner, who sounded worried.

'As close as we can. The closer the better.' At the time I don't know anybody who understood this. But when the great day came, it suddenly made sense. Bruce was not one to explain things, unless it was necessary. One reason why few people ever understood it. Or received advance notice of his plans.

'Wull they no' see us marchin' towards them?' was another question.

'Not with the wood at our backs. It's a wood on a slope, remember. They won't see us until we are right up to them. Anyway, we will start right at the dawn, before the sun is up.'

Bruce paused then, surveyed us and said: 'What matters most then, if all that is taken care of?'

When there was no answer, he said: 'Noise. They might hear us. That's why we have to be quiet. Say nothing at all, if you can. That's why we're practising. So that we can do this easily and in silence.'

Many days were spent descending the woods into the flat ground below, almost all of it cleared of trees because of flooding every so often which destroyed the seedlings by drowning their roots. But always in the early morning before dawn. Always the need for silence was emphasised and for order in everything we did. Every man went behind another and when a line was wanted it was formed up in silence, if dark, one hand went on the shoulder in front, the other was for the pike. There were five important moves.

First: the move from the camp to the top of the slope to a particular position, always in a line, about 100 in each, sometimes more, at the entry to the slope down which we would eventually move through the wood. There we sat down and waited.

Second: moving down the slope. Even this was not easy, especially at the beginning of our training. We soon put a youngster with really keen eyesight in the lead, the commander going as second man. Then, when the marshal gave the signal, a tap on the shoulder of the company commander, the move down through the wood began along the line of rags that curved around the obstacles down to the Carse floor.

Third: the careful positioning of our line by the marshal behind the other lines and waiting for the rest to arrive and position behind us.

Fourth: when everybody was down and lined up, Bruce, who watched it happening, would turn and move out from the wood and we would follow. Finally, when he had gone as far as he judged needful, he would stop and the standard would come nearer as we approached until we were right where he was.

Fifth: he would set his pike and kneel and then we would set ours. Every pike-butt was set in the ground, just an inch or so, behind the right heel. This meant we grasped the pike about four or five feet up the shaft, enough balance to move it to lodge in the attacking cavalryman or his horse when they would come on to us.[2]

All of this took time to understand and time to learn. Bruce made us practise so we could do it without thinking. Most of us thought it was just one of the series of manoeuvres we were required to practise in the course of becoming fully trained soldiers. That it might have a particular reason was never clear at that stage and for many, never became clear at any time.

'What are we doing this for, Sire?' he was asked often. The answer was always the same. 'Wait and see.'

'Can we really beat the English?' said another.

'If you do exactly what you are told, yes. But you need to do everything I say, so it is natural to you.' He always smiled then and we knew he believed we could win. He might not want to tell us, but he had a plan and it was going to work. Most of us believed this. We had experienced his plans before. They always worked.

During the day it was easier. We could see our whole company and all the others. We practised moving together under orders, combining to form a single line and setting the pikes. Then there were combats, man to man, as one fought another and there were some wounds and they had to be bound up to heal; for Bruce wanted us to be ready for the fight that was to come. So injuries were inevitable as man had to try his strength and skill against his fellow. There were also forced marches of ten, fifteen, twenty miles and more, always at a rapid pace that tired you out to start with but got used to. Three or four a week there were and sometimes in the dark over unknown territory when getting lost was easy. This was dangerous. Some men were badly hurt by it, falling down into holes and gulleys, colliding with tree trunks, even sinking into marshes. But Bruce persisted and we learned as never before to trust the man in front, having a hand on his shoulder, listening for his whispered comment and passing it on behind. And we were made to swim across rivers like the Forth, and if you couldn't swim you were supposed to learn or you drowned. Most people learned to swim by copying those that could. Beginners in the art were invariably thrown in, whereupon, though frightened near to death, nature would take over and they would swim as a dog does or a horse, paddling with both hands and kicking the feet. A few, the uncoordinated few, could not master this and drowned if the river was deep and powerful enough to carry them away before someone jumped in to save them.

Then one day, when our division was stretched out across the Carse, 400 men wide, Bruce mounted his horse and rode at us just for the practice, gently, slowly, so that no one got injured. And it was then that the full effect of his manoeuvre began to be understood. Before Bruce's lance could hit anyone, his horse had to stop because of the forest of pikes in front of it. When he dismounted in safety, he cried out to us in a loud voice, as if he had just realised what to do. 'Every man should be as close as possible to the man in front because then more pikes will hit the horseman before his lance hits them. And leave a gap between each man and the next man on either side, for in that gap the pike can be manoeuvred to lodge in the charging horse and rider, the point can be shifted from one side to the other, with one hand, though two are available. The main things are: kneeling down and the butt of the pike stays in the ground. It is the ground that takes the pressure of the horse and rider, not the man himself.' The message was repeated by Bruce himself. Every ten yards he stopped and spoke to the men of the company facing him. He was always very deliberate about this, making sure everyone understood what was needed. It took too long even to get round our division, a problem that would soon be solved.

'But the English wullnay go oot here just because we want them to!' one complained.

'Wait and see,' said Bruce. And we did. And, eventually, we did see.

Scottish armies had always mustered in the Torwood because it was rocky and wooded and on the road to the north and Stirling, where was the castle the English were coming to take back, for at mid-summer day, if they did not come, it would be returned to us. What we never understood until later was that we were not going to fight there. That was a surprise.

As the days lengthened, the task of moving in the dark became easier, not only because our eyes got used to it but because there was more light, especially near dawn. We soon saw that it was the dawn Bruce wanted to catch. We always got into line before dawn and waited for that moment and the march began just as the light was beginning over on the eastern hills. Of course, knowing the ground so well by day made it much easier to traverse at night.

We stationed look-outs everywhere. I was one myself when it was my turn. Our group was to watch the road south of Torwood and if anyone not of the army was near we were to turn him back along the road. Bruce did not want anyone to see us practising. It might have given them an idea of what he intended and the information could have been taken to the English for money.

But it was not all straightforward. I was near Bruce when it happened one time. The lines were marching across the Carse one dark morning and someone in the fifth rank stumbled in a hole or slipped on the wet grass. He fell onto the man at the side and that man fell and hit the next man and in a few minutes twenty men had fallen down like dominoes and a few had even been injured by pikes falling, spiking friendly flesh at their front, accompanied by crying out and cursing.

'You see why this matters?' said Bruce, running up to the fallen men. 'We have to be under control. This kind of thing is fatal. So everybody: take care where you set your foot. And leave a good space between each man.' So we were not to cram together until we were in our final position. Even then, realising the danger, we did not cram as close as we might: there were plenty of pike points to hit the charging horse and rider with a space left all round each man. At least a dozen points, coming from two directions, one on either side of the rider.

The message went around the whole camp; and, as usual, Bruce made sure of it by doing it himself after the company commanders had already done it. When he told you in person, you really did pay attention. It took a while for him to get round everyone but it was worth it. It made us realise how important it was. He was not taking such a keen interest in what we did for nothing.

The other manoeuvre we practised was making a big semi-circle at the foot of the wood. This time, only half the division was used. What we learned and Bruce could see for himself how it would work, was how to get the companies into the position he wanted after coming down through the wooded slope. He tried out several sizes of semi-circle and when formed, stood in the centre looking at everyone, judging how it would be on the day. Forming the semi-circle with men on the slope was tried but abandoned because there were always trees on the slope which made everything more complicated and the men were likely to fall over on the sloping ground, especially when kneeling.[3] By trying out the possibilities, Bruce eventually realised that the best way, the most reliable formation, was to have every man on flat ground. That was what determined the size of the circle. So at least I judged. But it had to be a certain size. That was a factor too. It was to be about 30 yards in diameter, it seemed.

Messengers came up every day, reporting on the events at the border where the English were collecting as usual at Berwick. The important question was when would they leave? But we knew it would be about the middle of June, for they had to be at Stirling by mid-summer day to relieve the castle. That was the arrangement Sir Thomas Mowbray had made with Edward Bruce, the King's brother. If the English did not reach the castle in time, it would be given up to us, the Scots, without further conflict. Edward Bruce had agreed because this castle was unusually difficult to attack, perched as it was on a high rock, too high for the rope ladders which had been used to take Rothesay, Perth and Roxburgh, among others. These ladders[4] had sides of rope the height of the wall, with thin bits of wood for rungs; but the priceless addition in them was the top rung. This had an iron bracket in the middle which just fitted over the top of the parapet. And then, glory be! There was the wee hole just off-centre in the top rung beside the bracket. Into that hole, the end of a very long pole would be stuck, tapering, so it did not go in more than an inch. To set the ladder, the pole was raised up in the air and the ladder rose along with it. The bracket could be fitted over the parapet easily. Most parapets were the same, about a foot wide or less, but they could be seen from afar and judged for size. Even so, somebody in our army would know the parapet and what size it was from past experience, having served on the very same battlement as a defender in time past. Once the bracket was in position, the pole could be removed and laid down and the first man could put his foot on the bottom rung. As soon as he did this, the ladder could not be thrown down from above, because it was held fast by the bracket. The weight of the man on the bottom rung made it impossible to throw down from the parapet.

Rothesay and Perth were taken this way. The pole was carried across the moat by one man and another carried the ladder. Roxburgh was similar except there was no moat but a river on both sides which had to be crossed. The attack there was from the east because the wall was lowest there and the hill in front less steep. To ensure that the top rung did not split, the hole could have iron rings on either side hammered in. To keep the ladder away from the wall, fenders were fastened to every third rung and rags used to reduce the noise of scraping when it moved against the wall. The rungs were about eighteen inches apart. The rungs were held in place by knots under them.

What made Stirling more difficult was the fact that three walls stood above a precipice, hundreds of feet high and the fourth was barely fifty yards long and defended night and day by lots of men who could interfere with the ladder as soon as the brackets reached the parapet. It had always been possible before to find a part of the wall which had no sentry. Then the process of putting up the ladder could go on unhindered. At Stirling, all the defenders were on one short wall only, because the others needed no defence.

In an army like that you soon make friends because of the shared difficulties successfully overcome. When you ate, slept, pished, shit, fought and farted together, you had to accommodate other people and their wants and they had to accommodate yours. And if not, you changed or you changed them.

How did I, John Craufurd, come to join the army? More to the point: where did I learn to scribe and acquire the skills that go with it, to be able to tell this tale?

2

THE ORIGIN OF MY INSIGHT

I had come to the army only six months before. I had been standing at the Mercat Cross in Ayr when a group of riders came into the town and dismounted. It was then that Bruce saw me. It was winter, it was beginning to grow dark and I had just recently left the schule in the Sandgate after extra time spent with the dominie, Master Waleis, a Dominican friar from the monastery nearby. There had been a schule for half a century and our dominie was the latest of four or five. He had been sent there from Oxford as a kind of missionary when the English took over the land. From him I had learned to be silent, speak only when I was spoken to and to obey, things others found difficult and for which they were regularly chastised. After a few initial failures, I succeeded better than anyone, obtained the favour of the Master and never needed to be punished again. It was not that I was better than the rest, I was just different. The words that came from him seemed to me the greatest treasure, better than the treasures of heaven, whatever they were. I listened with my full attention and absorbed everything he said, like a sponge. When my fellows wanted only freedom from the discipline to act the goat, play pranks on each other, wrestle and fight with whatever weapons came to hand, I wanted more words.

The dominie spoke the English and I loved the sound of it better than my own language. There was music in it, rhythm and even promise in it, that was the main thing. The Scots we all grew up speaking was a rough noisy tongue devoid of what I dimly recognised were ideas. Ideas of great men and their doings, ideas of tournaments and wars and tales of derring-do, though there was some of that, I concede. Ideas of the church and its history and of God and the men who served him and the missionaries like our dominie who gave up their lives in his service. But there were other ideas, ideas from other worlds I was eventually allowed to enter into and they were not found in the Scots language. The town then had been in English hands for a dozen years, only recently returned to my people, the Scots, by our new King, Robert Bruce who was that very day travelling from Glasgow to his castles in Carrick, where he came from.

Though the town had changed hands, it never occurred to our dominie to leave. Probably, he had been instructed by his order to remain and civilise us, come what may, him being sworn to obedience. Anyway he remained and I was delighted. What I would have done without him, I know not: despair and depression, probably, but of these I knew little at that time. From him I learned counting and scribing and measuring and then Latin and even Greek. It was the Latin that made the difference. It was, said Master Waleis, the language of all educated men. Thus, if you travelled to France or Italy or Spain or the Low Countries or even to the freezing north or the many islands in the warm seas beyond Italy, the home of the Pope, everyone would understand you because they all had Latin—if they had been properly educated, that is. It was soon his ambition to educate me and I loved every minute of it.

Every day and even after the day was supposed to have ended, he would spend dropping plums into the limitless basket of my mind. These I tasted and savoured, swallowed and digested and he saw my delight, tested my acquisition and when I satisfied him, as I almost always did, the delight shone in his face. I expect my own delight shone in mine. And so I learned about the Romans and their world and the Greeks before them and the Carthaginian, Hannibal, who had terrorised the Romans in their own homeland for a while and then been defeated in his turn by the great General Scipio Africanus. And Julius Caesar. Who could not be captivated by him? I read *de Bello Gallico*[ii], his account of his wars in Gaul as though it were the greatest pleasure of my life. It was the quality of the mind that lay behind it, of course: the prose, the beautiful simple, soldier's Latin, the energy of the man and his skill as a leader and, above all, his success in overcoming, again and again, overwhelming odds. His achievements filled me with awe, reverence. Had I but known it, I would eventually transfer that feeling to another.

[ii] *About the war in Gaul,* which was France, Switzerland, Belgium and some of the adventure even in Germany. Caesar bridged the Rhine in ten days and crossed over with his legions. Later, it took him three.

How did I get to the schule? That was strange. I was walking early one morning from the steading where I lived between Alloway Kirk and the town when I came across a man. At first I thought he was asleep, had lain down in the road. I examined him and could get no response from him. He was dead, I eventually realised. It was a fine morning. No one had passed that way yet. So I had been the first. What should I do? I was then around seven years old and without experience to guide me. An older person would have known. I wondered how he died and began to scrutinise him more carefully. There was a pack on his back that looked as if it had been rifled, for it had been pulled out from under him and was open to the four winds. There was no obvious wound until I turned the head and saw the blood. He was bearded, about middle height and age and had lost some of his clothes, I judged: barefoot and bare legged. Probably his shoes and stockings too had been taken. Around him, fluttering in the breeze, were some things I had never seen before: parchments they were. I picked one up and studied it carefully, for there were markings on it. These were very strange. What I know now is that they were numbers and letters and the letters combined into words and these were in Latin. To me, then, they were mysterious. This man, it seemed to me, had understood their meaning; whoever had killed him had not, and had left them behind with his corpse.

So I gathered them up and returned to the steading where I told my father. 'Was there any siller?' said he, throwing down the parchments on the table in our house.

'No, nothing. He had lost some of his clothing and his shoes. There is a back pack but it is empty, open. What shall we do?'

'Nothing. Leave him to others.'

'What do these things say?' I said, referring to the parchments.

'How should I ken?'

That was the day I discovered that my father could not read. When I asked him the reason, he beat me as usual. It was his way. He had also beat my mother until she died that same year. Since I had loved my mother, I hated him. In the middle of it—the slaps and cuffs—he said: 'Why do ye need tae read?' and with a sweep of one hand sent them fluttering to the fire. 'It's no' fur the likes ae us.'

'I want to read because they have things to tell me, things I might know.'

Some caught fire. I seized the rest and ran out of the house. Back along the road I went to the town away from my father. I sat on a stone by the roadside and pondered the parchments. It soon occurred to me that perhaps the man himself had made them. But how? There had to be a method and, I dimly realised, an instrument of some kind. When I reached the man I saw his hat, a small brown hat, lying under a bush. In it, stuck in the brim, was a feather and something about it caught my eye: the end of it, the last two inches or so, was black, sharpened to a point, when all the rest was white or grey. Was this the instrument? I began to search his pockets more carefully and in a small pocket on his waistcoat I found, wrapped in a dirty clout, a small wooden box with a lid on a hinge that fitted exactly and was held by string round it. Inside, there was treasure: a black liquid. I got the lid open and put my finger into it and brought it out: black! This was what had made the markings —and the end of the feather, that too, dipped in it.

All this I discovered for myself, but understand the markings I could not. Sitting on a low tree branch, I took one of the unspoiled parchments with no marks on it and began to try to copy the marks onto it, after dipping the end of the feather. My efforts were not much good, nothing like the man's. I needed a flat surface, a table and a chair.

I contemplated my world: the steading or farm, a rude shack of one room shared with the animals and, worst of all my father and his other bairns, all of them older than me, all of them accustomed to abusing me like our father. Using his table for this purpose was out of the question. My father would never allow it. I knew that there was more in this world than what his had to offer and I made a sudden resolution to find it.

I spent an hour or so down by the shore trying to make out the meaning of the markings. I sensed that they were important to me. And I made no progress. It was so frustrating that I wept. I did not even have a table I could use! It seemed so unjust!

Sitting on the beach with the parchment flattened by stones at the corners, I tried to copy the symbols and made a bad job of it at first. But I persisted and became slightly better, after many mistakes. But what did it sound like? I had no idea. Of course the ink blotted and spread and I got sand on it. But it never occurred to me then that sand was often used to dry the ink.

The problem of the sound would not go away. I realised that had it been my own language I might have been able to compare the letters with the sounds I knew, but this language was foreign to me. I had been to church like everyone else but the words were usually mumbled and I had not the slightest notion what they meant. I thought of sounds I had heard: 'spiritus sancti, pache, dominus'—there was one at least that sounded familiar: it was like dominie, a word I had heard before. Maybe these were connected. But I could see I needed more than this. I wanted to be able to read the Latin of the parchments. There, I felt sure, was the route I had to take in the world, to escape the drudgery of the farm and mindless beatings of my father. Sometimes, I feared he would kill me altogether like my mother.

And so I went to the town that afternoon, determined never to return to the steading and my family. I needed to find someone to help me. From workshop to workshop I went and no one I asked was able to read the parchments, though many had some idea of what our own tongue looked like when written, though evidently it rarely was written. From some I was chased, as if I had demeaned the owner by establishing that he could not read. Finally, I was referred to the small monastic community in the Sandgate near the bridge. There were people there who might know, I was informed.

This is how I met Master Waleis. He was a tall man with a bald head, dressed in a black cloak under which was a white cassock. I met him in the street outside a small building and when I had been seen to have parchments and was questioned about them and I explained my needs, he invited me inside to sit down on a bench at a table and there he interviewed me. I explained how I had come upon the dead man and found his parchments and scribing materials. How I wanted to be able to read them and how I had failed because I did not know what the sounds should be.

As he sat studying me, he seemed to perform some actions with a rosary he had, a habit of his, it turned out. He took the parchments from me and began to read them. 'These are Adam le Baker's papers,' he told me. 'I hear he died last night. Would you like me to read them to you?'

'No, Sir, I would like to be able to read them myself. I would dearly love to learn to read and I hope to teach myself if I can only learn the sounds.'

'You would need more than that. But I can teach you here if you wish to learn. I see you have been trying to copy the letters.'

When my position was explained and that I had no money, he said it was not important. I could stay in the building and eat meals with him and some others who could not get home every evening. I would be expected to do chores to cover my expenses.

I agreed. I told him I would not go and tell my father, for it would mean a beating and he would never allow it. This was accepted. If my father were to come for me, Master Waleis would deal with him, I was assured.

In this way I became a student and it was a great happiness to me. This is where my love of learning began, where I learned the Latin and the Greek and met Julius Caesar, the great general; Seneca the wise ruler; Marcus Aurelius, the best emperor and scholar with his Meditations; and Cicero, the lawyer who demolished the criminal Verres in court, so that they became my friends, to replace the ones I did not have—and Plato, Aristotle, Thucydides and others too numerous to relate. Above all, I learned to think as they did, to plan and make insights and to write and speak in their languages. I even studied the five ways of Aquinas and under Master Waleis insistence, the *Summa Gentile*, but I never took to it. Unlike the Greeks, Aquinas did not take the logic as far as it would go. The answer was already determined by belief. The idea that an infinite regress was an impossibility seemed wrong to me: are there not infinitely many numbers? And in both directions from zero, positive and negative? Some things really can go on forever. And that women were inferior to men just because they were mostly not so strong was another objection. Some women were just as strong, I could see. Some were even cleverer and more determined. So I never acquired the mind-set the Dominicans were eager to instil in me. Though admiring of their dedication and goodness, I remained sceptical of their dogma. But there was something else I learned.

When Bruce saw me about to begin my evening exercise of walking for miles, he stopped me and waved me to join him. When I did so, he asked me how old I was, said he needed men and that he wanted me to join his army. I told him of my work at the schule with the Dominicans and so someone was sent with me to collect my things and explain to Master Waleis. There was no talk of refusal. I was wanted by my country and my king and that was enough. After a very hurried farewell to my tutor, in a very short time I was trailing behind the riders with my few possessions in a sack over my shoulder. 'How will I keep up?' I said, when they began to ride off southwards. 'We are for Turnberry, the Castle. But you must run to keep up. We will see what you are made of.' The riders laughed at this.

Others were collected, some my age, most older. We were made to run by a sergeant on horseback put in charge of us with two more riders to see we did not escape. When we stopped running, they would smack our arses with a long switch cut from a tree. When none of us could run any longer, we were allowed to walk.

This was my initiation into the army. Of course we could not keep up and it took us most of the day to reach the Castle where the horses were tethered. Nobody paid me any attention when I arrived, except to throw me a few crusts of bread, all that was left. I soon lay down to sleep and I could not, even with the fatigue, for thinking of what I had lost.

In the morning, when Bruce had completed his business, we set off back to Ayr again and this time we rode straight through, or rather they did. When they set off across the river, which was near the schule, I managed to slip away into the building for a few minutes. There was no sign of my teacher or his pupils. He must have been on an errand of mercy, perhaps helping someone on his way to heaven, a task that often fell to him and came before any other.

So there I was in the one place I had learned to love beyond all others and it came into my mind that I had to commit an irredeemable wrong. I had to steal a book from the library, for I knew I would never be allowed to borrow it. There was only one and it was a prized possession. It was a copy of 'The Elements' of Euclid. There were about a hundred parchments copied out in Master Waleis' own hand. I had begun its study not long before and was entranced by its intelligence, for it was like another world, very different from the narrative histories. Here, I realised was real power. This book, I had seen, contained real knowledge, the kind that was unquestionable. Julius Caesar might have written *De Bello Gallico* but how was I to know it was true? I *believed* it was true, that he had conquered the whole of Gaul in battle after battle, succeeding against odds of 10 to one in Alesia against Vercingetorix. I believed it because his soldiers knew the truth, so how could he tell lies about it? But that was not the same as *knowing*. Euclid's work was completely persuasive and brooked no questions, doubts or disputes. I had never seen anything like it, never imagined I would ever come in contact with such intellectual power, such certainty. As I left the schule for the last time, as I expected, I almost wept at what I had left behind me. A man who had helped me and given me treasure immeasurable and none but he was aware of it. I would gladly have remained, but Bruce had cast his spell over me; the country needed my aid to repel the English invaders. I knew where my duty lay. We all did.

For the next six months I defended that book with my life, read it whenever I got the chance and thought about it often when I could not. Somehow I preserved it—well, most of it. I came back to camp one night to find someone using parchments from it to wipe his arse, laughing at my discovery. I called him all the bastard names of hell and wrestled him into his own shite, punched his face and made him swallow the stuff. Never had I known such fury. They left my book alone after that. It was better than eating shite.

I tried to clean the shite off and failed. He had scrunched and torn them and the marks had all but disappeared. A few weeks later I managed to steal some fresh parchments and was able to remember most of what had been stolen and scribe them almost as they had been.

3

MAKING AN IMPRESSION IN THE ARMY

In that single trip, Bruce had collected about 40 men and boys like myself, almost men. In the course of half a year, a dozen had succumbed to disease, killed by accident or fighting in one skirmish or another. Because we fought together in Boyd's company we knew one another which helped. Even had we not, we would have become friends of a sort, for in an army when you must forage for food together, eat out of the same pot, pish and shit in the same place (for safety: nothing is worse for an army than doing it anywhere; it spreads disease and kills the army before the battle), sleep huddled together for warmth in winter, and survive fights of various kinds, bonds are formed between you, and they are lasting.

My invariable companions were Magonigal, a dark bearded baldy-headed bright eyed soldier much older than myself, and taller, who sort of took me in hand after I had proved myself, Kincaid, an older man yet, who could put a cow on its back singlehanded and MacFee, a tall thin slow-talking quiet person who could turn his hand to anything. Then there was Tam Quincy, a well-built fine looking man until he had lost an ear in a sword fight which was stinking because it had got dirty. It caused him a lot of pain until one day Magonigal who liked a drink like most of them, came across a stone jug of aquavittie in a Galloway steading where we were terrorising the Balliols. Before he could drain the lot, I pounced on the jug and tore it away from him. 'Haw Sur? Haw Sur?' he bellowed in that Twechar[iii] twang he had, 'Bae Christ, whit are ye aboot? Ah'll fucken cuff yer lug, ya wee bastart,' he erupted.

[iii] A village in Dumbartonshire between Kirkintilloch and Kilsyth

'This is the very thing,' I said, seizing Tam by the arm with my other hand, shouting orders to the rest, and dragging him protesting to the river. 'I am going to clean that wound before it kills ye.'

I got him to lie down by the river bank where I could remove the dirty bandage and cleanse the wound first with water sooped up in a clout which I washed out and drained by squeezing every few strokes. When the place was cleaned with water I observed it carefully and decided that I should first remove a flap of skin that was red and angry looking. 'I am going to cut this wee bit off, Tam. Hold his head, MacFee.'

'Wull it no' be sair?'

'Of course. But it will get better, I think. So just put up with it.' And so it was I used my knife to cut off the flap and managed well enough, despite his screams.

'Are ye finished the noo?' said Tam at last through his tears.

'No, there's red bits and there will be pus in them. I'm going to cut them and clean out the pus.' So once again I slit the swollen areas and wiped off the pus which seeped out.

'Are ye done yet?' cried Tam.

'No. I need to get these really clean and then I will cauterise it.'

'Yer no' gonny heat a knife, are ye?' he said, fearfully.

'No. It's too near yer brains. It might kill ye quicker than anything.'

Kincaid laughed: 'Whit brains has he?'

MacFee: 'How can ye cauterise it then?'

'With the whisky. What did you think?'

So, with the wounds at the place where the ear had been cleaned as far as possible, I laid him on his side and poured the whisky into them and all over them. What a screaming and crying and struggling there was then! Finally, when all was ready, I called over Kincaid who was standing ready by arrangement with a bunch of lighted twigs and set fire to the place which went up suddenly with a whoosh! Mercifully, Tam passed out. When the flame died away there was the smell of roasting meat, the place blackened and dirty again. I cleaned it again with water and bound it up with a clout freshly rinsed in water.

'That's the best I can do,' I announced to the assembled group. 'Take him back to the broch and lay him down.'

That was the day I proved myself. Book learning might be secretly admired, openly resented, even joked about because it was a peculiar obsession, as they saw it, but I knew enough to try and repair a battlefield wound. Henceforth I was to be applied to if anyone had a wound or an ailment. Of course I knew little: only the feeble efforts at physic I had seen done by Master Waleis, which was not much. I merely exercised the brains God had given me. I was not a leech but I was better than nothing. In that army that was something. We were all used to men dying every other week, even if there was no fighting. For many it was just a natural condition of life. God took you when he was ready and it could be any time, in any number of ways. It was a complete mystery to me then too, but as time went on I began to have ideas about it.

Before leaving Torwood, all trace of our presence was removed and Bruce himself checked everything, as usual. All the tents and equipment were packed up, all the camp fires doused and the ground returned to its normal state, spreading dirt over everything and leaves on top. Most of all, the rags were collected and carefully preserved and carried with us for future use. Then we marched off half a dozen miles to the north along the road (the only road) to Milton Ford, crossed the Bannock burn, moved off the road to the west into the New Park; and there we set up camp again all along the north bank between the Ford and Gillies hill.

There was a lull for a few hours while Bruce, with a single company to help him, selected the routes down the slope of Balquhiderock Wood, cleared a few branches that might impede descent of anyone with a 15 foot pike in one hand, ordering others but often doing it himself, and marked each entry point at the top of the slope. There was little chance of this action being noticed from the castle a full mile away to the north because of the presence of trees and especially whins and scrub in between, all over the Dryfield. When Bruce was ready, all the rags in places where they would just be seen when darkness fell, he ordered every company to come to the top of the wood, one by one, and let them see the ground in daylight, the better to be able to traverse it in darkness as we had practised so many times. Every company was allocated its route of descent. Every tree root and hole or slippery place was pointed out and marked by every eye, to make us more aware, more able to manage the manoeuvre. And then the ground was vacated and left empty until after we had breakfasted at three of the clock in the cold darkness of morning. Once again, we assembled, the whole division, each man within his company at the top of the slope and the beginning of his route to the Carse floor.

At the silent signal from the marshals, we began to descend the wood and line up in our ranks, each man with his pike vertical in one hand, that wrist with a small axe dangling on its string, leaving the other with the targe on the forearm to touch the shoulder of the man in front or grasp a branch or tree trunk as seemed best.

Our company stood in the second rank and heard the men behind us move into position even though there was little noise. When that stopped it was time to go. A squire passed between the companies, went out to Bruce who was watching ahead and whispered to him that we were ready. Ahead of us, the standard, barely seen in the gloom before dawn, began to move and so did we. After a march of ten yards, the standard stopped and we closed up on him. He set his pike and knelt down and we did the same. And all those behind us did likewise. We waited, every man lost in his own thoughts. Then, still in silence, Bruce rose up and, without a word, moved back the way he had come, in the space between our rows, which parted to admit him, and led us back to the foot of the wood, back up the slope and back to our camp. By the time the sun came up, we were back in front of our fires and no outsider had seen anything of our doings.

For weeks, since our arrival, the whole area had been closed to travellers unconnected to the army. Companies took turns in turning away anyone who had not come to enlist or bring provisions. So one day I was stationed at the back of Gillies Hill; another day, I was down on the Forth where the burn enters it. Others were at Cambusbarron, a hamlet north of Gillies Hill and west and south west of there. Several groups were south of the Torwood and even the banks of the River Forth were patrolled as well as the Burn and the Pelstream and the great bogs, especially Skeoch and Livilands. The Castle itself was surrounded and no one allowed in or out.

There was much traffic by ourselves as we hunted the deer, rabbits and fowl in the New Park among the bogs, and fish which were plentiful in the two streams and even as far as the Forth where, at Polmaise, a fish pond had been constructed into which salmon and trout were collected and hunted. Every day, parties went out as far as Dunfermline and Falkirk and even Perth and Glasgow. Wherever provisions could be obtained they were requisitioned by order of the king. A paper written and signed to be presented after the fighting was over. Or not, if it went against us. Every tradesman, every fletcher, fisher, weaver, shoemaker, smith, armourer, grocer, brewer and farmer knew this, but they all said nothing. All, I am glad to say, were on our side and hoped and expected us to win. So the provender was given gladly. No one thought of asking for coins. It would have been viewed as treason. Anyway, there were none. The Scots were as poor as mice. Normal trading conditions were suspended. The issue was not, have we made a profit today? But, will we be alive tomorrow? And maybe, what kind of life will it be? Endurable?

Of course men for the army were arriving every day and they were welcome. But they had to be trained and for that they had often to be absorbed by companies which would provide the training by keeping them in close contact so that they understood what they were to do. Especially in the early morning practice involving our secret move through the woods in the gloom before dawn.

The habit of training was dinned into Bruce in childhood and all his days he engaged in it to keep his own personal warlike skills in trim. He would fight several people at once, a practice which led to the loss of his front teeth, though that was after the great battle when he was much older and less capable. He shot arrows at targets, fought on horseback, with lance and without, and man to man, using every weapon and sometimes none but his bare hands and feet. And we all followed him in this as in everything and learned from his experience and that of his sergeants and company commanders who taught us what they knew.

Bruises and wounds of various sorts were inevitable but the training was necessary. Apart from the increase in skills, it kept the body muscled and ready and able to fight for long periods. Many people lost fights, we were told, because they lacked the stamina to continue and, when exhausted, they ceased to be able to resist attacks which therefore became fatal. For this reason we were all expected to march many miles every day and even at the run, this being the foundation of our fitness. So much so, that we were often out of breath and exhausted.

In time, we tired less quickly, could fight with all our speed and strength for longer. But all the usual weapons' training went on every day, with sword and shield and dagger and axe. The two handed swords of some knights were largely dispensed with, for as Bruce pointed out, they would not be much use to deal with men in armour when we were to be lightly armed, when our ability to strike quickly and decisively would be an advantage. Yet every man had his preferred personal weapon and none was disallowed. A few carried a broad bladed axe, there were one or two large swords and many swords of the smaller variety since their owners were accustomed to cut with them rather than chop with the small axe which the majority preferred. But pikes of course were the standard and anyone with other ideas was consigned to the rear of the army where few wanted to be. So, unwieldy weapons were quickly thrown down in favour of pikes. Training in the use of these was frequent and effective.

The first thing, surprisingly, was that the pike had two positions of safety: flat on the ground in the channel between the standing rows of pikemen; and vertical, where the point could not engage any friend. Their use was mostly limited by us to defence, set behind the right heel and pointing upwards clear of the shoulder of the man in front but in the channel between the men where it could be aimed easily. One of our practices Bruce devised was to run a man in armour at a short line of pikemen and see how many could lodge the pike in the gaps to bring him down. This was very expensive in broken pikes and even broken heads, other bones and bruises of every kind, but Bruce insisted that everyone try this, hoping they would recover by the time of the event. A team of carpenters gradually assembled who kept us supplied with fresh pikes, the timber being brought from the far side of Gillies Hill, for Bruce would not have a single tree cut anywhere around our defensive position on the Dryfield, the New Park or its surroundings, not even south of the burn. Every tree, he told us, from Falkirk to Stirling, was a friend to us. Even our wood for camp fires had to be brought from afar, cut down and hauled by horses to the camp and chopped up there as needed.

Everyone knew what was about to happen. An English army was about to arrive to raise the siege on Stirling Castle, which, by arrangement, would be handed over to us the Scots without a bolt fired if the English did not come before mid-summer day. If they failed to arrive on time the dishonour would be grave to every Englishman. So it was certain that their army would arrive by then. That is why for a whole year[5] since Sir Edward Bruce arranged the truce with Sir Philip Mowbray, Robert the King had been preparing for his defence of the castle.

With about a week to go, riders suddenly appeared galloping up the road to the Ford, among them Douglas, who reported that the English were on the move. Bruce was surveying the Ford at the time, deciding on his final preparations and dispositions, many of us kneeling in ranks around it in a semi-circle. Douglas drew up beside him, leaped down from his horse, nervous with excitement and, I think, fear too, for his eyes were bulging out of his head. He stood, tall, dark haired and swarthy in a once black, mud-stained gambeson, in front of Bruce, saying nothing, sweating in the summer sunshine, after such a long hard ride and panting from the exertion. 'Well, I take it they have left Berwick?' said Bruce. 'Get some water at the spring[6] here and then we'll take a flask or two of wine in my tent.'

I never found out what was said. But soon after, hearing at last of my power in patching up wounds, Bruce came to visit me particularly, and after examining Tam and hearing his version of what I had done to him, he said to me: 'How did you know what to do?'

'I didn't know.'

'Did you see a leech do this where you came from?'

'No.'

'Well, how did you come to do what you did?'

'It was just common sense. He had a bit of skin that was black and looked angry at the edges nearest the head. I decided it was no use to him and should come off. After that there were bits that were red and swollen. I knew there would be pus. So I let the pus out since it was making it swell and sore.'

'Why was it sore?'

'Because it was swollen. The pus was pushing against the skin making it sore.'

Bruce smiled and seemed to accept this explanation. 'And then what?'

'There must still have been pus in them. So I washed out the places with whisky.'

'And then set alight to it?'

'Yes.'

'Well, his face is not very pretty now.'

'How could it be when he lost an ear? At least he's alive.'

'But did you have to use whisky? And did you have to set fire to it? It burnt his face.'

'What do you expect? The whisky had to go everywhere. Of course some of it was on his face.'

'Maybe whisky would have been enough without the fire.'

'I don't think so. The pus would still have been alive in him. The fire killed it.'

'Aye, but it jist aboot kilt me tae,' said Tam ruefully.

Bruce thought for a moment and then said to me: 'There's some men up at my tent with wounds. Maybe you can see to their hurts.'

And thus it was that I accompanied Bruce to his tent where on the grass outside were a handful of men sitting or lying down. I stopped by a man on his back, the worst, whose lower leg was black and above that purple. The stench was awful. 'What do you say about this one?' said Bruce.

'If that ear was anything to go by, this leg is a goner.'

'What do you advise?'

'It's not going to do him any good and it might kill him. So I would take it off.' I examined it more closely and saw that the origin of the problem was far down the leg near the shin. There was a pus-filled ulcer. 'What caused that?' I asked the man.

'The point ae a pike. Somebody ahint me fell doon in the daurk and he's pike fell on ma leg.'

'So first you got a yellow bit and then you tried to scratch it off and it got worse and then it turned black and started climbing your leg?'

'Aye, that's aboot it.'

'So that purple bit is where it's got to and it will carry on climbing unless you cut it off.'

'I don't understand,' said Bruce. 'What is it that's killing him?'

I guessed he knew already and was just trying me out. I replied: 'The black bit is full of pus and rot and the leg there is dead and useless. It's like rot in a tree, I expect. The rot travels up the tree and kills it. If it goes on like this, the whole leg will be black and the purple will move onto his body. That will kill his vital organs.'

'And you want to cut his leg off?'

The man howled in protest at the very idea. 'I don't want to cut his leg off. But unless somebody cuts it off he won't live.'

Bruce signalled to another man nearby and said: 'What do you say?' I learned later that this was Gloag, Bruce's old tutor, a know-all who had been at Oxford. Gloag was tall and thin with a large cyst in the centre of the mostly bald head surrounded by a tonsure of white hair, with a single wisp of hair in the centre at the forehead.

'Ye canny cut his leg aff. He'll jist dee onyway. Ye micht try a potion or a poultice, baith wid be guid.'

'What kind of potion?' I said.

'Wan wi' a wheen ae brandy and a deid cat's ee, and a coupla frogs legs. And mibbee a piece a shite aff a strang buull.' For an Oxford man he still spoke with a very peculiar accent which further knowledge of him proved to be from some wilderness in Galloway. Maybe he hadn't lasted there very long, long enough at least to lose his accent; maybe he was even driven out because of it. So at least I speculated.

'You have found this to work from experience, have you?' said Bruce, sceptically, knowing it untrue.

'Aye, Ah have so. The verra thing.'

'Well there's no brandy,' said Bruce.

'Wull, whusky wid dae, ye ken.'

'And there's no frogs round here at this time of year,' said Bruce 'and any cat found hereabouts was killed and eaten, eyes and all, weeks ago.' Looking at the man sternly but also compassionately: 'What do you want? If the leg is cut off you could live. If not, you will die. So he thinks,' pointing his thumb at me, 'and I think he's right. It's what always happens.'

The man said: 'Ah don't waant tae dee.'

'Well then,' said Bruce to me. 'Take it off.'

'I'll need help to hold him down; and whisky, lots of that; and dry clouts and water, lots of that. And twine and needles to stitch him up. And a really good sharp knife and a sharpening stone and a rope. And maybe buckets for the blood and such.'

'Can you do it?'

'I don't know. I've never done this before.'

'Well, do what you can. Use that trestle table in my tent.'

I sent off for my comrades and got the other things by sending them in various directions. Bruce swept his parchments off the table, the remains of a half-eaten fowl and a goblet with some wine still in it. Soon we were ready, a handy knife belonging to him had been sharpened and I began by giving the man a strong draught of the whisky. The others holding him also took some drams but the man more than anyone. Meantime, with the man laid out on the table, I took off the clothing up to the groin and began to apply the rope to the flesh above the purple bit. Tighter and tighter I pulled it until the man screamed: 'That's too much! Dinnay dae that!'

'I have to do it. The tighter the better.' I got a short strong rod of wood and inserted it under the rope and twisted it and turned it until it would turn no more, the man screaming and whimpering by turns. 'Here, Kincaid, hang on to this and don't let it move.'

Another piece of wood was found, bound in a clout and I showed it to the man: 'This goes in your mouth. You can bite down on it.'

'What for?' said he anxiously, very frightened now.

'It might help to bear the pain.'

'Magonigal, you get a bit tinder ready to light at the fire outside,' I ordered.

'What's that for?' said the man, now tipsy with drams.

'To cauterise it, what else?'

Nothing more was said. I just stood over the man with his outstretched leg and tried to imagine how it would be. 'Pull the leg to one side. Gently now,' I said to the men. Again I stood and surveyed the problem. 'Fetch me a big stone, a clean one. A smooth one if you can.'

Mercifully there was one nearby. It was dirty but smooth. I gave it a wipe with my sleeve and put it under the leg where the flesh was good, but high up. So the whole leg was off the table now, resting on the foot and that was what made the slight difference that could save his life. I studied it again. Imagined how it would be. And it would not work, I realised. There was a bone and I had to get through the bone. I needed a saw. 'Away and find Crabbe, the Fleming, and borrow one of his saws,' I told MacFee. This Fleming was the man who had made the rope ladders for taking castles. He had a box full of useful tools and even a small forge that he carried everywhere on a cart.

The saw when it arrived was fine-toothed, which was good, as it would pass through the bone more smoothly, causing less pain. I took it to the fire outside and heated it there. 'Are we ready now?' said Bruce, who had come up to observe.

I thought again about the sequence of events to follow.

'No,' I said, finally. 'Not quite. Give me that roll of twine and the needle.' I threaded it through and for good measure made several lengths, one of them very long, each of which I dipped in a goblet of whisky poured out of the stone jug.

'Why are you heating the knife?' said Bruce, as I passed it back and forth through the flame of the fire just outside the tent.

'I don't know. I just think it might cut cleaner and maybe if it's really hot, it might kill what's killing him. Isn't that what fire does: kill everything?'

I told the man on the table to bite down hard and look to the other side away from his leg. 'Hold him, then.' And I cut very quickly with the knife, right through the flesh on top of the thigh below the rope and all the way around which was easier because of the leg raised up off the table. The man screamed as if his life was being taken. Then he went limp and passed out. Blood seeped out, but not very much to start with because of the tourniquet. I seized the saw and sawed through the bone as quickly as possible and a spout of blood came out, showering everything like red rain. But the leg was off and it was free, dripping blood. It fell off the table. I poured more whisky over the place. 'Light it, quick!' I said. And Magonigal did it smartly while I made sure of the tourniquet.

A blue flame flickered, barely seen in the summer sunshine, and then the smell of roasting meat assaulted our nostrils. I applied a thick clout to the wound, smoothed it up the sides of the leg towards the rope and began winding the twine around it. In the event, I did not use stitches at all. I simply kept on winding and fixed the twine finally by the end under the binding which I had laid along the limb at the start and tied it off.

'What about this rope?' said Kincaid, meaning the tourniquet on the upper thigh.

'Slacken it off. I can't do any more. The blood needs to get to these sore bits or they'll get the pus too.'

And so the job was done. I was suddenly dog tired and I lay down flat on the grass, like a dead man and rested. 'Haw sur?' said Magonigal, looking down at me, without the usual rasp, 'Ye did weel.'

Presently, another voice above me said: 'Do you want a drink?' It was Bruce, holding out a tankard of ale.

I sat up, took it from him and drank it down. 'So what happens now?' he said.

'We wait and we pray.'

'Will it work?'

'I don't know.'

I spent the night with my company and was up before dawn for practice. By then we had become quite good at managing in the dark. Of course on nights with a moon and few clouds it was easier, but every man's eyesight had improved at night and we made fewer and fewer mistakes. Using the same route to the Carse floor was one help, for we soon knew every twist and turn of the path down through the wood and the rags[7] showed the line clearly even under the foliage that largely shut out moonlight. Of course we knew exactly how many rags there were. The marshals had learned to better judge where to set the first line and the others fitted in behind them. In the beginning, they had put the first line too close to the wood which meant that the rear lines had to form within the wood itself. That was no good, for the trees got in the way. The whole formation had to move as one unit at the same speed. This was never stated but was obvious to me.

Back in the camp around the fire, after breakfast, I decided to go and see how the man with the black leg full of pus was doing. I found him lying outside the tent on the ground, his eyes staring straight up. Bruce came out to talk to me. 'He died in the night; never woke up. What was it killed him do you think?'

I knelt down and closed the eyes and studied the stump with the bloody clout round it, bound on with twine. There was not a great deal of blood, so it wasn't that. 'It's the purple bit. It has gone further up the leg.'

'Where did you go wrong, then?'

'I should have cut further up, I think. Maybe some of the rottenness was still in the bit that was left well below the skin where it could not be seen. So it carried on climbing up the leg. That's what did it.' My grief at failure almost reduced me to tears.

Bruce clapped a consoling arm about my shoulders: 'You did your best. It was well done. Next time you'll do better.'

'Will there be a next time?' I queried, uncertainly.

'Of course. Your way is better than frogs legs and bull-shit.'

He took me into the tent again and this time I was invited to sit in his presence on a stool. He was in his favourite chair which had arms and cushions for the arse and the back. It looked comfortable and Bruce leaned back in it with the front legs off the floor which was strewn with reeds from the bogs nearby. On the table were the parchments I had seen before. While wine was poured out by a servant, I noticed that they were mostly lists. He saw my interest. 'You have knowledge of parchments, have you?'

'A little, Sire.'

'Do you mean you can scribe?'

'Yes, Sire, a bit.'

'Who taught you?' said Bruce, leaning forward to grasp his goblet and take a mouthful.

'The dominie, Sire. I was taught the figuring and measuring.'

'And have you any Latin?'

'Yes, Sire, some.'

He reached across the table and picked up the wadge of parchments, extracted a few and handed over the rest. 'Can you read these?'

'These are lists of companies and the men in them. And these others are the supplies we have and the supplies we need: barrels of flour, barrels of salt-herring, loaves of bread—lots of them—and barrels of ale—many of them—some even of wine; and sheaves of arrows; bows, arrowheads, axes and horses and their harness,' and scanning the rest in more haste, 'all the needs of the army.'

Bruce smiled: 'I see where you got the skill you just showed. A man used to parchments can represent a whole army by a few symbols and plan a campaign on parchment when without it he would forget everything and it would make no sense.'

He was right as usual. Few of my companions could count and measure, only those involved in the commerce of trade and then only sparingly, enough for the trade.

'My brother Alexander was the best scribe and counter I ever knew. Only Baldred Bisset here is near as good.' This was a monk who attended to some of the King's clerical work, aided by a few assistants.

'Have you read the book?' said Baldred.

'Yes,' I replied, 'most of it.' He meant the Holy Book of course. In our kirk, only the dominie and his brothers and I could read it. But I could read other things: every book Master Waleis owned and these were many, all copied out at Oxford and carried with him wherever he went.

'Your brother, Sire? What became of him?'

Bruce's face saddened and he turned away from me, so that I could not see it. 'He was the finest Cambridge student of his generation. Dean of Glasgow at 21. Murdered at Carlisle on the orders of that bastard, Edward Longshanks.' He turned and I could see the grief rising in him as he remembered this splendid young man. 'He was the ablest of us all. He was just unlucky. He was hardly ashore when they captured him.'

Suddenly, seeming to remember something, Bruce laid down the other parchments he had not shown me on the table and rose. 'Come Baldred. There is a man I must see. I will return in a few moments. Enjoy your wine and have some more.'

When he left, I found myself with nothing to do. So, sipping the wine which I enjoyed and sitting on the stool, I looked around me and absorbed the small details of the King's tent. There was not much. A few oil lamps which were lit at night but being miles from anywhere and between hills among trees, were no signal to an enemy. Then my eyes fell on the parchments I had not been shown. I saw lines of small circles, each with a short stubby line between and other things that looked the same but were more roughly drawn, or had bits scored out. There were even diagrams with longer lines, parallel, at an angle to the top of the parchment.

As the chest of parchment books lay open beside the table. I decided to investigate. Several I recognised, such as Plutarch, a Roman scholar of the first and second century AD, whom I had heard of but never read, one by Tacitus, another Roman, and Seneca, whom I knew and admired, even some in Greek which I had not seen before. There were some of the Gospels in Latin and a book which I immediately picked up because of its title: *De Rei Militari*[iv] by Flavius Vegetius Renatus, a 4th century AD expert in military training. I began to read it and soon found that the author recommended that infantry should be taken on route

---

[iv] *Of Military Matters*

marches over rough country in full kit three times a month—obviously Bruce thought this insufficient, for he was driving us twenty miles a day and more by then, three times a week. And where Renatus expected 20 Roman miles in five hours, which I calculated was about 4 Roman miles an hour, Bruce drove us much faster: the same distance in four hours. If you couldn't keep up you got your arse slapped with the blade of a sword. Partly, but not completely, in fun. There was some shame in it. Renatus also recommended running (which I had experienced from my first day in the army) and swimming which I had also learned by the simple technique of throwing me into a river, the standard method in that army. You either swam or drowned. If you were too stupid to learn you were no use.

When Bruce returned, he sat down and studied the parchments carefully. 'I see you have one of my books?'

'Yes, Sire. I see where the training comes from. But you have extended it, made it harder.'

'Should I be following Renatus, then?'

'No, Sire. You should do as you think best: mould it to your own needs.'

'You did not move the parchments then?'

'They are not my business, Sire.'

'But the books are fair game. Quite right. Did you look at the parchments?'

When I admitted I had done so, he said: 'Why did you do that?'

'They look odd. I am sorry. I should not have. They must be private.'

'What do you think they are?'

I thought for a moment, looked again and replied: 'It's the plan for the pikemen[8], I think. Each small circle made with the quill is a man and each short line his pike.'

'But there is more than a circle. What else do you see?'

'A short body and two arms.'

'Why are the men shown apart?'

'So that the pikes have room to manoeuvre. The points need to be aimed with the butt fixed in the ground.'

'Now you see how useful scribing is. It helps to make plans that win battles.'

All of this I already knew. The control of an army was very easy when reduced to numbers of men and companies on a parchment. You could even do without the parchment: remember how it was when you last saw it! That was the real value of scribing. The mind could hold the image—many, many images—and you could have them in front of your inner eye in a moment, any time you wanted. That was power!

'What do you make of the figure with the parallel lines at an angle?' said Bruce, finally.

I had wondered about this, been troubled by the puzzle. Suddenly, I understood. I think it is the formation of the pikes. If the men are kneeling and every head is behind the one in front, the pike, which is set in the ground, is free to be aimed at the attacking cavalry.'

'Very good,' said Bruce, smiling. 'But what else do you see?'

But I had to admit that was all I could see. Only much later did I understand the full meaning of that figure.

The Bannockburn Area, 23rd June 1314

4

PREPARATIONS FOR A BATTLE

That was also the day the Islesmen arrived. Most were called Macdonald. So they had two names to distinguish them. Roddy John or Wullie Marut or Angus Dubh or some other combination. They spoke a dialect of the Irish that was hard to follow, though Irish was used a lot in Carrick at that time. There were many of them and their lord was a cousin of Bruce, so many that he undertook their training himself. Thus, that evening we were sent to guard the area around the Torwood while they alone stumbled about in the dark learning what was expected. Some extra routes were made on the slope for them alone so that they could get down to the Carse quickly but their first practice was down south at Torwood during daylight that very day, so that they could see better. The English had only just left the Border at Berwick and it would be safe. Even so, scouting parties were sent all around to make sure of the surrounding countryside so that no one could see what was happening.

There was an eerie silence about the countryside, an emptiness, as if everyone not involved had gone off to some distant place in the north or west to hide in the wilderness and wait upon the outcome, taking possessions, like wagons and animals, with them, probably having buried most of their goods and stored food in a tree trunk, a cave or underground, though anything left there would do badly because of the dampness. Keeping things dry underground was impossible, unless it was in a wooden chest and these were rare, took a long time to fashion and needed a good carpenter. They would even warp and split underground, as I knew.

The Islesmen rejoined us beside the Bannockburn in the morning, taking up any places they could find for their tents, some, without tents, making rough brochs of the kind we had ourselves, stone-sided with turves and branches for cover or just reeds over some poles, using a tree if one was handy. So many Scots had arrived by now that there were almost too many, a situation that Bruce had never expected. It was his doing of course and he could not have understood just how highly he was valued. It was him they came for as much as the country. He was our inspiration. Even so, no doubt many men stayed at home. It was safer there and they had families and farms to look after. If they lived far away there had to be a good chance that the English would never reach them, no matter what disaster took place. Some, no doubt, left for the wilderness, taking their families, livestock and possessions with them in the hope of somehow staying clear of the usurper, after the expected battle had been lost.

To most of us that seemed inevitable. We spoke of it among ourselves all the time around the campfires in the evening, then especially, resting after our training. Magonigal, who was older than most of us, had seen an English army ten years before when they invaded this very place and lay outside Stirling for months besieging it into submission with huge siege weapons never seen before that threw big boulders at the wall and broke it down.

'What was their army like?' I asked him one evening as we sat together.

'Every diveesion has a different uniform fae aw the others. They're no' like us, in broon or green hame-spun. They huv fine tunics and guid weepons, all o' them the same. Ye never saw sae mony archers and sich big bows. I saw a man shoot an arra as faur as the hill ower there,' pointing.

'I don't believe it,' I said. The hill was three hundred yards away.

'He did, Ah tell ye.' said Magonigal with a stern face.

'But how is it possible?'

'The bow wis taller than him. But he was ower strang and he could puull it richt back tae his ear. Ah'll niver forget the noise it made. I was atween him and the hill and Ah heard the whirr ower ma heid. It smacked intae a tree as if it wid split it in twa.'

'How could it go so far?'

'It's the power in the wid. The light coloured yew is on the ootside o' the curve and the daurk colour inside. The sap wid is better on the ootside 'cause it bends easier and the ither kind gangs best inside. The shaft is cut fae the tree and they ken whit tae dae tae get the maist oot it.'

'Why don't we have them? Bows like that, I mean.'

'We dae, a few. No' many but some.'

'Well then? Why don't we have people like that?'

'They huv the skill. It takes years tae learn. I spoke tae a Welshman wance—some are Welshmen. His Irish is like oors, near enough. He said he sterted on the bow when he wis a wee laddie and his faither changed the bow makin' it bigger as he grew. The main thing is he fired it every day, often. Huntin' in Wales is the way tae feed yoursel'.'

'Are there not poaching laws, for taking the King's deer?'

'Mibbe. I don't ken. Mibbe the Welsh jist go their ain way.'

Kincaid said: 'What about their cavalry? Do they have big horses?'

'Aye, horses higher than a man; and broad, wi' muckle thick legs like tree trunks.'

'Wan slash wi' a knife in the neck wid dae them in,' said Crosby, a wee man with a squint and bandy legs but a feisty rascal.

'Haw sur? It's no' sae easy,' said Magonigal. 'They're protectet. They huv trappers that cover the hale horse wi' a thick cloak o' leather and tapestry or sich, wi' the colours o' the man that owns it; and the heid has a leather covering and blinkers.'

'Whit are blinkers?' said Crosby.

'They cover the eyes so the horse doesnay see the armit men in front. So it jist runs intae them and ower the tap ae them when it knocks them doon.'

'And does it always knock them doon?'

'Nae bother. The horse is a ton weight, a huge thing, that knocks ye doon flat—aye, it wid knock ten men doon flat. That's how big and strang it is. When ye hear the thunder o' they big hooves comin', ye better get oot the way. And there's a man on the back ae it, mind. And he's in fuull airmour and weighs anither hauf a ton.'

Magonigal stared at us, as we had nothing to say and then laughed. 'Haw sur? De ye think that's aw?'

'I suppose there's a lance, too,' I said.

'Ye suppose richt!' said Magonigal, chuckling. 'It wid skewer ye and pin ye tae the grun'. —Aye skewer twa or three o' ye and pin ye aw thegither!' He laughed at our discomfort at our future —conveyed by bloodless faces; and the image of us all stuck together on the lance and pinned to the ground.

There was a silence then until Kincaid suggested: 'But their leaders are no' like Bruce?'

'No, but they're all verra guid jist the same. They've aw fought wars in France and won their battles. Aw tried and tested men.'

'So we are in difficulty, then?' I concluded. 'How are we going to manage it?'

'It will no' be you that does it. But we dae huv Bruce. Mibbe he can dae it.'

'What are we gonny dae?' said Duns, a grey-haired man with an accent from some border village, obviously nervous at the prospect of the conflict, like many of us.

'Haw sur? Whit dae ye mean?' said Magonigal, affronted.

'I mean what happens when they come?'

'You tell him,' said Magonigal to me, smiling at having set me a test.

'Where are they coming from?' I said to Duns.

'Berwick on the border. No' far from ma hame.'

'And where are they going to?'

'Stirling. The Castle. And if they're no' in time, the castle is forfeit tae us.'

'So they will be on time, you can rely on that. Where do they go after Berwick?'

'Emburgh. Anybody kens that. There's nae ither way for horses and cairts. And they'll huv hunners ae thaim.'

'And where after that?'

'Fawkirk.'

'And then?'

'Stirling.'

'And how do ye get from Falkirk to Stirling?'

'Alang the road. Whit else?' he replied, irritated by the obvious answer.

'How does the road get across the burn?'

'How do Ah ken?'

'Weel, is there a bridge?' said Magonigal, impatiently.

'Naw, there's nae bridge,' Duns replied confidently.

'So how does the road get across the burn?'

'There's a Ford, of course!' I said.

'Haw sur? Does that tell ye whit Bruce will dae?' But Duns was looking blank, as if the question was beyond him.

'Bruce will fight them at the Ford,' I said.

'Richt', said Magonigal, approvingly.

'But whit if they don't go by the Ford?' said Duns.

'How can they?' Magonigal and I said together. He added, 'It's the only way across for their cairts. Even their horses couldnay cross for the trees and banks on baith sides. But it's no' that maistly. It's the high grun oan baith sides ae the burn. It's packed wi' trees and horsemen couldnay get ower there.'

'How wull Bruce defend the Ford?' said Kincaid.

'With a battery of pikes, what else?'

'Well, why are we no' practising this?' said Crosby angrily.

There was a silence for a time and then I said. 'There's no need. It's simple.'

Magonigal smiled, thinking he had found me out: 'Haw sur? Ye mean we line up oor pikes alang the bank?'

'No,' seeing suddenly that there was a better way, I said: 'No. We will leave them a nice space just across the burn so that they will cross it and then we'll set our pikes in a big half circle. And they will charge onto our pikes and we will hold them and the more of them that cross and charge the better it will be for us, for they will come roaring across the burn charging into each other and soon be too close-packed to do anything.'

'But Ah thocht they were huge horses that ran ower the tap of ye like thunder?' said Crosby, annoyed.

'They have to cross the burn first and that will slow them down and then they have to ride up the far bank. That will cut their speed. Best of all, the space left to them to charge on the north bank will be too little. Just twenty or thirty yards, at most.'

'But why?' said Crosby. 'Why no' line up the pikes at the burn bank?'

'Because they might not cross, then,' I said. 'We want them to cross. We want them to charge us because we can hold them when they have little speed. Mostly we want as many as possible to cross into the space for they will soon fill it up and be unable to manoeuvre. That means they will be stuck fast in a wee space filled to overflowing and we can pull them down and dispatch them with the wee axes under the visor or the spike on the back of the blade in the back of the head right through the helmet.'

There was a gasp from those present as they suddenly understood and then some stood up hurriedly, for Bruce had quietly approached in the darkness and was standing there listening and they took off their caps or helmets as signs of respect. But Bruce would have none of it, no ceremony was wanted. 'Sit ye down, men,' he told them. Then, looking at me, 'I see that you have made a good plan, Craufurd. Maybe I'll use it.' He smiled then, and I knew it was not new to him and that he had made this very plan himself some time before. He said: 'There's one thing missing from your plan. What makes the Ford special?'

I thought for a minute and pictured it in my mind's eye and then I saw. Excitedly, I shouted: 'Because it is a ford, only a few knights can cross at one time. It's like...like, the neck of a flask or a bottle. Ye stop the wine getting out by plugging the neck with a cork. Our pikemen are the cork.'

Bruce smiled: 'And the cork is on the north bank.' He took a sook of our jug when invited and chatted a while and then left us to visit other parts of the army and it was then that Kincaid asked the question that had been rising in my mind.

'What happens after they get beat in the space on the north bank?'

Magonigal looked across at me expectantly, in the firelight. 'They will have to retreat,' I told them. 'There's nothing else they can do. They can't make progress against us. They can't get onto the Dryfield. That's this place, all the way to St Ninians and all the way to the Carse. It's called the Dryfield because it's always dry: no streams and no pools of water. We have to use the burn for our water and camp beside it. They will have to go back the way they came and go somewhere else. They must reach the Castle and smartly, or forfeit the prize. They can't go west because of the bogs. They'll have to go north east down the slope towards the Forth.'

Magonigal nodded, approvingly and raised the jug for a sook. Then he passed it to me and said: 'And then what?'

'They go on to the Castle,' said Duns. 'That's what they came for. They must go there.'

'How can they?' said Crosby. 'Livilands Bog's in the way.'

Into the silence, I eventually asked the vital question: 'Where did they camp when they came here ten years ago?'

Magonigal slapped his thigh and laughed. 'That's richt, sur! Now yer talkin'. They camped in the Carse, where they always camp. It's the best place for miles roon aboot. Twa fine burns either side and the Hillock in the middle for the King's tents. Where else could be better?'

'But what about the Castle?' said Duns.

'The Castle's nae problem when their army is sae close. The Castle disnae matter. It will never be given up when the English army's in plain sight.'

It was then, staring into the fire while poking fresh flames into the peat and wood on it, that I suddenly put two and two together. My head lifted and I saw Magonigal staring at me, move his head from side to side and, for emphasis, wag his forefinger telling me to say no more. My mouth opened wide to spurt it out, what it all meant. But I said nothing. Gradually, I realised that silence really was best for these men. They would find out soon enough what Bruce intended and they would be fearful then. For what Bruce meant to do was as dangerous a move as I had ever heard of. At first sight, it was downright madness.

Next day, while Magonigal and I were told off to climb a hill to the south west and keep an eye open for our horsemen returning from a scouting party, we were left alone for a time, he and I. It was then, just the two of us, that he raised the question of the practice in getting down a slope in the dark.

'Haw sur? Whit's Bruce gonny dae wi' us then? De ye ken?'

'The English will camp in the Carse as before and he means to get up early and catch them unawares. He's going to march right up to them and confine them between the streams. That makes another bottleneck.'

'Ye'r richt. Why's he gonny dae that?'

'Because they won't expect it. They'll expect us to run away and be chased and hunted down, fleeing like the times in the past— like Falkirk.'

'But dae ye see the rest ae it?'

I thought for a moment and then asked: 'What do you mean?'

'How close to them is he gonny march us?'

'I don't know. Enough to close off the space between the streams: the burn and Pelstream. Once that's closed off they are trapped there. They can't escape to the front or the sides. The streams will be muddy and impassable with an army scattered all about there for a while.'

Magonigal laughed at me for a young stupat then. 'You think aboot it, just think aboot it. Eventchally you'll get it.' He left me, laughing as he went.

'Tell me,' I shouted after him.

'Naw, ah willnay,' he shouted back. 'Ye wid niver believe it.'

'Did he tell ye, then?'

'Aye, me and a few ithers that ver' near guessed it. But we're sworn tae keep quiet. Ye widnay credit it.'

'But will it work?'

He stopped all of a sudden and turned then to face me as if for the first time he had doubts. 'That's whit all the practice is fur.'

'I know that. But will it work?'

'Aye,' he said uncertainly. Then, with more confidence: 'Aye it will work! Because ae the practice! Everybody kens whit tae dae. Even if they huv nae idea whit it's fur.'

A few days later came the culling of the army. There were so many that only the best were to be kept. The entire Dryfield and all the way to the burn as far as Gillies Hill was alive with men. And they were getting in each other's way. Everybody in our company was lined up in the usual order at the edge of camp, as if for the morning march in the dark and Boyd himself and two marshals looked us over. Several were taken out of the line. When they came to Crosby a marshal said: 'You are to go to the camp at Gillies Hill beyond Halbert's Bog. When we need you we'll send for you. It's a fine place up there among the trees. There are many good glades. '

Crosby was incensed. 'Why me? Ah'm as guid as anybody!'

'You'll do as yer telt. Ye ken the rules. They are the difference between winning and losing. Ye've been telt till wur blue in the face. Now go wi' these ither buggers. Begone.'

'Ah wullnay! Why me fur Goad's sake?'

Boyd, who did not like losing good men, was angry: 'Yer too fucken wee. No' five fit tall. How kin you deal wi' a six fit high knight in airmour? Ye've nae chance! Ye jist dinnay have the strength.'

'Bae Christ, ah'll pit you oan yer back, ya big bastart!' And Crosby was as good as his word. He kicked Boyd in the crotch and when he bent double, Crosby hit him over the head with the shaft of the pike which was already in his hand. Boyd lay on the grass for ten minutes recovering. Crosby moved not one inch, stood above him ready for more conflict.

When Boyd got up—was allowed to get up, in peace—ruefully fingering his bloody scalp and curbing his anger with difficulty, he said: 'Weel, you can stay. But only you. Ye're a violent wee bugger and maybe we need ye after aw.' The others, who had not complained and demonstrated their temper by fighting back, were sent off as already determined. When they had gone, one marshal said: 'Are you sure that's the right thing to do? What if the King hears?'

'The King kens fine. What we need are fechting men. And that yin's wan ae them.'

'But what about his short size?' said the marshal.

'It micht jist be a good thing. He can run among them quickly and hit them ower the heid wi' he's axe. He's a wild cat yon wan.'

When the cull had taken place, the next morning there was a practice with the whole army before dawn. By this time, there were over

100 routes down through the trees on the slope which stretched from the burn at the Carse to the Pelstream east of St Ninians, about a mile northwards, every route identified at the start up on the Dryfield with a standard or pennant or a shield bearing the colours of the leader of the company. This was a reminder of where to sit in our line before the marshal tapped the leader on the shoulder at which he would set forth into the wood, following the path that he (and everyone else) now knew so well and we followed, every man's hand touching the shoulder of the man in front to make sure we did not get lost, though now that was unnecessary for most of us, even in the dark, for it was nearly midsummer and never did get completely dark. Indeed, as dawn approached, the light was better than ever before.

There must have been about 100 companies in our division, with different numbers of men, all of whom knew each other well by this time, except for new comers, probably about 150 men in each. So over most of the length of the wood, the three divisions would descend, leaving the ends for Moray at the Pelstream side and Douglas at the burnside. At the south end of the wood, the slope was severest of all, very dangerous for men even in daylight, fully sixty feet high and steep. Because of this, Douglas was to reach the Carse from the valley floor containing the burn itself, moving into the Carse and rounding the corner to the north to get close to the south end of Bruce's division. Moray did the same: led his men into the Carse from the north side of the wood beside the Pelstream where the ground is more flat and the going easier in the dark. Even so, there was woodland in both places and several routes, each with some rags, were put in place and practised beforehand. There were also a few markers in the ground to show exactly where the left flank of Douglas's division would line up and the right flank of Moray's. These markers were something low and natural that no one else would think twice about. A big stone with a white mark on the side facing the wood: we could see it but no one else. It was not very big, just big enough for us to see as we approached the starting line. Moray wanted to do the same but Bruce would not allow it. Nor would he allow a wooden stake or even a bit of a bush or a tree that might have been taken from afar as a useful piece of kindling and removed. In the end, that marker was a short stake no more than a foot high and six inches wide. On one side, the side facing us, there was a white rag, not more than five inches wide. Since the two markers were different, natural seeming, low down and about 400 yards apart at that stage of the Carse which was just under 1000 yards apart[9], they would never be noticed or connected in that flat, slightly undulating, ground at a distance of 500 yards or more. In the case of the wings, the markers showed the end of the front line of the central division.

In this way, the central division must have had about 15,000 men; the other two on the edge, about five thousand each.[10] The Islesmen accounted for about 3,000. So the two Bruce divisions had been about the same as the wings.

It was very unlikely that any Englishman would venture close enough to the foot of the wood to see anything; they would all congregate well out of bowshot of that place.

Did the men realise what was planned? A few. Most gave it not a thought. It was just one of the exercises that we did habitually, like moving inland to the west in the dark or marching 30 miles in daylight or exercises with pikes or hatchets and forming companies and divisions in daylight so that we all, the commanders especially, could see very easily what we were doing and learn therefrom. Those who thought this particular morning exercise might have a bearing on the coming battle immediately discounted it, usually under the scorn of others. Why would Bruce desert a fine natural fortress like our Dryfield, with its dense palisade of trees on mostly steep slopes to get down on the flat Carse with all its manifest disadvantages of lack of trees to form a protective screen? Of course that was madness. Besides, we would not be going anywhere without our cavalry going first. That was the thinking of ordinary men.

5

THE POOLS IN THE CARSE

There was a lot of rain that week. Indeed, these years were bad for rain and the crops everywhere suffered: drowned in the fields, which were soaking. When it started, the King was worried. Every day he went to the Carse to look and see what effect it would have. And I realised what ailed him: if the rain did not stop, the Carse might actually become a sheet of water which sometimes happened, as he admitted to me alone, when the River Forth could even burst its banks carrying so much water down to the sea. But it wasn't just that. Rainwater not only poured down the bounding streams of the Carse (the Bannock burn and the Pelstream) it came off the escarpment all along its length, all the way to very near Stirling itself. So Livilands Bog became much worse than usual, for the escarpment drained into it from three springs, at different places, a very extensive area that stretched a long way towards Stirling and a long way[11] out into the Carse of Stirling, bounded as it was by the River Forth, almost as far as the Forth, indeed. No bad thing from our point of view, because it made the Bog a far worse obstacle than usual in summer.

The other effect was that the Carse soon had its pools of water. Some of us who were trusted to keep our mouths shut went down there every day with Bruce after that, just to count them. The reason for our interest was of course that if the Carse did become a sheet of water [12] (and few of us had ever seen this) the English would never camp there. So all the best laid schemes and all the training we had done would go for nothing.

So for a few days, because of heavy rain, the Bannock burn became a brown torrent. To try and cross on foot was to risk being blown over and drowned in it. On the northern boundary of the Dryfield, the Pelstream, which started in a dozen springs on Gillies Hill, tore right through the centre of St Ninians, right across Main Street, the only street north and south; and it wasn't just the water landing on Gillies Hill that caused this. All the water on the west half of Coxet Hill drained into the northern part of Halbert's Bog and that drained into the Pelstream during its surge towards St Ninians and the Carse and the River and, eventually, the Firth of Forth and the Sea. The water raining down on the eastern half of Coxet Hill also ended up in the Pelstream, though a bit further down near the beginning of the Carse in a tributary. So, for a day or two, the citizens on the north side of St Ninians were cut off from those on the south side and there was no travel on foot from north to south anywhere within fifty miles. That's how important the road was and the ford at Milton on the burn and the ford at St Ninians where the Pelstream blasted through the village into its own narrower gorge on the way to the Carse. Nor was that all. Almost all[13] the water that fell on Gillies Hill fed the springs of the Pelstream, right at its source. So these also had a formidable effect upon the width, depth and power of the stream.

Another effect of so much rain was that everything got soaking wet, weapons rusted, armour (for those few who had any to wear) and mail, the same. Life in tents for those who had them was still bearable but, for those like me and my companions from Carrick and elsewhere who depended upon laying our heads down in a broch made of stones, turfs and branches, the constant fall of water from the skies could not be kept out and it was a serious, irritating source of discomfort.

One day, I was standing naked outside the broch trying to wring out my clothes, so I could the more easily hang them up to dry inside on a string above the fire. The smoke had been arranged to escape through the roof at an angle in a corner, so that water did not so easily penetrate. Bruce came by as he did every day several times a day. He laughed at me.

'You don't like the rain, do ye?' he said.

'Does anybody?' I shouted back, scunnered at the inconvenience and the impossibility of improving it.

'What do you think the English think of all this rain?'

'They will all have tents. It won't trouble them.'

'Don't you believe it. They will be in full armour and it will rust and all their weapons. And their arrows will be wet and their bow-strings. Did you ever shoot with a wet bow-string?'

'I never shot with a dry one,' I replied. 'I have nothing to shoot with. But I expect they have a way of keeping their strings dry.'

'You are right, of course.[14] But they are having to travel and the road will be very muddy and difficult. I believe they will dislike the rain far more than we do.'

'What can we do, Sire, about this rain?'

Bruce, on the point of moving away, turned and grinned: 'Pray for sunshine.'

His prayer was answered. After several days of intense rain, the next day, the sun shone and it was a fine summer sun. We ran down through the wood to count the pools in the Carse, Bruce among us, the knowing, silent few, who had penetrated the plan. I counted 35 pools, one of them a hundred yards long and a yard deep,[15] another at an angle, about the same, and a very big one almost as long on the north side of the Knoll, a hillock[16] or large mound about a quarter mile by an eighth in size and about sixty feet high in the Carse-centre. Bruce did not agree. 'There are other pools behind the Hillock that you can't see,' he told me.

'How do ye know that kind of thing?' I asked him, for it was genuinely puzzling.

He smiled and tapped his nose with a forefinger. 'I have been here before many times,' he told us. 'Winter and summer. The pools are always in the same place. They form in the undulations of the land but they are none of them more than a yard deep.'

I was still puzzled. 'Why are there pools at all?' I said. 'I don't understand it. There are no pools anywhere else.'

'It's all the rain from the Dryfield that comes running off the escarpment and down through the woods. That's the water you can see because it's on the surface. But underground there is a lot of other water moving downhill in the direction of the River Forth, which is only a mile away. Between the two of them, there is no room for the absorption of the water still falling. So pools of water form in the undulations of the flat ground.'

'But they must eventually dry up? We've seen the Carse without pools of water often enough.'

Bruce explained: 'They do dry up, of course. But it takes a few days. With this amount of rain having fallen, it will take several days for the pools to disappear.'

'But how do you know that?'

'I have seen this many times. I understand it. I have even been here many times this last year because I knew a problem had to be solved. Understanding the ground is the key to winning the battle,' he told me quietly.

That night I wondered about the things he had told me and there was still a question without an answer. I had to know. Brought up as a scholar, the demand to know was all consuming; nothing got in the way of it. In pursuit of the truth, the world would be turned upside down. So the very next day I sought out Bruce again and when I got him on his own I put it to him: 'Why should this Carse have pools of water when the others on either side don't have any?'

I think I never saw him smile so broadly that whole week. He came and ruffled my hair. 'That's a miracle that question. That you could even ask it, is a miracle. Few people would think of it. But it is fundamental, as you can see.' He paused to think how to convey the answer and then asked me a question: 'How does this carse differ from the ones on either side?'

This was hard and we were standing looking at the carse, our Carse, below the wood at that moment. Of course I couldn't see the edges of the Carse and it made it harder. So he decided to show me and we walked together off to the Bannock burn and then down the burnside. Since there was only the two of us and the King wore no regalia of any kind, no one would have given us a second glance. But then, there was nobody about. The whole world around was locked up safely somewhere else. The very air itself smelt of trouble and sweat and tears—a lot of them—and blood, that too, of course. That always goes with trouble. Especially our kind.

'I did not see Julius Caesar in your library, Sire?' I said, as we crossed the Carse to the burn below the wood.

'That's one that got lost, during all our moving, often in a hurry. But *The Gallic Wars* is an important book, I grant you.'

'The Romans were great engineers,' I remarked, thinking of the fortifications thrown up sometimes during a battle like Alesia and bridges like the one across the Rhine.

'Yes, one day perhaps, in more settled times, I will take up ship building.'[17]

'We don't need engineering here, do we Sire?'

'No. Do you understand why not?'

'We have a natural fortress to defend here. It would not be improved by fortifications. The enemy would be wary of it and we don't want that. Best if it remains in a natural state. Then they won't understand how good a defence it is.'

Bruce smiled and ruffled my hair. 'Right again. What else could I learn from Julius Caesar?'

'His habit of taking off suddenly, expecting his men to follow him where ever and whenever he wanted; even on the darkest night.'

'Why do I not do that here, then?'

'I'm not sure, Sire. Caesar was such a great general, I would have expected you to do this.'

'I need to be able to go off alone like this, with just you and I. I do not want to be followed by the whole army all the time. Some things must be kept from them.' The daring move he planned to make in the battle, for example, I thought. Knowing that in advance would panic everyone. It made me feel faint just to think of it.

So down the burn side we went, keeping the Hillock with its trees in the centre on our left and staying on the north bank, our territory, as we had decided. Once we passed the Hillock there, sure enough, were two more pools I had not counted. We came at last to another stream and, as we began to walk upstream along its bank, Bruce, said: 'This is the Pelstream.'

'Of course,' I agreed. 'It has to be, for there are no streams in the Carse at all. That's all this could be.'

'Do ye understand now?' Of course I did not. 'Notice that you are not quite right. There are a couple of shallow pools to the east in the next Carse. You can't see them from here. Why do you think that is[18]? This carse is full of pools as you can see. I've counted 37 so far. Some you can't see for the Knoll. But you are right: this Carse is unique. Full of pools. The Carses on either side are quite different, none or almost none. But why?'

I was still baffled. We began to walk up the other side of the Carse along the bank of the Pelstream around the Hillock with it on our left and the Pelstream on our right, heading now back to our wood on the slope and the camp further over across the Dryfield and St Ninians too, up the tree-clad slope. The Pelstream, because of the intense rainfall, was a raging brown torrent when it came out of the wedge it had cut for itself. I looked behind me and noticed that the Carse of Stirling was not the same. Suddenly, I saw the difference. 'This Carse of ours is hemmed in by the two streams, the burn and the Pelstream. They join behind the Hillock.'[19]

'That's it,' said Bruce. 'This carse is enclosed by streams and the two carses on either side are not. Why does that make a difference?'

'Because the water level under these other carses falls all the way to the surface of the river. But that's thirty feet down! That means there's plenty of room for water falling from above to be absorbed! So there are no pools there.'

'Good,' said Bruce with as much delight as I ever heard from him till then. 'But what about this Carse. Our special one? What's the difference?'

'It's hemmed in by the streams…', I said haltingly, half seeing.

'So how deep is the underground water in our carse?'

'Very near the surface! There's no river surface thirty feet down in this case. The streams meet at the ground surface. So there's no space for the rain falling to be absorbed in.'

Never before had I experienced ecstasy: the intellectual kind. I understood what Bruce had understood and it was a miracle, what he had found. And I had followed him. And with little prompting, I had seen it for myself. I knew myself that day to be a scholar, a person who could think things out for himself, could see what others would never see for themselves in a million years.

But Bruce was not finished with me. Like my old dominie, he left me with a question to ponder. 'Why are there two pools in the carse across the burn?' I had no idea and he left me to think it out by myself.[20]

6

FILLING THE GAPS

The next day was like all the others: practice and more practice and by nightfall, I was exhausted and fell asleep like a dead man but I did not remain asleep. I awoke to find my mind teeming with anxiety. Somehow, during the night, a doubt had formed in my head, grown, erupted and gradually became so enormous that it surfaced as if from a great deep pool and suddenly it broke through like a great whale, with mouth so wide open, it might swallow me. I woke with a start, feeling like Jonah, sat up on my bed of heather and twigs and knew instantly that I must go and take immediate action. There was no need to reflect further. This was important! I had to find Bruce and tell him.

I sprang up and, saying nothing to my snoring colleagues, I went outside and ran along the path in the darkness to the King's tent where lights were still lit. I could see the figures through the canvas standing around the table and I pleaded with the guards to admit me. 'I must see the King,' I said. And when I was turned away with a sneer, as if I was of no account, uttered the words again but this time I shouted them. 'Let me in for God's sake! This is important!'

That sentry drew his sword and, hearing it come out of the scabbard, Bruce himself appeared. 'What's this? Craufurd, is it? What do you want at this hour?'

'Sire,' I pleaded. 'There is something you have forgotten! I need to speak to you privately.'

'Privately is it? Well, you better come in then.' And I was allowed to follow him inside. There I found half a dozen company commanders,

Moray, Douglas and Sir Robert Keith, the Marshal, all gathered around the table and the King's chair which he promptly returned to. The atmosphere was fraught with conflict, seemed to lie in the very air like smoke, among steaming nostrils and large bodies shuffling restlessly on the benches as if about to strike. Intimidation hit me like a hammer. I felt as if I had no business there: a child among adults.

'Well, what is it boy? What have I forgotten?'

'Filling the gaps, Sire! How are we to fill the gaps?'

Bruce threw back his head and laughed and laughed, and looking around, said: 'See, I told you! This lad has the Latin. He can scribe parchments and he knows what that means. You should all get it. Your lives might be spared if you do.' Yet, as he looked around at them, few of them over thirty, all of them grey before their time and bearing their share of wounds, healed or partly healed, he added, consolingly: 'Well, maybe not. Maybe it's too late[21] for letters. You have all spent too many youthful years at war to play games with a dominie.'

To me he said: 'You may join us, lad. You might understand better than some of these. Sit there beside me and look at this.'

And so a space was made for me and I sat beside the King on a bench and was shown the parchment that all had been studying. There were two lines which were apart and then tapered but did not join. 'What are these, Craufurd?'

'The bounding streams of the Carse, Sire. The Pelstream on the left and the Bannock burn on the right. That rectangle in the centre is your division standing between the two markers. These other smaller rectangles on either side and ahead are the Earl's and the Lord Douglas's.'

Bruce was delighted. His face shone. 'See, what did I tell you? And did you see how quick he was? That's because he was tutored. To him, reading parchments is as natural as breathing.' Then to me: 'Go on boy what else do you see?'

'You don't know how far into the Carse you will get. So you must have gaps between the divisions. The question is: how are you to fill the gaps you must start out with, when you don't know how wide the gap will be?'

Bruce was suddenly the soul of happiness. He stood up and shouted to his attendants: 'Wine! Bring wine for all here!' And so it was that I found myself seated in the King's company with him standing—at a table on which I had only recently killed someone by cutting off his leg too close to the disease that was killing him—surrounded by a group of youngish veterans, grey-bearded before their time by a hundred conflicts, who mostly glowered at me for my book learning.

'Now boy, what is your answer?'

'Aw Sire,' growled Moray, 'This is not a time for children! They will be here in a few days.'

'Patience, Thomas, patience! Let the boy speak. Have faith. Come on now, lad. What do you see?'

'You must fill the gaps from the rear ranks of the centre division, your own, Sire. Half the back rank goes to fill the gap on the left and the other half goes to fill the gap on the right. That means 200 men will go to the left and 200 to the right. If the gaps are each fifty yards, that means four ranks in each gap. Not enough. So after them, the second rearmost rank, now the rear, because the other has left it, will do the same. That would make 8 ranks deep. And if you want more depth, you could send off the new rearmost rank as well and that would increase the number of ranks in each gap to 12, more than enough, Sire.

'However, there will not be as much as fifty yards in the gap because the width of the streams is only about 1000 yards at the very start of the Carse. You must be able to get into it some distance at least. The three divisions measure 800 yards. If you get as far as the narrowest point which, you told me, Sire, is 830 yards, the gap is only 15 yards on either side. 200 men would make about 14 ranks deep there. Enough, easily enough, to hold cavalry.'

'But why do we need gaps at all?' said Douglas, angrily. 'Why not just set off with the whole army in a line across the Carse?'

'Tell him, boy,' said Bruce, smiling.

'Because the Carse tapers! The men at the edges are going to end up in the water. What good are they there? Hundreds of our men struggling in that fast, deep, brown, muddy water. They would mostly drown! It might set up a panic among our other men. That must not happen. Some of the men in the battle lines might even jump into the streams to save them. Leaving other gaps!'

Bruce chuckled delightedly: 'That's what we want to happen to **them**: get **them** stuck in those muddy bounding streams. With their armour, they'll die there all by themselves with no help from us!'

Moray said: 'But Sire, why not decide where you will put the front row and then just have a line that length?'

'Because I don't know exactly where I am going to set the pikes. It will depend on them. The circumstances.'

'But you can't just change the length of the line in the middle of the march.'

'No, but I can change it at the end of the march. I can move men forward from the rear as he says and fill the gaps then.'

The two main opponents, Moray and Douglas, stood silently staring at the parchment diagram for a while until Douglas concluded: 'It's too dangerous, Sire. It could all go wrong.'

Moray said: 'What if the wings do not reach the bounding streams?'

'You must move your rear ranks to fill them,' said Bruce. 'How many would you need?'

'I don't know,' said Moray, uncertainly. 'It all depends.'

'What do you say, boy?'

'All three divisions measure 800 men across the front. That is 800 yards. Then there is the gap between them at the start. That should be fifteen yards.'

'Why?' asked Bruce, with a grin.

'Because the total frontal length will then be 830 yards and that is the shortest distance across the Carse, the best place to be, if we can. If we reach it, there will be no gaps to fill at all.'

But Moray was worried: 'What if we don't reach it—and I don't see how we can—and there is a gap between my division and the Pelstream?'

'You will do what the centre does', said Bruce: 'fill that gap from your rear ranks.'

'How many would I need?' asked Moray, again.

I said: 'The Carse is less than 960 yards across at any place we must reach. So that makes 130 yards short. And a full 100 yards is on the right wing that Lord Douglas must defend. That means the biggest gap you would have to defend is 30 yards.

'Your rear rank of 200 would make 6 of these gap filling ranks.'

'So you would need to take 2 rear ranks to fill that gap with 12 ranks. Enough!' said Bruce.

'In fact, Sire, it would be 13 ranks.'

Moray nodded agreement but Douglas was unhappy. 'If I am short of the Great Bend,' he said, 'I could have a hundred yard gap to fill on my right. That would take me 1200 men to fill with 12 ranks deep. That's six of my rear ranks.'

Moray and Douglas were both unhappy about the uncertainty of the size of the gaps.

Bruce said: 'There is not much danger and what little there is will be mended by practice.'

But a silence descended upon us. Bruce sat staring fixedly at some point on the tent wall, unwavering, evidently deep in thought.

It must have lasted several minutes, this moment of deep calculation. Some of us were becoming restive. Then it began, our joint lesson in how to plan a battle, from the master.

He took his hands which had been, like the rest of him unmoving until then—so worrying, this statuesque pose, that Gloag who knew him and his ways better than anyone, even began to murmur protests; that Bruce, still seated, adopted an attitude of prayer, his elbows still on the arm rests. And for a few moments the trance continued until finally, he moved and sighed and smiled at me and started:

'What are the problems we face, boy?'

'We have to get our men into the Carse. We have to get them formed up.'

Bruce was impatient: 'We can do that. What then?'

'We must advance and close off the Carse so that the English, when they charge, as they must, are hemmed in by the bounding streams.'

'So what is the difficulty?'

'We can't form a complete line because it will be too long. The Carse tapers and some men would end up in the streams and they would drown and they might panic the rest.'

'Should we aim for a particular point, in that case?'

'That might be wise, Sire.'

'Where should it be, then?'

I had no idea. Nobody else did either.

'Well, look at it this way: how close do we want to be?'

Again nobody knew.

'What is the point of getting close?'

'To confine them between the streams.'

'But why close?'

'So that they cannot get up speed when they charge.'

'Right,' said Bruce, smiling. 'So we **want** to get close to them. What is stopping us?'

'When we march out from the wood, they will see us and they will charge before we can get close. We just do not know how close we will get before they hit us.'

'Assuming they charge us while we are approaching, what should we do?'

'We must set our pikes and we must cover all gaps. —Immediately. Then they can't break through. If they break through our gaps, we're done for, Sire.'

'So that's what we must prepare for: them charging while we are still short of their lines. We can cover the gaps best if they are as small as possible. But we have no control of the gaps at the edges of the outer divisions: that will depend on the shape of the streams. It might even happen that one wing gets ahead of the other and no bad thing, if it is Douglas's: he needs to get as far into the Carse as possible to cover the bend in the burn.'

There was a dead silence for a time as everyone thought about this. Presently, Bruce said quietly: 'The smaller the gaps in the centre the better. There is less to do when their charge hits us.'

'Does that mean a single front line right across, then, Sire?' said Douglas, who had advocated this previously.

Bruce thought for a time and then said: 'No, I don't think so. Remember how the men fell like ninepins when someone tripped? No, making a single division is a recipe for disaster. We will keep the army in three divisions. They will be separate but close, so that the gap can be filled in a moment.'

'How close, Sire?' I asked.

'Five yards. Enough to keep the divisions apart and independent. Ten ranks need only fifty men to fill the gap. That's fifty off the rear rank of the centre on each side. That takes care of these gaps.'

'No matter where in the Carse my division is placed,' said Moray, 'I can easily fill the gap between the division and the Pelstream.'

'Yes,' agreed Bruce. 'Douglas's is the difficulty. He might have a gap of a full hundred yards to fill.' The King, looked at Douglas and laughed suddenly: 'You will just have to run your men down the Carse into position so that they get there quicker!'

As time would tell this is exactly what Douglas got his men to do. Moray was having none of it, however: 'We need to remember to make no noise, Sire. The sound of men running would alert their sleeping camp and get them up and at us quicker than anything.'

'Right, Thomas,' said the King, who added, smiling at Douglas: 'you will just have to get them running in silence. We can practise that tomorrow.'

Some laughed at the joke. Douglas was not one of them. He was worried about covering that 100 yard gap. But everyone knew he would be teaching his men to run quietly across the soft turf of the Carse the very next day. Except for one thing: by now no one was allowed anywhere near the Carse in daylight just in case a manoeuvre alerted a distant watcher to what was intended. So the practice would be elsewhere, out of sight.

'So that is what we need to do, folks,' said Bruce, finally. 'We could widen the front lines of our divisions and that would mean less gaps to fill in the centre and the edges. But I do not think it is wise. They must be kept apart and fully independent, so that anybody falling affects only one division, not all three.[22] You must be very careful to remind everyone to take care where they put their feet. They must march together and if someone falls, hit by an arrow, say, he is to be left and walked over. Preserving our formations, our independent formations, is everything. The two small gaps in the centre are easily filled. Moray's gap at the edge is easily filled by his own rear rank. Douglas's is harder to deal with because we do not know what will happen. But you can manage, Douglas, can you not?'

'I can that, Sire. I will train my rear ranks tomorrow on a variety of gaps between us and the burn. And we will soon see them running quietly and without so much as drawing a panting breath. You have trained them all well, Sire. These 30 mile marches have made everybody fit.'

And that was what we did. In the morning at first light, the first two rows of the three divisions were paraded in their usual positions with gaps of five yards between each. Extra men were drafted in to stand where the ends of the divisions would be. The full rear ranks were positioned where they would be expected, that number of yards from the front: about thirty. Then with the 3 divisions well defined, though not filled with men, two marshals, one at the rear and one at the front instructed the men when to move and where to move to, and all of it by sign language. At first there was an occasional curse and a little noise. But after several attempts the move was seen to be easy. Every man in the back line knew where he would be positioned in the gap, starting with the front and filling backwards. Control, as usual, was everything. The men moved when they were told to and not before and they went where they were wanted and not just anywhere. The entire arrangement was orderly and disciplined. And it was all done in silence. Instead of filling the central gaps with fifty men from the rear rank, Bruce had them filled with half the whole rank: 200; which meant the gap was 40 deep, making it even stronger than any other place in the entire formation. But that was only to happen if there was time. The first fifty to fill the gap were crucial: they had to fill the gap quickly. Once that was done we were in no danger. The rest could form up behind them very easily at leisure.

All of this work was done in a flattish area, mostly clear of trees to the west of the New Park, far from any prying eyes but just in case, watchers were sent out everywhere with orders to turn anyone away or capture and imprison anyone who so much as caught a glimpse of our doings. The main thing established was that the men in the rear line of the centre division were used to filling a gap of five yards by moving to the front at the command from the marshals. One marshal at the rear and one at the front at each end.

The practice then changed to filling the gaps at the streams. And here, different widths of gap were practised: twenty yards, thirty, right up to the full hundred in the case of Douglas's division, the men being changed, his men, this time. The rest all stood as onlookers.

Near the end of the practices a strange thing happened. Bruce spoke to the whole back line of the centre and then the second backline and the third of Moray's; and the last six of Douglas's, addressing them all in groups, division by division. Whatever happened, he told them, they were to consider themselves independent of the lines on either side. Once everything was in place with the three divisions stopped or marching, they would be under the control of the two marshals stationed at each end. These men would decide when to fill the gaps and if they were filled, and the divisions were taken forward or backward, these men would remain where they were until the marshals decided to fill the gaps that arose because of the further move. Only then, would they move to fill the gaps. I did not understand this at the time, could not see the reason for this. And I never had an opportunity to question Bruce about it because in the final period before the battle, he was involved everywhere, seeing to everything, checking and double checking, as was his way. Only later did I understand Bruce's remarkable foresight, during the battle itself.

When this practice at filling the gaps[23] was over, Bruce came to me and clapped me on the shoulder and walked me back to my broch.

'That was well done, Craufurd,' he told me. 'Do you think we're ready for them now?'

'I believe we are, Sire.' But as we walked towards the burn and the Dryfield, I said: 'How far do you think we will get into the Carse on the day itself?'

'It depends on several things. How much noise we make getting down to the Carse through the wood. How much noise getting into line. Not much, I fancy. How much noise they are making, for every noise of theirs makes it harder to hear ours. It depends on how ready they are, of course. If they are all up and mounted and facing us, they are bound to see us when we're still a few hundred yards away. If they charge then, we will have to be quick filling the gaps and setting the pikes. It could be a close run thing. If they get to us before we are ready, every gap filled, they might get around us and charge us from both directions. That would be unfortunate. Could be a disaster.'

'But how far, Sire?'

Bruce laughed: 'You really are a boy, Craufurd. You just never give up. He scratched his grey head, turned to me and said: 'It is impossible to say. But I would expect them to be overconfident and if they are, they will not be ready and they will not see us for a while and we might get close enough to them to do them some damage. The difficulty is Douglas's wing. He needs to get to the bend. That would make a big difference. '

'But Sire, he has enough men to close down the gap no matter where in the Carse he has to set his pikes.'

'That's true, boy. But it would just be nice if he had only 200 yards to cover and not 300.'

7

THE CHANGE OF PLAN

One evening, after vigorous weapons' training followed by a long march in our companies in every direction, which had a dual function, I see now, of not only increasing our stamina but of scouting all the land within a dozen miles of the Bannock burn and frightening away any scouts the enemy might have sent out, Sir Robert Boyd and I were called to the King's tent. There, around the trestle table on benches and a few stools, with Bruce at the head on his favourite chair with the arm rests, we found a number of others: Keith, the chief marshal, a tall thin man with hair prematurely grey, the dark haired Douglas, swarthy faced, brooding, but still a rather beardless giant, stooped over the table, and beside Bruce on his right hand, the Earl of Moray, his sandy haired nephew; several men I did not know and had not seen before and no one bothered to make introductions.

When the order to attend the King arrived, Boyd had quizzed the squire who brought it: 'Whit's the boy fur? Are thur wounds tae be patchet up?'

'I'm not sure,' was the reply. And as we marched along, Boyd, who was obviously irritated by my presence, said: 'Why do you think you're tae attend the King?'

I suppose I was a little puffed up about being invited along with Boyd. A great deal of attention had been paid to me by the King and it was natural I should be resented for it, especially as I seemed to get things right (because of my education in parchments) that other, older persons like Boyd could not understand so easily. I expect I rather fancied myself an important man with advice that was valuable.

I was about to be given a priceless demonstration of Bruce's own intellect in action. Until then, I had sometimes imagined that I had played a royal role in the planning. I was soon to see that this was an illusion, that Bruce knew all along what should be done. He would often pretend otherwise as a means of determining who among his associates had the faculties of the general that he himself possessed in such abundance. His questioning was the same sort as the dialogues of Plato which recorded the technique of Socrates, the great philosopher of Athens. This was the key to the illusion. Bruce's questions were his way of getting us to see what he had already seen.

What was about to take place was a kind of tutorial between him and us of the same kind I used myself to experience with the Oxford educated Dominican, Master Waleis, but far more impressive because it was completely original, spontaneous —dictated by circumstances—and brilliant, the kind of thing no other person could even be imagined to be capable of.

I was soon seated at the table among a dozen others on one side of him. He seemed very happy and relaxed, had been chatting to Moray on his right and the dark giant Douglas on his left, the prized lieutenants. Walter Stewart, his son in law (Marjorie, his young wife having died, however, a few years before), at the other end and myself crammed on a bench in between Boyd and Keith opposite Sir William Vieuxpont[v] (a grizzled, grey headed knight from some village in the eastern borders) and others.

Bruce began quietly enough. 'Are we clear what we are going to do?' There were several grunts of agreement.

'Is anyone unsure of what he is to do?' No one was. There was even a general feeling of happiness that we were ready for any eventuality. Moray spoke for us all:

'Sire, you have brought the army to a fine state of readiness. The country owes you a great debt.' Several assented to this loudly.

'Well, you might be happy, **but I am not**!' Bruce announced.

There was a dead silence. Disbelief filled the faces round the table. 'We have a hundred routes down through the wood and we are used to marshals telling every company when to go and where to line up. And it does work, I grant you. But is that the best way to deploy?'

Bruce waited for reactions. When there were none, he said to me: 'Well, boy, what do you say?'

---

[v] Norman French for 'Old Bridge.'

'It works perfectly well, Sire.'

'What are the critical factors in our descent of the wood?' This was the important question that opened up the topic to detailed examination and improvement.

'Silence, speed and order,' I replied. 'You have made that clear at every stage of our practice.'

'What have we left out?'

'I don't know, Sire. We have all three. The men are very quiet, the moves are made without conversation, sign language all the time, the movement is quick and the formation is orderly.'

'But there is something missing. What is it?'

No one could think of it. A few suggestions were made. All dismissed as irrelevant by the King.

Presently, Bruce called for wine and we each had a drink to give us further time to think about it. Yet, despite the additional stimulus and passage of time, no one could think of an answer.

Finally, he said: 'We have taken no account of the ground itself.' And still no one understood.

'What is the problem with the descent of the wood?'

'It is on a slope, Sire,' I volunteered. 'We need to be careful.'

'Right, boy. So?'

But none of us could see what he meant.

Bruce was annoyed. 'What is the next question?'

'How can we be more careful?' suggested Moray.

Bruce shook his head. 'We are careful,' said Keith, irritated. 'I don't see how we could be more careful than we are already.'

'Are all the routes down through the wood equivalent?' said Bruce.

'No,' said Moray. 'Some are easier than others.'

'At last! Which ones?' said Bruce.

'The centre.' I said. 'It is very much less steep there. Both ends of our bit are much worse.'

'Then,' said Bruce, 'why don't we use the centre for the most important moves? The place which is least likely to result in a fall. What would they be?'

'The front rank must be got into position correctly and first, for once it is set, the others can line up easily.'

'And what else?' But I could not think of it.

'Once the front rank is set,' said Bruce, 'the movements of the others will not be seen for the presence of the front rank which they are behind. So getting the front rank in place quickly and in silence is very important. It conceals the other movements. Get that first one done correctly and the others are far easier.'

After a pause to absorb this, Bruce continued: 'What else is important?'

'The rear ranks, Sire,' said Douglas.

'Then they should go down the centre too, later than the front rank but along the same route. They will be the last to go.'

I began to see what he intended. 'Do you mean to put all the companies down the centre?' I said.

'No. Why would that be a bad idea?'

'Because if something goes wrong on one path it could hold up the travel of thousands of others. It is better to have separate paths for most of the companies, despite the difficulty of the slope. Then their descent is independent of every other.'

'Right,' said Bruce. 'Only the front rank will use the centre and when all others are away, the three rear ranks can also go that way, for that will be quickest and safest.'

'Now, Douglas,' he continued, 'there is an area of flat ground in the valley of the Bannock near the Carse a few hundred yards in length and fifty in width and it has a priceless asset. It has no trees.' Everybody had the picture of the area in his mind, for we knew it well. 'Why is that, boy?'

'Because the burn bursts its banks every so often and floods the area drowning any seedlings.'

'Right! There I want you to assemble your force, Douglas, 25 ranks wide. There will be 200 in each column, the exact number needed to cover your front. You will march them down the valley to the Carse along the burnside and then make a left turn along the foot of the wood, using the marker as your guide and take up your position. When you reach it, you will already have a front of 200 men, 25 deep, the right hand side of your initial formation.' Douglas was delighted but objected: 'But there are a few trees there, Sire.'

'Ignore them. The 25 yard wide ranks will divide at any tree and reform beyond it. So the formation is secure. Just make sure the ranks are spaced out by a full yard, then going round a tree will be no problem.'

'That really is much better, Sire,' Moray agreed, smiling. 'I could do the same. It would save time collecting companies and marshalling them. There isn't the space beside the Pelstream but up on the hill there is. There are trees there, though.'

'Yes, but there are some good clear spaces just below the escarpment when the slope to the Carse is much less.' Bruce smiled at us. 'Then there we have it finally,' said the King to Moray. 'You will move down that slope along the side of the Pelstream, Thomas, and make a right turn when you reach the marker, nephew, and your left side will become your front rank.'

'What if someone stumbles in the dark?' said Keith. 'And they fall like ninepins?'

'Each man will have his hand on the shoulder of the man in front. They have practised this many times, their eyes are used to the dark and, anyway, it is a lot less dark now that we are nearly at mid-summer day.'

'So we have wasted a lot of our planning, then?' suggested Vieuxpont.

'Not at all,' said the King. 'We learnt a great deal from it. We trained ourselves to manage in the dark and we have found the best way of deploying. That is what all the practice did for us. Without it, we would never have seen it. Nearly all our routes down through the wood will be used: those in the centre division. Only the front rank and the last three will go by the centre. Marshals will be needed for the centre division as before. These changes will be easily accommodated, for everyone knows the ground very well by now.'

'What about the few rags we have on the wings to guide us to the Carse?' said Moray.

'Get rid of them. See to it yourselves,' looking at both him and Douglas. But everyone knew that Bruce would check in person. Bruce did not want anything unnatural that was not absolutely necessary to be left where it might be noticed.

When all this had been agreed, Bruce seemed satisfied and called for more wine and sat quietly staring into space while the rest of us chatted among ourselves.

Presently, he spoke again, as if awaking from a sleep. 'Maybe we are missing something. I feel it.' All talk stopped.

'Why is this new way of forming up the wings so much better? Because they form up before they ever get onto the Carse. That saves time. As soon as they arrive they are ready to march. That is a marvellous advantage. Can we not deal with the centre in the same away?' He looked around at us, wonderingly. 'Suppose we form up half the centre division on the flat ground of the Dryfield just before the top of the wood: 35 ranks wide and 200 columns and march the 35 ranks right down the centre and turn right at the bottom? And march them into the Carse parallel to the wood? The left hand side would then be the front rank of that half! There are trees there, of course on that slope but they are spaced out because they are big. Any man faced with a tree just goes around it and picks up the formation after he is past it. The main thing is that the slope is far easier there. And there are glades because of the big trees.'

'What about the other half of the centre division, Sire,' I said. 'Would you send them down afterwards?'

'No, boy, I believe I would send them both down at the same time! The other half would just turn left and then their right hand column would become the left half of the front rank.'

Everyone thought about this and the King drew it out on a parchment and held it up so they could see.

'This is the best way!' said Bruce, grinning. 'The whole centre division will be down very quickly, all in a onenner!'

'But that would take a seventy yard wide movement down that slope, Sire. A lot of men would be going around trees.'

'But the slope there is not so steep, boy. That's the key! They will be able to get around an obstacle like a big tree easily enough without falling. And because of these big trees in the centre, there are much bigger spaces between them. Tell every man confronted with a tree to take a single step to the right. Always to the right. That would do it. And make sure each column is at least a step from every other. Then there will be enough room to get round the tree without disturbing neighbouring columns.'

'Do you want to take the whole central division down the centre, Sire?'

'Yes, I think I do.'

'But will it work, Sire?' said Moray. 'Is it not a gamble? After so much practice?'

'We will try it out tomorrow before dawn. It means assembling the companies on the field above the centre of the wood, right at the top of the wood, at the beginning before we start. Do that tonight and have them sleep at their posts. That will save a great deal of time! We will have 35 ranks with 200 men in each rank for the left and the same number for the right. And the two columns right in the middle will end up as the front rank when they get down and make their turns, to right and left. That is what I want to do,' he added decisively. 'That is the best way by far.'

'Is it wise to change everything after so much practice at different things?' said Vieuxpont again.

'All that practice showed us the best way of doing it and gave us great experience of travelling down through the wood in the darkness before dawn. It was not wasted time. This method of assembling before we even head down the slope of the wood is far better in every way. The key is that the slope is not much in that place and the trees are big with good spaces between them.'

Douglas said, suddenly: 'One thing I am not sure of, Sire. When do you want me to set off? I can form up my men the night before when it is still light, but I need to know exactly when to move them onto the Carse.'

'Well boy, what is the answer?' Bruce turned and smiled at me.
'As soon as there is just enough light to see by. When the dawn has just begun. And with every step they take the light will be better!'

And everyone knew that was the signal and even if it were misinterpreted, the effect would be the same: the two divisions on the edge would form up and they would be in very good position to join up with the centre.

'You will be in the Carse first, Randolph and Douglas. Why is that, boy?'

'Because there are far fewer trees on both sides of the Carse. It is open ground. So there will be more light. The centre division will be starting above the tree line close to the big trees at the top of the slope and coming down through it, so they will be slower to see clearly.'

'Even so, the centre will soon be in position,' added Bruce. 'And because of the backdrop of the wood on its slope no one in the English camp will see anything of our divisions forming their positions. '

'And the wings are to be slightly ahead of the centre?' I enquired.
'Yes, boy, why?'
'To help to keep them independent?'
'—And I will be able to see them far better.' But that was something I did not understand until the day itself.

Just to make sure, there were two morning practices when these new arrangements were tried out. They worked far better than the others. The King's genius had worked his usual magic. Taking the actual conditions of the ground itself into account had made the entire problem of forming up the army very much easier and quicker with no loss of silence and good order.

'This new way of forming up the wings is beautiful, Sire,' I told him with pleasure. 'And the centre too. That is the logical extension of the idea. It is marvellous.'

'Remember this: it was only possible because of so much practice. We have perfected our manoeuvre by the efforts we have all made. And if we had not found this, we might have failed.'

As ever, the practices were made in the dark before dawn, and we never did walk into the Carse any distance just in case of being observed from afar, even in that dim light. Always, by the time the light came up we were all safely back among the protection of our forest. Never at any time did we practise the march more of us realised by now was going to be made into the Carse itself. The uncertainty of this was worrying of course. But Bruce would never allow the least sign of his brilliant plan to be known to our enemies. To make that march just once close to the day itself was to leave the traces of it in the grass. The effect of thousands of feet might be noticed, even if the grass-stems had a day to recover from trampling. Even the ranks when formed up would be hard to see by anyone, so close were they to the wood with its dark background; present only for a few moments; and then vanished. Anyone who had seen them from far off would have thought he was seeing things. But the ground was cleared for miles in every direction. For some time now, we had not done anything except practice the move into the formation. The movement forward we did not need to practice. That was easy.

A few evenings later—each with the new-fangled morning practice before the dawn—as I made to return across the Dryfield to my broch to rest, Bruce, standing at the door of his tent, smiled at me and said: 'Well, Craufurd, scribing pikemen and divisions on parchments is not the whole story. We have to take the ground itself into consideration. It always has so much to tell us. It has the last word. The Great Bend, that really matters! And that slope in the centre of the wood that is a lot less steep there, where the trees are big and well-spaced out. Because we know these things, have noticed them, we can make use of them. Imagine it! If Douglas gets as far as the bend! He will have a hundred yards less to defend! That would be marvellous. And I think he might manage it. And we are going to be able to assemble the army in the Carse, hidden from the enemy by the wood, in just a few minutes! Think of it! One moment we will be on the Dryfield and the next we will be lined up in the Carse ready to march! That's what knowing the ground has done for us.'

8

HOW DID BRUCE SPEAK TO ALL HIS MEN?

By this time, the problem that presented itself at Torwood and was solved by our leader for a single company (by having them sit close together around one side of a tree) had become intractable. When you have 20,000 men in an army, that makes 200 companies of a hundred men in each. If Bruce spent just twenty minutes speaking to each company and getting to where they were arrayed to hear him, another ten minutes, say, that would take him 200 half hours or 100 hours just to get around them all. That was four days to get round them all just once!

There was not time for that. What Bruce wanted to tell us had to be conveyed efficiently. In many armies, the commander never did communicate with the men, only with officers who then went off to speak to their companies, often passing on the message inadequately because their understanding of the message was not clear. Their own words were never as good as Bruce's own.

This became clear to Bruce himself when he overheard Boyd pass on instructions to us one evening, by the campfire, after one of the company commanders' meetings in Bruce's tent.

Many moves made by Bruce, often original ideas, contributed to his success. This one, I now think, would never have been seen by anyone but Bruce. It took an original mind like his, a very rare thing. And if he had not done it, had been content to leave the ordinary men in ignorance of his own personality, power of expression and inspiration, I do believe that things might have turned out differently. It was, you see, more than just a matter of conveying instructions. The best of it was the inspiration he was able to give us all by this discovery.

What led up to it, I do not know for sure. Only that the next morning after our dawn practice in descending the slopes of Balquiderock Wood, Bruce came to us and ordered us to follow him.

He took us to the north east corner of the Dryfield, about a quarter mile south of the Pelstream and the same distance south east of St Ninians. In that place, the ground falls sharply to a depth of about fifty feet, creating a natural amphitheatre[vi] about 100 yards wide. We arrived to find that Crabbe, with some assistants had been busy the night before at his forge. There was a pile of spades and shovels.

Bruce himself began to show us how to construct a seat for one person. A foot up from the bottom of the flat ground of the depression he cut out a turf making a platform about a foot high and 2 ft wide on which a man could sit with his feet on the bottom level and another man above him could have his feet on the seat behind the back of the man below him. Soon, we were all deployed at this task all along the slope. Soon after that, we realised that only the platform mattered: the back on which the seated man's back rested could be left untouched as the slope itself was good enough.

The object of the exercise was to get as many people crammed together as possible, yet in comfort, so that they could hear him when he spoke. Once we understood what we were trying to achieve, we made rapid progress and the work went on all day, other men being brought in to help. Other men still, cleared this area of trees and the scrub that grew thereabouts. The high trees up on the Dryfield were left, of course, and all those between us and the Carse. The trees were part of our defence, even screened the amphitheatre from the Knoll in the Carse, half a mile away to the NE. Weapons too, were left at the brochs of their owners, lest men were injured by them, when tight-packed in their seats, coming and going.

Once a lot of places to sit had been fashioned in this way, we began to try out the best way to deal with it. After much trial and error, packing men close together, and with Bruce speaking to us, we soon

---

[vi] You can see this on the map on p48 and the coloured battle maps which come later, easiest on the map of the battle area where the ridges and the elevations show the depression which creates the amphitheatre very clearly. It lies to the west of Balquhiderock Wood, south of the Pelstream and SE of St Ninians. As always: go and look. 114'-81'=33'; 151'-81'=70; average 51.5' See p179 herein where there are photos of it.

realised that he could be heard well enough with 100 men in the front rank and every other rank up to the top of the slope. That made about 50 rows of men, a total of about 5,000. Then, at Bruce's command, carpenters constructed a platform about six feet high which they set down about ten feet from the front. This gave even better reception, given Bruce's naturally powerful voice, so long as he spoke slowly and distinctly, which, in any case, came naturally to him.

The final move was to position men on the ground all around him and even behind him and we even filled the 10 ft space on the flat ground around his platform. Seated men there could also hear him and he could see them by turning to one side and the other, thus maintaining eye contact, an important factor in a speech to a large group: because the speaker's eye moves across the line of vision of every spectator, each man in the audience believes the speaker is addressing him personally. In this way, 6,000 men, tight-packed could hear what Bruce had to say. Every man was about 2 ft wide at the shoulders which meant that 100 men took up 66ft sitting in a row about 33 men on either side of Bruce. He could be heard by them all. Best of all, his personality, his determination, his courage, self-belief and passion were then available to the whole group. They were fuelled by his incandescent will.

By evening, all this had been arranged and Bruce ordered his own division to sit together so that he could try out this method.

'I know this is going to work because at Cambridge I once met a Greek who had come there via Padua and Paris to study. He told me about an open air theatre at a place called Epidaurus in his homeland. It is still there, 2000 years after it was made. It has seating for about 15,000 people and you can hear what was said on the stage even at the far back of it because of the fan shaped design with seats rising all around in front of the stage. The Greeks performed dramas there to audiences of 10,000. The Romans extended it, so that means it works even then. I believe we should try tomorrow to make a better version than this one. This is very good work, I think. I see many heads nodding that I am being heard even by those at the farthest parts. Tomorrow, we will concentrate on extending this and create a fan shape of our own. We do not even need to have seats at all, I think. It should be enough to sit on the grass. The raised edges of the sides will focus the sound, like a scallop with raised edges. I believe we might be able to accommodate 10,000 in that case. But even if not, what we have is sufficient.' He paused to consider the question anew and said with excitement: 'Do you know, I think it would almost do as it is. Several more thousand can easily cram in here on the remaining empty areas of sloping grass.' As experience was to show: he was right.

One other thing we did was to check that nothing could be heard of what Bruce said and nothing seen of our goings on down in the Carse. Between the ranks of packed men and the Carse there lay a huge ridge and even a plateau of ground 70 ft above the Carse, much of it covered by dense woodland, some of it another 100ft higher. Behind all this, everything we did would be out of sight and sound of our enemies.

From that day on, Bruce would harangue the army in very large groups, improving with every performance at the task of throwing his voice out among us. He would speak of our training, encouraged us, made us feel we were fast becoming very good soldiers and educated us in the best way to manage the pikes and even the axes and shields, sometimes demonstrating their use with a few folk chosen for the purpose.

There was room for questions but never at any time would our leader reveal the plan. So many different formations and moves were being practised that a lot of people were unsure how we would be deployed when the enemy arrived. Some, like myself and Magonigal, had guessed the plan but we knew better than to tell anyone. It was so daring and so dangerous that it might frighten the men.

In this way, yet again, because of this unusual knowledge of the ground and even his education at Cambridge, Bruce had managed to solve a problem which could only be solved here at the ground itself. That our battle area—the area we had chosen to defend—should have such riches within it, (the burn so difficult to cross, the bottleneck at the Ford, the Dryfield which was a natural fortress, Balquiderock Wood which shielded us from the English camp in the Carse around the Knoll and the pools of water which made it certain that no army would ever think of camping anywhere else— in summer, especially, when water was vitally necessary for men and animals) which no other area anywhere in the country possessed, was amazing. That he saw this, is a small miracle, like all the others. Many years later I came again to this sacred place. By then all signs of the amphitheatre had vanished. The sharp edges of the seats had been washed away by rain, frost, ice and snow; and the ground we had cleared had returned to its former state of grass, scrub and small trees. Only the natural amphitheatre remained, now in its original state. In the end, it was enough just to sit on the grass: the slope was just right for this.

Much later, I learned that the theatre at Megalopolis could hold 20,000.

9

THE ENGLISH ARE COMING!

The very next day, close to the deadline, riders arrived hot foot from the south thundering up the road. Soon, the news was everywhere about: the English would be at Falkirk that day! Everybody was shocked by it. I was beside Bruce at his tent helping to attend to the wounds and sickness of those who had presented themselves for his aid. I could see the shock in his face. He stopped dead and seemed to lose the colour in his cheeks, a high colour that was a characteristic of his, right down to the beard, mostly grey though it was after so much travail and hard lying, often in the open, sometimes in winter. His mouth fell open and he took a big draught of air, perhaps to steady himself. So he was human after all. The news had hit even him like a punch in the guts, for he bent over. He was afraid, just like all of us. But in a moment, he remembered his position. Stood up straight and grinned happily at all of us. 'We'll soon see if all this training has been any good,' he said confidently.

Soon after, I was able to query him about the shields and standards that now stood at the top of the wood to guide us to our posts, prior to making our descent down the centre. These were all very well in daylight but in the dark, what then? 'Sire,' I said to him, 'I hope ye don't mind my saying this but these shields and such do not show up in the dark. Could we not show a wee light at the head of every route through the forest? Even if there were only two, one for each half of the centre division. It would help us to form up in the morn. Surely the forest would hide the lights? It's on top of a hill and there's two hundred and fifty yards of big trees there.'

Knowing the significance of the question, he looked to right and left, decided no one could overhear the conversation and replied: 'You may be right. But I don't mean to chance it. Surprise is everything. There is another answer: we will spend the night before we move, sitting or lying down at the right place. Just like Moray and Douglas. The shields and standards at the centre just help us to get into position in the evening when it's still light.'

So that was it, Bruce was not going to make any sign that we were ready above the wood to move down through it when it suited him. Bruce said quietly to me: 'You know to keep quiet about this, I trust?' I nodded.

Quietly, I said to him: 'How do you know they'll go there. Into the Carse?'

'I don't know, of course. Only time will tell. But there's nowhere else they can go and that's the natural place. The place they always went before.'

'What about the ground down near the Forth?'

'It's too far away. We could easily escape and they'd hate that. They want a pitched battle. The Forth's two miles away. Too far.'

'What about the land east of the Castle? Could they not go there?'

'How could they get across Livilands Bog? It stands in the way. After all this rain, that bog's in a terrible state: awash all over. It will reach right across to the river. And they can't get onto the Dryfield because we will be at the Ford to stop them. It's like a fortress, as ye ken. Steep sided all around, densely packed with trees, aye, on both sides of the gorge. No army in the world could get onto the Dryfield where we're standing right now. That Ford is our Thermopylae.'[24]

'What's that, Sire?'

'The place, the very narrow passage in the mountains of Greece, where 300 Spartans kept out a million Persians.' I had heard of this but never read it for myself in Herodotus. Evidently he had.

'But how could they do that?'

'Only a handful of Persians at a time could fight in the narrow space and the Spartans killed every one of them. They could have held that pass for a month.'

'You mean they didn't?'

'They were betrayed by a shepherd who showed the Persians another route round the mountains, so the Greeks could be surrounded and attacked on all sides. Even then, they fought until they were all killed. No Spartan was allowed to return from battle alive unless he was victorious, except on his own shield.'

'Can I tell my folk about the Spartans, Sire?'

'Aye, that'll do no harm.'

In the late afternoon, the question of the pottes was raised. My division was down at the Ford when Bruce was asked where he wanted them. He waved at me to join him. It was Boyd's men who were to dig them and Boyd wanted to put them on the north bank right beside the water. They were to be square holes in the ground about two feet deep and the same width. In the centre was to be a short stake hammered in and then pointed, which would hopefully damage the feet of any horse that stepped into it. The issue had been left late because there was to be a covering of freshly cut grass, reeds and twigs arranged to conceal the trap. Had the covering been done in advance it would have dried out, shrivelled and seemed unnatural, defeating its purpose.

'What do you say to that boy?'

'Putting them right beside the water is a bad idea. If a few horses get lamed there and maybe killed, the rest of their knights will not try to cross over.'

'Why not?' Said Bruce.

'Because they can't get over for the bodies in the way.'

'Exactly!' said Bruce. 'We want to encourage them to cross over into our killing ground. If they don't cross over, they might just wait for reinforcements of archers and infantry. That we don't want. They could do us a lot of damage then.'

'So where should the pottes be, then, Sire?'

'What do you say, boy?'

'We don't really need them here at all.'

Boyd was incensed. 'We must ha'e them. They wull definitely help. We canny dae withoot them!'

'The boy is right,' said Bruce, mildly. 'What we really want is to give them a taste of our hedgehog. We want them to run at our pikes and discover just how painful it is being pricked by all these steel points.'

'Whit good is that?'

'Because it will make them unsure and circumspect the next time,' I said.

That was close to the truth, one that Bruce was not ready to make public. So he shut me down. 'Well, that's it decided. We will have no pottes here at all. We want them to cross over and get in each other's way and discover what they are up against. Our training and discipline will be very telling, believe me.'

'But you must ha'e pottes, Sire!' Boyd insisted.

'Why must I?' There was no answer to that. Boyd had not really understood the plan in all its wonderful logical detail. But Bruce relented:

'Well, if you must have some, put them on the south bank to deter cavalry from moving upstream.'[25]

'Whit good will that do?'

'Tell him, boy.'

'It means that they will not so easily get upstream to cross and outflank us. And if any of them ride to the west, upstream where they can cross, it will be the cavalry at the rear mostly. They will be young men, inexperienced and less well armed. That will make it easier for Lord Edward Bruce to defend the gap in the Bogs.'

To Boyd, Bruce put a question: 'What is the most important thing here at the Ford?'

'The pikes, oor formation, Sire.'

'But given the pikes, what then? What are we going to achieve here?'

'You mean gi'e them a taste ae oor steel, Sire?'

'What do you say, boy?'

'We want them to cross in great numbers for then they will get in each other's way. Soon, they will be unable to do anything to attack us or move forward or back. We can push them off their horses at our leisure.'

Bruce patted Boyd on the back, consolingly: 'That's what letters do for you, Robert. You learn to see everything with dazzling clarity. To see what counts and what doesn't. It's the key to leadership. Maybe you should borrow some of my books.'

But Boyd was not finished. 'Surely, Sire, we kin put some pottes richt in front ae the pikemen?'

Bruce raised an eyebrow and looked at me.

'Pottes there would damage our own men. They need to be able to run about safely without stepping in holes with pointed stakes. Our men will be pulling them off their horses and hitting them with the hatchets.'

That evening, the evening of the first engagement, we slept little. Our fires, all of them along the north bank of the burn between the Ford and Gillies Hill, kept us warm and our spirits rose and fell intermittently. One minute we would think we were going to win and then the awful realisation of what lay ahead hit us and brought a harsh dose of realism. These English had been here before. Some of us had seen them, seen what they could do. What injuries they could inflict after their training which, since it went on all the time in far better conditions and with better equipment, just had to be better than ours. And there would be so many of them! That was the clincher. The King of England would never venture forth into Scotland without the biggest army he could muster. That just had to be far bigger than ours.

Bruce came to our fireside, squatted down on a thick bit of kindling and spoke quietly about the forthcoming battle. He was taking a sook of our jug when wee Crosby started it. 'What are our chances, Sire?' Bruce laughed: 'If they're not good we should be somewhere else!' and we laughed with him. 'Seriously, though, we have a good plan, the best I ever heard of and we have trained for it very well. Of course something can always go wrong. But I think it will have no effect on the outcome. Everything we need to do has been tried and tested. It works. Moving in the dark was always going to be a problem. But it's not really dark now because it's midsummer. It just never gets completely dark at this time. And we have practised and our eyes are used to the dark. So we should manage very well in this half-light we have, especially with the moon shining. If it clouds over it will be harder but the rain has stopped and everything is drying out nicely. So we might have a clear sky like tonight. Even the stars will give us more light.' He looked up, as did we, marvelling at the wonders of the universe above our heads.

MacFee, who had said little, said slowly, what many were thinking: 'How many of us will dee the morra, Sire?'

Bruce was unperturbed by the question: 'Some will die for sure. There will be a battle and men always die in a battle. But the plan is very good. I hope few Scots will be killed.' He paused to think what else he might say to us and continued: 'I always think the best thing to do before a battle is to begin with the idea that I am going to die in it. Once I get that idea into my head, the question becomes: how many of the enemy can I kill before they kill me? So if I am still alive afterwards I will feel very happy. And if I am not, it won't matter very much.'

There was no early morning march and practice down through the wood to the Carse. It was too late for that now. We slept late and breakfasted at our leisure and then set off in our companies under good discipline to go to the Ford. By prior agreement some of the Islesmen had been allowed the place of honour in the front rank of the semi-circle that Bruce now arranged around the little amphitheatre on the north bank of the burn at the Ford. The space there was free of trees because so often in the past travellers had been unable to cross in wet weather and camped there until the water level went down and the force of it no longer carried away people and animals crossing. There they would light a fire from the trees nearby, using twigs for tinder, cutting up branches to keep it going all night long. There they would make their bannocks and this would be the reason for the name of the burn. From this empty space, cleared by successive generations and kept clear against the overwhelming power of woodland to preserve itself by incessant seeding everywhere, the road wound up the escarpment turning right and then left until it passed the farm; and then straightened out again by turning right and heading across the Dryfield to St Ninians Main Street, on its way past the Kirk to Stirling Castle, another mile up the road. The slopes[26] on the north bank and the south were just enough to be manageable by a horse and cart which was why it was so important. In no other place was this possible for a full mile in either direction; and, far worse, there were huge bogs in the way, both west and east.

There was no need for the entire division here. Anyway, Edward Bruce had kept his part of it near the camp we had just left so as to defend the gap between the two bogs and, more importantly, the right flank of Bruce's force at the Ford. About a mile up the burn from the Ford, you see, there was no escarpment for it had swung north away from the burn to Coxet hill and two great bogs were between it and Gillies Hill. So, without the escarpment on either side, the burn at long last could be crossed very easily, despite the torrent that still flowed, for the banks there were low and between the trees that lined them, were passages across. Outriders from the invading English cavalry might move up the side of the burn on the south side seeking a place to advance. Some of them might know about the great bogs in that direction. It was the narrow gap between them that Edward Bruce was guarding with his division. And our right flank, that too. If he failed to stop a crossing of the burn, cavalry could run down the burnside to the Ford and attack us in the flank.

The other divisions were disposed [27]as follows: Moray held the route up onto the Dryfield from the Carse near St Ninians, which was sometimes used in summer by folk travelling there or to Stirling from the north east: Dunfermline and St Andrews, that direction. But as the slope was long and steep this route was rarely used. Moray had to be there to defend the rear of Bruce's force, for if cavalry say, rode up that way after a flanking movement through the Carse, then, instead of proceeding onwards to the Castle to raise the siege, taking that for granted, they might turn and attack the rear of Bruce's position at the Ford. Douglas, by contrast, was not involved. He was to stay in the middle of the Dryfield[28] and take his men to assist any of the other three forces that might need help.

All of this was clear to me from the movements that morning long before I took my place on the north bank of the ford in the tenth rank on the west side of the great semi-circle. And there we waited for their cavalry who, because of their speed and thirst for glory, must arrive first. The entire outcome was predictable, could hardly be otherwise.

MARSHALLING

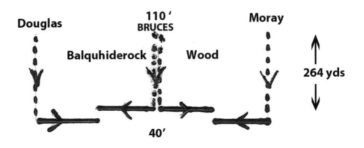

10

THE FIRST DAY: THE DEFENCE OF THE ROAD[29]: de Bohun

Bruce knew that their cavalry would arrive first but not when they would arrive. They might start early, though, knowing their commanders and their lazy habits, and, in their arrogance and overconfidence, expecting a day of sport foxhunting rebels, he thought they would reach us in the late morning. An army like that one would take a long time to clear up after the night before. But Bruce was taking no chances. So we were there long before we need have been.

After kneeling with our pikes set with the butts in the ground, pointing upward at an angle, as we had practised so often, Bruce told us to put the pikes vertical and sit down to rest. We would learn soon enough when the invaders were near. Our scouts were out on both sides of the road to the south and Falkirk, concealed by trees. And so we sat, rested and waited.

Bruce alone was mounted. A fine chestnut horse, the best in the country. He wore a simple breast plate, strapped on, all the armour he deemed necessary. His tunic was brown homespun and his breeches. He wore no helmet and no gloves, no sword and no lance even.

'Should ye no' pit oan fuull airmour, Sire?' said someone. 'Aw they Inglish'll hiv airmour. Ye micht suffer a sare wound if ye gang this wey.'

'All the armour in the world, won't save them. And it's not what we need. We need to be fast. To be free to move quickly. In and out with the axe before they so much as turn round.' The axe, everyone knew, was his favourite weapon. Just how useful it was and what he meant, we were about to see.

After a long time waiting, there was a cry from the road behind the hill on the south side, from a scout hiding among the trees there, soon followed by sounds of a few men scampering towards us[30] down the slope on the south side of the Ford. Then, splashing across, they appeared in the middle of our semi-circle of pikemen. They were dripping, soaked with the water from the burn which was a rippling brown torrent they only just managed to cross because of their own haste and power.

'They're coming doon the brae the noo, Sire,' one of them said pointing in the direction he had come from to the south and Bruce motioned to us all to set the pikes and kneel down, as training required.

Bruce rode the horse to the rear of the space created by the circling pikemen and waited, as we all did, to see what would happen next. Meanwhile, the bedraggled scouts melted through the lines and climbed up the escarpment for a good view over the heads of the ranks of pikemen.

Bruce signalled to all of us for silence using both hands astride the horse, the small axe dangling from the right wrist on a string, as usual with every one of us, similarly armed; though all of us had targes on the left forearm and pikes set firmly in the ground, as we had practised so often and could do it in our sleep without thinking.

Presently, there was the rhythmic clopping of hooves battering the ground, growing in intensity as it neared, then the clatter of the stones on the bed of the burn and the spray blasting into the air as a knight in shining armour and surplice of red cross on white ground rode across amid a myriad gobbets of water to scatter glittering light in every direction like a bejewelled veil in the sunshine. The huge black destrier, bigger than Bruce's, rode up into the space we had left. The trapper of the horse had the blue and yellow colours of the de Bohuns of Hereford. Startled, seeing us, standing in his way in silence, the horse reared, snorted and neighed with shock and the knight nearly came off his mount with surprise. But he got it under control and threw his visor up with one mailed hand, the other clutching the reins, the better to see what confronted him. His face was red and sweating with effort on such a warm day and he looked to right and left quickly and then, not seeing Bruce off to one side at the rear of the semi-circle, hidden against the backdrop of so many ranks of Scots in homespun, and concluding that he could not hope to penetrate such a dense forest of pikes, he turned the horse and began to rush back to the burn and ride back across to make a report to his own commanders further back along the road.

It was then that Bruce moved, galloped his horse after the knight and twirling the axe into position in an instant, brought down the spike onto the back of the helmet of the retreating rider. There was a sickening thud and a jet of bright blood shot into the air. Off the back of the horse he fell and the horse ran off across the stream leaving the body of the dead knight lying just two yards from the water with a red rivulet pulsing upward like a spring from a wound in the back of the helmet.

What a shout of exultation there was then! Forgetting all their training, men stood up, pranced around, yelled and slapped each other on the back and even hugged and embraced in some cases. Bruce turned his horse and rode back and, as he saw our disorganised lines, shouted at us. 'Get back into line! Kneel down! Remember what you were trained to do! And never do this again!' The anger was hot in him and everyone was shamed by it. 'You must remain under control,' he shouted. 'Lose this and we could lose everything!' As Bruce went through our lines, which parted to let him, and up the road, we heard him cursing the damage to his favourite axe. The shaft had split under the force of the blow.

Meanwhile, an esquire rushed in across the burn and tried to revive the dead knight. But there was nothing he could do and he soon tried to go back across the burn, unable even to move the corpse for the weight of it and its armour. A pikeman dropped his pike, darted forward, smote him with an axe and he too fell, never to rise again.[31]

There was a lull, but it did not last long. Soon, other knights, in gleaming armour on huge horses decorated in their colours, each with beautiful heraldic designs, each with the red cross on white, in twos and threes, were crashing across the burn in plumes of spray and, once across, up the short slope into the semi-circle, where they immediately tried to attack the pikemen and made no progress for the lengths of the pikes which took the brunt of the pressure and transferred it to the ground. First one knight and then another was stopped dead by the forest of pikes and once that happened, Scotsmen dropped their pikes, ran forward, grabbed the knights and hauled them down off their horses or just pushed them off with the pikes. Visors were lifted and the small Scottish axes smashed into faces of supine men struggling to rise. Meanwhile, the horses, quivering with fright, bucked and kicked, threatening to kill our men by their very size and strength and weight. One blow of these flying hooves and a man would be broken on the spot. There was nothing else we could do but slash their throats under the trappers with the axe blades. Then they fell and were less of a problem. Only the blood hindered us, making some of us slip on the grass. Had there been pottes, it really would have been harder for us; might have gone badly, for we ourselves would have been victims of our own devising.

There was great happiness among our men at observing how successful this strategy was against these magnificent warriors in all their finery. There were more important things than weapons, horses and clothing, we had begun to realise, and we had the beating of them. It was just as Bruce had envisaged. Knight after knight plunged into the burn and crossed over and was soon charging fruitlessly at our pikes, a forest of steel, impenetrable by anybody or anything, no matter how well armed. And so the slaughter of Englishmen continued and mindless of it, dozens more crossed over and soon the space was filled and they were unable to charge and, at the edges of the semi-circle, they were being pulled down in increasing numbers.

Those other knights on the south side, arriving later, shouted at those engaged, wondering what was the hold up. Nothing could be heard clearly for the tumult of fighting as men and animals were killed and the shouting and the screams and the cheers, these too. The burn itself was soon a mass of struggling horses and men vainly trying to reach the opposite bank of the brown rapids in spate, but could not for the numbers there already. First one horse fell and then another and the riders were blown downstream never to be seen again in that torrent which raced through a long deep winding gorge full of rocks at great speed in a whoosh of white water that looked like a massive block of ice in motion. Gradually, the mounted men behind who could not advance into the space and enjoy the fighting which was what they had come for, began to explore alternative routes and we could hear them ride off in large numbers behind the wooded hill, Catcraig, to our left, some we could see stuck in the little bog in front of it, heading for the Carse and some the other way, up the banks behind the palisade of trees that lined the south bank of the burn towards our camp. There Edward Bruce was waiting at the place they might be able to cross because the banks there were so flat, the escarpment having tapered to nothing by then.

In a little while the sound of fighting could be heard from there. Later, much later, there was even the clash of steel, the shrieks of the dying and the shouted glee of men, muted by distance, that heralded the sounds of battle across the Dryfield to the north, in the direction of St Ninians. So Moray too was engaged there.

In time, the space on the north bank of the Ford was cleared of knights, though many of them and their horses lay dead. There was a general withdrawal along the road to the south, back the way they had come, seeking some way to get around us and reach the castle, for there was no way across the Ford or onto the Dryfield which was a natural fortress that needed no defending.

But before that, there was another act of indiscipline: when the last Englishman rode back across the burn, some of the Islesmen, their blood up and unable to contain their desire to get at them, dropped their pikes and ran after them hoping to leap onto the retreating horses and axe their riders. Bruce was down again upon them like an avenging angel, running after them on foot, scattering them with the flat blade of his sword while berating them with his tongue in the Gaelic they understood. In time, he gathered them together in the middle of the space which had been our killing ground for English invaders and told them harshly what damage would be done to the army and the country if there were any repetition. And then, to all the rest of us who had not moved out of position, he called upon us: 'if ever you see anyone make a move that is not ordered by me or a commander, strike down that person instantly!'

'But Sire, how can we?' said several voices at once. 'How can we kill our own men?'

'Better that than indiscipline that results in the loss of the battle and the loss of the country.' Bruce was livid with anger. I never saw him so furious. 'One stupid man leads other stupid men and a few becomes a flight of stupid men. Can you imagine how disastrous that would be? The stupid men fleeing would be killed in the back with lances. It is dead easy to kill men fleeing. We must always go forward. We must act together, but only on orders,' he asserted, before going off to see how the others had managed, leaving us to guard the Ford, the road and the Dryfield against any further attacks by the invaders. But not before sending out scouts to the south to see what they were up to, what route they would take next, though it was obvious enough: they had to move into the Carse, for it was the only way forward for them. To the west were the great impassable bogs and the tents and brochs of our camp and, most of all, the division of Edward Bruce defending the gap between the bogs and the way across into our camp. We all knew that they would reach the Carse very easily. They would know it too, some having been before. That is where they had always camped in the past.

With the defeat and departure of the English, our division was sent off to cover the Dryfield just above the top of the wood down to the Carse. There, behind the trees, we were to sit in our lines, making as little noise as possible. Nothing was to be done to provoke an attack up out of the Carse. Meanwhile Douglas was on his way to replace our men, some being sent to replace Edward Bruce's who would also move to the Dryfield.

A few men were given the task of stripping the dead knights of their armour which was gathered and taken to our camp for storage under cover so that it would not rust. The bodies were left where they lay meantime. In all that fighting that morning, only one Scotsman had been injured. I was spotted by Bruce and asked to mend him as best I could. Presently, we were alone with the man, everyone else having gone about their business, even Bruce's squires who were sent off with messages. The man's arm was broken and the bone had come outside the flesh, a dangerous wound if ever there was one. He had fallen in the dirt across the burn chasing retreating knights after trying and failing to get his axe into the last one.

'I don't suppose they'll be back?' I said to Bruce, who stood above me as I knelt over the man who was sitting beside the burn, trying to clean the wound with a wet clout.

He said: 'Douglas will be here in a moment. But, no, they have taken a beating here and they won't come this way again. There is no point and they will see that. Anyway, our scouts would tell us in good time.' Groups of them had been sent to follow the retreating Englishmen and report back on their doings.

Suddenly Bruce stiffened and he took a dirk out of its scabbard. I looked up to see and there, looking at us across the burn was a mounted man. He even had armour, though not a full set: a simple plate on the breast and a shield. His visor was raised. 'It's Seaton,' said Bruce, quietly. 'I wonder what he wants?'

11

HOW BRUCE GOT HIS MEN TO BELIEVE THEY COULD WIN

Since Seaton just had to be one of the other side, being not of our army but on their side of the river, what could he want? Seaton was a Scottish knight but one of the Comyn clan, so inevitably an English supporter.

'May I come across and parley?' said Seaton, 'I come in peace.' Saying which, he dismounted and led the horse across the torrent, managing to keep his footing only with difficulty. A wise move: to have ridden across could have been threatening and Bruce would have dealt with that forcefully, as we knew.

'I would like to join your army,' said Seaton.

'Explain yourself!' said Bruce, aggressively.

'I have been travelling with theirs and the closer I came to home, the worse it has become. I cannot fight for them any longer.'

'Have you done any fighting?'

'No. I was at the back of the cavalry and when some went west to try and cross the burn there, I went with them. But I never did cross the burn till now. I could not bring myself to do it.'

'But you are a Balliol man, a Comyn, how can you do such a thing? You must have sworn allegiance to them and the King of England. Are you saying you are breaking your word?'

'Yes. What is my word worth when it means fighting against the men of my own land? I find I just can't do it!' There was a vehemence about this that was warming. Here was a soul in torment and he had made a decision.

'I think you should go back to your own folk,' said Bruce, more kindly than before. 'If you go now, you go in peace. We will not harm you.'

The young man was desolate, his face a picture of despair. 'I won't go back to them. I just can't do it. Don't you see?'

'They don't know about your defection. So they will accept you with open arms. It will be as if you had just got left behind, like many another.'

'I am not going.'

'Well you can't stay here,' said Bruce. 'Douglas's boys will be here in a moment. They'll not listen. They'll kill you for sport.'

'I have nowhere to go,' said the young man, despairingly. 'I won't stand by and do nothing and I could not ride away and wait for the outcome. I will just have to stay here and take the consequences. If I am killed by my own side, that's too bad. I could get killed anyway. What's the difference who does it?' The anguish was all too obvious. His face wracked with pain.

'So you are determined on this, then, Seaton? Well, what are you prepared to do to help us?'

'Anything. Name it.'

'You could get up close to Edward of England and stab him to death.'

'I wouldn't get near him. But I could try. If you insist, I will try it.'

'Go then and see to it,' said Bruce. And Seaton mounted and prepared to ride back across the burn. But seeing this, Bruce was not finished with him. 'Wait awhile. Not so fast. Will you swear allegiance to me?'

'Aye, gladly.' And he dismounted and knelt down and said the words Bruce told him to say and meant it. 'So I am your man, one of the Scots, where I should have been all the time. Thank you, Sire, thank you,' he said, clearly affected by emotion. 'My conscience has been tormented.'

'I must soon go and see to my other forces,' said Bruce. 'Here is what I want you to do,' pulling his grey beard while pacing about as was his habit at times when thinking deeply. Having made his calculations, he stopped and faced Seaton: 'You are to come to my tent in two hours time with these two, pointing at myself and the wounded Macdonald. Just make your way straight in, stopping for nobody and say that you must speak to me in person. You will be stripped of weapons. I will question you again about yourself and what you have been doing and what you have seen. I want you to say to me that the English are demoralised by their defeats today.'

'How do you know they have been defeated?' I said. 'You don't know that.'

'Yes, I do,' he said angrily. 'Can't you tell from the shouts? It was a certainty that my brother would see off any flanking move on the west side. It would have taken their whole cavalry force to beat him; and they were all down here where they could not beat us in a hundred years. Randolph was bound to beat the flanking move on the east. The slope he is on is too steep for heavy cavalry to attack up it. And there are the trees. These make an attack so much more difficult. Impossible, I'd say. It's another bottleneck but uphill. Worse than here. All three of us are defending bottlenecks, don't you see? That is why we have won today. Anything else is impossible.'

'But we heard the fighting?' I said. 'If they could not attack there, what was that?'

'Whatever it was, we'll learn soon enough. But Moray didn't lose. If he had, he would have sent someone down here by now to apologise and seek reinforcements.'

'Maybe they went onto the Castle.'

'A few might, I grant you. But their commanders? No. They would do the right thing: attack us in the rear. They haven't done that. So they didn't win.'

'So where are they now, then?'

'In the Carse, by now, like all the others. The foot soldiers from Falkirk far behind the cavalry will be tramping over there now, behind that hill,' he said, pointing across the Ford and the burn to the wooded hill, Catcraig, ahead southwards and on our left.

For the next 2 hours then, I was to take Seaton on a tour of the Dryfield ending up at Bruce's tent. Together we were to support and aid the Macdonald. He and I were Seaton's surety of fighting on our side, at least from now on, lest he were taken by our men as an enemy and slain on the spot. Seaton's horse was to be left to roam free, like many other horses without riders, for to retain it was to advertise the fact that he was on the English side, every Scotsman being on foot.

As Bruce left us, he called back: 'Don't mention this conversation to anyone. And the English **are** demoralised. You saw it here today. So you are just telling the truth. They are bound to be demoralised.'

'But they won't be, will they?' I said.

Bruce stopped in his tracks and bade me go to him. When I did so he walked me up the road and said, quietly: 'That was not a helpful question at this time. You are right. They're too arrogant and overconfident to be demoralised. They will think that when their whole army is assembled they will spend the day chasing us like a foxhunt. They will think we're going to run. But we're not. You must help Seaton to believe that they are demoralised. Can you do it?'

'I can try.'

'Try and succeed. Don't let him think he's telling a lie. And make no mention of this to anyone. Make sure that neither Seaton nor MacDonald speak to anybody before you bring them into the tent. In difficulty, you know what to do. You would be killing an Englishman intent on assassinating me.' Bruce turned back then and walked to where Seaton still stood.

'You must insist that we attack. That they are at sixes and sevens, because of their defeats today. Then the men will believe that they can win and because of it we will win! So you are doing a valuable service today, Seaton. Just make sure you believe what you are saying. Tell the truth about your own actions. The only lie is about their morale, and it's not really a lie. Many of them are demoralised! They don't know what to do about our pikemen. That's the lesson they were taught today.' Before hurrying off, Bruce went to Seaton, smiled at him warmly and clapped him on the shoulders with both hands, a move I had often seen him make. And Seaton was moved by it, became his man once again, emotionally as well as feudally. We all knew Seaton would try and give a good account of himself. But would he succeed? That was the question. He had to convince the men in the tent. Among them, Bruce's own commanders, who were not stupid. Meantime, as I could see, Bruce would arrange matters in his tent so that the scene that was about to be enacted would have a suitable audience.

'Shouldn't this man go to his broch and lie down?' I suggested. 'He could do with a dram of aquavittie.'

Bruce shook his head: 'No. Where you go, he goes. Find him a dram if you can but bring him to my tent with Seaton in a couple of hours.'

'But he doesn't have the Scots? Only the Irish. He doesn't understand what this is about.'

'You don't know that,' said Bruce. 'I won't chance it.'

'What if he says something about this at the tent?'

'He will be taken off by someone who'll fill him full of drams to keep his mouth shut or shut it permanently before he does.'

And so, with Seaton and I supporting the wounded Macdonald, we three shambled up the road which twisted up the sides of the escarpment among the trees and then turned off to our right as fast as possible to escape the attentions of the Douglas division and went along the top of the very steep slope that stands above the burn in its downward passage to the Carse; and for a while we shuffled along, hearing the Douglases moving into position at the Ford and, in the distance, the sound of the English army marching towards the Carse well to the south of us. It was like no sound I had ever heard. Trained to do so, the Scots always marched in silence. Noise was anathema for what we intended. Of course it was easy for us: many of us had no shoes, those we had were slight: things of soft leather which lasted no time, were soon holed and useless; so that many of us wore cloths on our feet or extended puttees which were all we could get. Some were even barefoot. The English were different. They could not have made more noise if they tried. Mainly, it was the stamping of the feet in unison, the mailed feet in many cases, but even then leather-shod boots and shoes which rang on every stone, so well made were they, so solid and strong, often—as we were soon to learn—reinforced with hobnails. And it was the regularity of the sound: a relentless, forward impulse that nothing could resist. What we were hearing was the infantry, of course, all their cavalry being, by now, in the Carse in their encampment, forming up as we watched. Their progress was like a great giant crossing our land, thumping the ground so that it shook as we listened. And we were fearful. The giant had come to kill us.

Coming out of trees into a glade above a flat area beside the burn we were at last able to see them as they crossed the opening of the great valley that carries the burn into the Carse. Men marched in regiments, some with banners bearing colours of their lord, archers by the hundred with bow staves unstrung across the shoulders, and men with swords that flashed in the sun, some with halberds, many of them wearing mail under the surplice with the red cross on white ground the English mostly wore to distinguish friend from foe. And carts too, mostly very large six or eight wheeled carts, but many little ones, probably the property of private persons. All of them laden with untold treasures from that far richer country than our own: tents, certainly, and beds and tables and food and wine and barrels of ale—the English were known as deep drinkers—and barrels of preserved food like herrings and bags of flour and preserved meat which their cooks would roast that evening.

Seaton, who knew them, had travelled with them, had camped with them, conversed with them, had lived with them, regaled us with the tales of their doings and the richness of their mode of life.

'You should see the King's tents. He has many. And many servants who attend his every need. Do you know he has a whole company of cooks who provide for him and his whole retinue?'

'How many?' I asked.

'A hundred maybe. His household has several hundred. And they carry their own kitchens with ovens and fires and spits for roasting. They live well on campaign. And he has musicians and entertainers of diverse kinds.'

At the sound of a woman's laughter, I said: 'Is that what I hear or am I dreaming?'

'It is just what you think. Rich men take all their comforts on campaign.'

The Macdonald was in agony and in the Irish repeatedly asked to be allowed to go to his broch and lie down but I could not allow it. Bruce was worried about what he might say. And so I was heartless and dragged him along with us, ignoring his grey complexion and gaunt features.

One thing I did after a time was to set off across the Dryfield to the west where the camp was and get him some whisky to ease the pain. We met a few women following their men in our army who knew where some could be found and so MacDonald got a good drink. And the women were glad to have helped a man wounded in the action that day. None of them knew Seaton or anything about him, so that was no problem. I even allowed MacDonald to lie down in an empty broch and rest for a while and there, after some more drams, he eventually fell asleep despite the pain, probably because of the exhaustion. Seaton and I soon succumbed to the same ailment what with the heat of the fire, the fatigue, the excitement and the drams. Thus, it was somewhat later than planned that I got MacDonald on his feet and set off with Seaton to meet the King. Evening was drawing in, the end of a fine summer's day.

Bruce's tent was larger than the others but, for ease of putting up and taking down, was not over twenty feet square. There was a matting of reeds on the floor and the chair he particularly liked which went everywhere with him since he had got control after becoming king; and other seats, smaller, scattered around and stools and benches around the walls where lesser folk could sit. In one corner was the table which was both writing desk and dining table; currently holding letters and parchments of various sorts, as before, and one on which he had been scribing recently in Latin. Beside it, was the open chest full of books copied onto parchments. Behind a canvas screen was a small sleeping place, where I supposed he would lie down for a few hours every night, not always alone. His wife, Elizabeth, whom I had never seen, had been imprisoned in England since soon after his coronation, when taken at Kildrummy. So of necessity he had recourse to alternatives, for the sake of health. But, in truth, he slept rarely, a few hours of an evening at most. In those days he lived his life at high intensity, consumed by thoughts of his task and what he intended to do and eager, anxious even, to see to everything himself, for that was one secret of his success. Nothing was left to chance. No incompetent was allowed to interfere.

The very air around the tent was on fire with delight, men laughed and joked and strutted and told each other their doings and what they had seen that day—with advantages. Since I was known, the three of us were admitted without ceremony, except for weapons which were left outside, watched over by sentries.

Bruce saw us and stood up. 'A wounded man, a brave man, I see.' And then coming forward to Macdonald, peered into his face and saw the agony. 'I am sorry for your hurt. But it was necessary...' he did not finish the sentence. 'Here Gloag, take this man away and find him a place to sleep beside your own and some aquavitae to quieten the pain. Watch over him and see to his needs.' When they had left us, Bruce sat down and invited us to sit. 'Sir Robert Seaton, if I am not mistaken? A Balliol man. What are you doing here? I see no flag of truce.'

'I've come to offer my services, Sire,' he replied.

'Ye mean yer changing sides because we won today?' said Edward Bruce, a tall man like his brother but fiercer, harder, less sensitive and aware.

'Not that. I am glad you won today. I am changing sides because I can't fight against my people and my own country.'

'Well, we don't need ye. So ye can go back where ye came from,' said Edward Bruce. At that moment, some other men entered the tent, some of them with wrists bound behind them. All had been stripped of armour and had wounds which needed tending.

'I won't do that,' said Seaton.

'Who are these men?' said Bruce.

'Prisoners, Sire,' said the tall fair haired Earl of Moray, Sir Thomas Randolph, a kinsman of Bruce, who rose and clapped him on the shoulders.

'You did well today, nephew.'

'It was nothing much, Sire. A skirmish.'

Bruce laughed: 'Not according to Douglas. He thought you were hard pressed. How many were there on the flank?'

'A few hundred only. They could make nothing of our pikes. These were unhorsed and thrown into the ring in the centre,' meaning the prisoners.

'So they never got above you on yon slope, then? Going downhill they would have caused you some trouble.'

'They never saw us at all. They rode past us in the Carse and we had to run through the village to catch them up. Luckily, they were stopped by Livilands Bog which was full of water after so much rain, so much worse than before. Eventually, they found a route up the escarpment through the trees. We fought them on flat ground and they waited for us until we caught up.'

'So the Castle was not relieved?'

'I'm afraid it was. Some of them went on to the Castle. We were unable to prevent them. They had got around us.'

'I see,' said Bruce. 'It matters little. They got close enough to be considered a relieving force. They won't give it to us now.'

'I'm sorry, Sire,' said Moray, blushing with the shame of failure.

But Bruce would have none of it. 'Your force is intact? You took prisoners and you held the ground. They were the ones that left. So you were victorious. Well done. Now, who are these prisoners? They'll make good ransoms.'

Randolph pointed them out: 'Sir James Caradine, Sir Thomas de Ferrers, Sir William D'Aubigny, Sir Thomas Gray. Oh, and Fermoyle, an Irishman.'

'I know them all, except Fermoyle.'

'He is an Irisher, a man of Earl de Burgh, your father in law, Sire.'

'How did he come to be with you Gray, and these others?' said Bruce to a knight with dark hair, a scarred face and other wounds, none of them serious, as I judged.

This man was afraid but still resolute and sore from bruises and cuts after some bashing about. 'There was much confusion, none of us could get into the fight. Some went by way of the Carse and others to the west along the stream. It was every man for himself.'

'I take it I have your parole, gentlemen?' said Bruce. 'You will be ransomed in due course.'

When all agreed to this and swore their oaths, Bruce ordered them untied. 'Get them some food and drink. There's no need to make their lives miserable. Their misery at defeat and capture is enough. But if you make a wrong move you will be killed instantly, I take it that is understood?' They nodded assent.

'You may sit at my table for now,' said the King. 'But when you are nourished you will be led away to spend the night under guard far from the battle area.' With that, as drinks were being brought, the prisoners sat down and Bruce said: 'There are not many prisoners, Thomas. Were many killed?'

'Not many, Sire, a few dozen. When they saw the task was impossible they rode off to the Carse to camp there. We have their armour if you wish to use it?'

'There is no need. It is not a time for armour. I take it you stopped both the gaps?'

'Yes, Sire. My force is divided.'

'And you left half to go after the flankers?'

Yes, Sire. It seemed best to leave your rear defended.'

Bruce now turned back to us: 'Fine, we will now deal with Sir Alexander Seaton.'[32]

'Did you see any action today?' said the King to him.

'I saw plenty. I engaged in none. I have felt for days like a leper. I could not bring myself to fight.'

'Then maybe ye'r not much use to us either,' said Douglas, big, powerful, dark-haired, with a lisp. 'A man who can't fight.'

Bruce interrupted: 'What do you think we should do now, Seaton? We were proposing to fold our tents and move into the western wilderness among the trees and rocks where they can't follow us.' There were gasps of annoyance and even disbelief from several men. 'Ye don't mean it, Sire?' said one. 'We can fight them here,' said another. 'This is an ideal place. So well-defended. Let them come to us.' Others were furious, puzzled, having already seen what Bruce intended, but he brushed their objections aside and shouted them down: 'What do you say, Seaton?'

'You must attack them, Sire. They are demoralised. They have no solution to the pikes and the pike formation.'

'When should we attack them?'

'Early, as early as possible.'

'Why early?'

'Because they will still be drunk from the carouse the night before. It's what they do.'

'But I thought they are demoralised?'

'It won't stop them drinking. Nothing could stop that. Most of them are on a hunting trip. They're not even organised in regiments and there is no proper leadership. Their commanders squabble whenever they meet about who's in charge of what.'

'So you think that we should attack them because they are demoralised,' said Bruce apparently ruminating, allowing the idea to circulate the people inside the tent.

'Why do you think they are demoralised? What did you see? Or hear?'

'They're worried about the pikes and the formation. They've never seen that before. It never occurred to any of them that pikemen could obstruct heavy cavalry. Some of them don't believe it even yet. But most of them have begun to see that this is not going to be a foxhunt of a few rebels. There are a lot of Scots against them and they have shown no tendency to run away. That is unexpected. Englishmen who were at Falkirk are all surprised by this.'

'And what is the difference between here and Falkirk, would you say?'

'The place is different. This is a difficult place for them. The burn is a serious obstacle. It's not just the water and the trees on the banks. It's the high ground on either side. Horses canny get up it at all and the trees make it impossible. That Ford is a death-trap. Then there are the bogs on either side, as you ken, Sire: the two on the west of the Dryfield and the other two south and north of the Carse. Get in there on a horse and ye'll get sucked under. It's the amount of rain that's fallen. The armour just makes it worse.'

'Will they stay in the Carse, do you think? For the night anyway?'

'Where else is there? Anyway, that's the arrangement made beforehand by the King. He's been here before, Sire. He knows it's the best place. Free of bogs, close enough to you to get hold of you tomorrow. His big worry is that you'll clear out in the middle of the night and escape. He wants a pitched battle.'

'So Edward is not demoralised, then?'

'No, Sire. He is like his father. He expects to carry all before him. The others are different.'

'But you really think the others have lost heart? What if I attack them early and you are lying to me?'

'I am not lying. I believe if you attack them you will win. The victories today are a sign of it. You have the method to defeat their cavalry. That's what has been shown. It's what some of them are afraid of: a surprise attack.'[33]

A beardless youth, Walter Steward, said: 'Maybe he lies, Sire. Wants to draw us into a pitched battle.'

Douglas laughed: 'We want a pitched battle.'

A few men shouted: 'Aye.'

'But what if he is lying?' said the youth. 'Let his life be forfeit if he is. Do you accept that?'

Seaton said: 'Of course,' and laughed: 'I would lose it anyway, what difference does my agreement make?'

Bruce surveyed the company and the prisoners eating and drinking at the table. 'What should we do?'

'Attack, Sire!' said every Scottish voice. Douglas said: 'If the English are afraid, they must have reason to be and our victories today have shown them what they are.'

The prisoners were taken away under close guard to sleep beyond Halbert's Bog under Gillies Hill, among the men rejected as unfit or unnecessary, well out of sight and sound of the forthcoming battle and we saw no more of them. Because I knew him by this time, Seaton was to fight at my side. I was annoyed about this, of course. Who wants to have a stranger foisted upon you to look after every minute of the day? Before we left the tent to sleep, Bruce took me aside and looked me in the eye:

'You know why I have had to assign him to you?'

'I know.'

'Well, just you see to it. The least trouble and you know what to do.' What he meant was: should Seaton let slip that his statements in the tent had been a ruse engineered by Bruce to increase the morale of the Scots, I was to shut him up immediately before any damage was done. Nothing must be allowed to undermine what Bruce's idea had achieved. The merest suggestion that it was a lie, a plant, and that the English were actually confident, even overconfident, would go around the army like wildfire, undoing all his efforts on our behalf. Of course they were overconfident! When had they ever lost to Scots? They had a huge army and the finest equipment. They had very experienced men used to winning battles. How could they be anything but confident? Well, Bruce had just persuaded his army that the English were not confident; that they were even afraid.

But Seaton was not happy with the arrangement either. As Bruce was leaving us, Seaton said to him: 'Forgive me, Sire, but if you don't mind I would like to fight with the cavalry. I am a knight, after all. That is what I am trained for: fighting on the back of a horse.'

Bruce turned on his heel and laughed: 'Cavalry? What cavalry?' Seaton could not understand. 'Doesn't Sir Robert Keith command your cavalry?'

'Tell him boy,' said Bruce to me.

'Every Scotsman is on foot. Our cavalry all dismounted. The horses are away up in the woods on Gillies Hill out of the way.'

'I don't believe it!' said Seaton with amazement.

'What good are cavalry to us?' said Bruce, taking him aside quietly, not to be overheard. How could we get them down that slope in Balquhiderrock Wood? And in the dark before dawn? That's what you're in for laddie: a march on foot down that steep slope through the wood, just like Keith's company and everybody else bar none. Do you think horses could do that? And what good would they be if they got there? They have ten times the cavalry we have and theirs is far better armed and horsed. No. We don't need cavalry. We don't want cavalry! Every Scotsman tomorrow will be on foot and carrying a pike, a hand axe on his wrist and a wee targe on the other arm. Horses would make a lot of noise and we have trained ourselves not to.

Thus it was that Seaton and I slept side by side on the Dryfield near the wood close to the shield of Sir Robert Boyd, the commander of our company. Before that, when we sat by our fireside, Boyd appeared: 'I don't like this man in my company but I've nae choice. The King's orders. He micht faw doon in the daurk and ye ken whit that means. Aw our trainin's fur naught. So you tell him whit's expected,' he told me. 'And if he disnae make oot, jist gie him a clout wi' yon wee axe ye have. The spike on the back o' the heid wid dae fine.'

'So you will go in front of me,' I told Seaton. 'You will see the rags every so often on our route and line up beside me when it comes to that in the Carse.'

'Why afore ye?' said Boyd.

'So that if he fails or falls I can hit him on the back of the head with the spike of the axe. That will solve the problem.'

I could see Seaton's face blanch in the firelight and I laughed. 'I only make a jest. Of course he can follow me and hold onto my shoulder. Anyway, the man behind him, MacFee, can do the honours if there's a difficulty.'

'But it might be dark, impossible to see,' Seaton complained.

'It will be dark, impossible to see. We've been practising the move for weeks.'

Worried now, Seaton, grabbed my shoulders and said earnestly: 'What if I canny manage?'

'MacFee will see te ye and puush yer deid body out the way. Will that do ye?' said Boyd. But when Seaton said nothing, Boyd added: 'Ye can stay behind if ye like.'

'I couldn't do that,' said Seton, finally. 'I want to fight, I want to be part of it. It is right.' Then with resignation, he concluded: 'I will just have to do my best. If it's not good enough, I can't help it. At least I will have tried.'

Late that afternoon, before we arrived at his tent, Bruce had addressed most of Douglas's division and all of Edward Bruce's, less the men left on guard at the various possible points of entry to our natural fortress, the Dryfield. Those we met after it, were plainly very fired up by the experience: eager for battle, confident of victory. What had he been saying to them? I was soon to find out. As the evening worn on, we in his division were called to hear him at the theatre we had constructed so recently. Many of Moray's were there too, only the companies guarding the two exits from the Carse up to the plateau with St Ninians, remaining in place. These together with the Macdonalds and other guard companies would be addressed after a decent interval for Bruce to rest and regroup. Thus in three performances, spaced out that day of all days before the battle, Bruce communicated with the whole army.

Used to taking care in all we did, formations being the rule of our lives for weeks of training, the task of seating ourselves in our theatre was undertaken without much mishap. There was a certain amount of noise, banter and braggarty from our group until Bruce himself appeared and ascended the platform to speak. What would he do? I wondered.

He stood tall and still and, at first, did nothing. Gradually, the sounds of talk were muted. Then, the grey-bearded, high complexioned face turned and surveyed us, slowly turning across the massed ranks above and below him, the bright eyes seeming to see each one of us, so that you thought he were about to address you alone, particularly. Again, he was in a yellow tunic with a red lion rampant on it with yellow hose. No armour, no weapon, nothing else.

He began to speak and was so quiet all talk was stilled as men strove to hear him.

'Tomorrow is the greatest day of our lives,' he began, pausing to let us absorb the idea, speaking so low he could not have been heard at the extremities of the seated crowd before him. Men craned forward to listen.

There was a silence. Then he repeated the sentence but louder this time. And paused again. And then, a third time he stated it but this time with a loudness that was riveting, arresting in its power: 'TO MORROW IS THE GREATEST DAAAAY OF OUR LIIIIVES!' The ferocity, the aggression, was like a wall of impending thunder he was about to unleash.

'We have over there, under a mile away,' pointing to the left (NE) collected together, all our enemies. All the people who have terrorised us for twenty years: raped our women, frightened our children, burnt our homes, stolen our lands, our crops, our lives and even our country!

'They have come here to do it all again. They are perfectly placed for us to defeat them, to repay them in their own coin, to take revenge upon them! But we are not just going to beat them, we are going to murder them! It is them or us. And we will do it! Why?' he paused again to allow time to absorb the effect, turning as he did so to search out every eye before him.

'Because we have a brilliant plan. A plan so marvellous men a thousand years from now will wonder what it is and where it came from.' Standing tall and still, yet shaking with passion, he raised his arm and shook his fist, so that all could see. 'They are never going to understand our plan! That is how good it is. I do not think in the entire history of the world there has ever been such a plan. Not in the Greek Wars or the Persian, not in all Europe, not even in the entire battle-ridden events of the Holy Bible that lasted thousands of years, has there ever been such a plan.

'And you are well trained. You know what to do with your pikes, your axes and your targes. Remember the pike must he held straight up in the air. It must not fall to one side or it may injure a comrade. If it does, he could die of it. You must not allow that. And watch where you set your feet. You must not fall—EVER. Your company could tumble like a set of dominoes. That must not happen or our plan could come to naught. Take the greatest care in everything you do. Your eyes are well-trained now. You can see in the dark far better. And by dawn, it will be easier than at any time before. So you will manage. We will be up before dawn. As the dawn comes up, we will be on the move. Take water and food this night, so that that there is no wasted time in the morning. If it worries you, fill a flask tonight. There is no time for anything in the morning! We will sleep, as before, in our companies, right here on the Dryfield above the wood. Do not leave your position. When you are roused in the dark before dawn, do not go off to pish and shit. Do it where you stand, if you must. Remain in your companies. For you will be moving almost immediately. No one is to wander off. Stay together in your own position and move only when instructed.

'This will be the greatest day in all our lives. Nothing matters except that we see it through. When the battle begins, fight hard and let nothing stop you. Do not let up for a moment. When they start running—AND BELIEVE ME, THEY WILL—THEN YOU MAY BREAK RANKS but only then. I WILL TELL YOU WHEN THE MOMENT COMES. UNTIL THEN, you must remain in formation. These formations are the key to our success. Along with the plan. You know the drill, now. Execute it. Do what you have been taught to do. I tell you this. YOU WILL DO IT! I know you will! You are the finest soldiers in the world. I feel sorry for these men over there. You are going to make them all rue the day they ever came here. And once they are gone, they will not be back. YOU ARE GOING TO TERRIFY THEM!

'That is how good our plan is.'

Suddenly, from the body of the group a voice shouted: 'But Sire, what is the plan?' Closely followed by a few others shouting the same thing.

Bruce laughed and grinned broadly for answer: 'You'll find out tomorrow.'

But this was not good enough. 'But how, Sire? How kin ye no' jist tell us?'

'Because you do not need to know! It will not help to tell you. Just do as you are told and your training will do the rest.

'We are going to win tomorrow. Tomorrow is the greatest day of our lives. They are afraid and we are fearless. Be like the lion. And every year henceforth at this time, you will remember this day and be as proud as you ever were that you were here with us and you were part of it.'

The King raised both arms and seemed to embrace us all. 'You are my friends. I admire who you are. What you can do. I am proud of every last one of you,' his voice nearly cracking with emotion. 'Go now and eat and drink and then sleep well, my brothers. And when tomorrow comes be like the lion. Competence, Cold rage and Courage. You do not want to reach the end of tomorrow without having given everything you have in you: all the heart, all the mind, all the soul. Everything in your bones and body and blood, that too. But I tell you,' waving his finger at us, 'you will be shedding other men's blood. You will still have your own.'

Bruce did not get around the whole army that night before the battle. And what was the need? Everyone at that meeting came away feeling as if a divine fire had just been lit within him. A hour or two later, there was another meeting there with the rest of the army at which the Macdonald, Lord of the Isles, spoke in Gaelic and Bruce in both Scots and Gaelic.

In the remains of the evening before dark, he got around many, just the same, stopping at camp fires, chatting to the men, always with a kindness here, a helpful comment there and exuding absolute confidence in us and our plan, which was imperfectly understood even then. A night move was on, that was all most of us knew. Only the few, who had the insight and the knowledge of that ground in the Carse, so very dangerous to an English army—especially one that was so overconfident that carousing and drunkenness were inevitable—understood it, and that, except in my case, imperfectly. But even I did not quite see all of it beforehand, not the half of it.

I wondered why he had not revealed the plan. He judged it unwise, that was all. Someone, a spy, could have slipped out of our camp and gone to theirs. Maybe that was it. Or perhaps he wanted them to be brave and feared that some would lose heart at the knowledge that in a few hours time we were going to attack the biggest, best-equipped army ever seen in these islands. And they were so experienced, with a long record of success. Maybe that was it. Maybe it was just that they really did not need to know. All they had to do was stay in the formations they had been trained in and do the things expected. Bruce would move us all somewhere else and there we would win. Many realised that we were going to descend the slopes of the Wood and form our divisions. We had even practised the new method for getting there. But what was to follow was unclear to many. I did not even see it myself fully until it actually happened.

Seaton and I were seated by our fire among the men of Boyd's company, when Bruce strolled in amongst us and crouched down, heating his hands, though it was a very warm evening. 'That's a fine moon, we have tonight,' he said, looking up. 'Maybe it will be even less dark than usual. That will help.'

'Huv ye thocht whit we're tae dae efter, Sire?' said Kincaid.

'Och, we'll have a fine time, no doubt. Feasting and celebrating on all that food and wine the English have brought us.'

'So ye really think we kin win, Sire?' said Crosby, whose small body lay stretched out along a branch of kindling, like a viper ready to strike.

Bruce laughed. 'What are we doing here if we don't? Haven't we practised and practised so that we can do the needful in our sleep?' He looked around and some men nodded. 'Well, then, that's all it will take. Just rely on your training and you won't go wrong. Be careful, mind, where you put your foot, make as little noise as possible. But you know how to do these things. You've made your share of mistakes and now you know. So you won't make mistakes when the time comes. '

'Will we have any prayers, Sire?' said Duns, 'Ah mean, any prayers for the hale army?'

'Say your own prayers. And not out loud. Keep them to yourself. It's not a time for praying.'

'What is it a time for then, Sire?'

'For killing. This is the day we get even; send them packing back over the border.'

'Do you think they'll le'e us in peace efter?' said Boyd.

'For a while. For years. They're in for a shock and they won't recover for a while. Eventually they will come back but we'll see them off then too. Depend upon it.' And we did. His confidence was real, it was present among us, and we knew he meant what he said.

'How many of us will dee, Sire?' said MacFee, quietly, this tall man who rarely said anything.

'Some will die for certain. But not many. I have planned for that. Wait and see.'

'What if you get killed, Sire, what then? Will the plans still work?'

'They'll still work. Everything is taken care of, believe me.'

'I hope ye're wearin' airmour, Sire, this time?'

'No. I don't need armour. A helmet and a light breast plate is all I need. Speed is what I need, just like you. Quickness , accuracy and force.'

'Do you worry about dyin', Sire?' said Crosby.

'No, what good would that do? If I am going to die, what is the good of worrying about it? I'll just wake up in hell or heaven, whichever. And there's nothing I can do about it. I would like to take a lot of these Englishmen with me, if I go. I don't mind it very much if they eventually get me, so long as I get a lot of them.'

He seemed to smile ruefully, reflecting on what had been said, his face framed in the firelight. 'If die I must so that we win, then I don't mind at all. I would just hate to be left alive if we lost. I would feel I hadn't done enough. That my life was ill spent.' He paused again, reflecting inwardly as he was wont to, as if transported to another inner world. Then he rose suddenly: 'But we are going to win and I expect to be here to enjoy it. And you too, all of you. Wait and see.'

Before he went off, he turned to us all and said: 'If you get knocked down tomorrow, wake up and you're being fed by angels, you know you have died and gone to heaven. They say heaven's a very nice place. I wouldn't mind an angel or two to share my bed tomorrow night.'

Amid the laughter, he said finally: 'Make sure ye get some porridge in ye before tomorrow morn. Do it tonight. There's no time tomorrow. Just be ready, as usual, well before the dawn.'

Messengers came around giving us all last minute instructions, reinforcing what Bruce had told us though they were, thanks to all the practice and the talk in the theatre, largely unnecessary. A few things were new. 'You are to make sure you have a really good drink of water from the Pelstream last thing tonight. There will be no time in the morning. Eat hearty tonight. And make sure you have your porridge or bannocks ready tonight, if you must eat when you are roused. Nothing must interfere with the move we will make. But we must be ready to fight hard with a full stomach and plenty water in us.' Just before the light went altogether, I took Seaton down the hill to the Pelstream through other lines of men seated, lying down or standing, snaking out from their positions at the top of the wood and their camp fires. When we had drunk all we could, we returned to our sleeping place and there we tried to rest but very few slept.

Through the trees we saw in the distance a thousand points of light which lit up the sky. Who were these men we would meet in the morning? We would soon find out. The Carse was full of them and even beyond it, all of them out of long bowshot of the front edge of the wood. There were many of them. Oh many! As this occurred to me, it occurred to others and a new quietness fell upon all of us, a stillness. And then we heard the sounds that carried right across the Carse, far below beyond the trees. There was laughter and music and singing and even wrestling by the sounds of it. Those of us who understood smiled, for we knew they were getting drunk.

By this time, the Dryfield at the centre above the wood had been changed. All the whins, brushwood and the few trees that survived there on that dry soil had been removed and were, even now, burning in our campfires which were everywhere else. That spot about 600 yards by 600 was now sacred ground, for that was our assembly point. By the time it was dark, we were all to line up there in our companies where the commander's shield indicated, lay our pikes flat out of harm's way at our side and lie down there to sleep, each man behind the man he would stand behind in the line. It was midsummer, the weather was fine and warm. What need of brochs and campfires? We would sleep in the clothes we would fight in, as usual, weapons to hand. Any food wanted for breakfast was now to be made the night before and kept ready for the morning. If you needed to pish or shit you went off somewhere else before settling to sleep but not too far and return as soon as possible. There were limits. But Bruce wanted us ready. Between each line of men were just two yards. Once we were afoot, this distance would be shortened to a yard or so just before we entered the wood. The marshals would see to that just before we began the descent. Anyone who had to leave the formation was ordered to use the nearest six foot path between the lines of resting men which led backwards from the top of the wood into the Dryfield right as far as the first ridge 250 yards away and curved back again, so that we were assembled, together, all on the flat ground.

The men were almost all so used to taking up formations by this time in the dark and moving in the dark, that few bothered about it, or even understood what was planned. There was a general feeling of tension. Everyone knew that battle was imminent but whether it was a defensive move we were to make in opposition to an enemy attack up the slope from the Carse or a further move by us, was unclear. When you are used to following orders, you do not wonder too much about what the future holds in store. You just know you will soon be in action and that is focus enough. Nobody had ever set foot in the Carse except at the very edge beside the wood, so no one really expected to go there to do so in the morning. Besides, the English were there. And we were defending an invulnerable natural fortress which we had just that day defended very easily against everything the English could throw at us. All of this was clearly believed by most of the men, as we sat, Seaton and I, and listened to the talk around us.

'They don't know. Do they?' was all he said to me, quietly, tapping me on the shoulder so that I turned my head to look at him in the gathering gloom and I whispered back: 'No. Most have no idea what is planned.' Of course Seaton did not understand the half of it. But I did not tell him what I knew.

And so, in time, in spite of the fear and excitement and the knowledge that an event that would shake the earth was about to happen, we became tired, and lay full length and slept fitfully. In the distance, across the Dryfield we heard the sound of the revelry of the enemy in their encampment around the Knoll and feeling the cool air from the river two miles away which had been heated in crossing the ground, wafting up through the wood where it warmed the sleeping forms. Because the Dryfield was only 250 yards from the top of the wood at the centre, our column of 200 men had had to swing around to the east to keep it on flat ground. The alternative was to take the columns up the ridges into the crater. Since that was another world, it was unwise. We did not need a straight line. Once the men were in motion they would follow each other with the hand on shoulders, as often practised.

How did some men know when it was time to rise? It was a question I had often asked myself. The answer was that some never went to sleep at all the night before such engagements and caught up on their sleep only after all the excitement was over, late in the morning or afternoon. So there were always plenty of folk to get us moving at the appointed time, despite the dawn not having been reached. The first I knew was when a marshal touched me on the head as he went by along the 2 yard space between one company and the next. Already, others to right and left were upstanding. I did the same. You stood up, stretched and then knelt to take hold of pike and axe and you were ready. I had slept with my targe on. Remembering a bannock I had made the night before, I knelt again, collected it, stood up again and began chewing. There was one rule we had all learned above all others in such situations: the pike had to be kept vertical. Otherwise it might damage a comrade. It was not yet dawn and yet, because of the midsummer day, so close to the longest day of the year, someone had said, there was more light than we had ever enjoyed before. There were few clouds in the sky and the stars still twinkled.

12

THE SURPRISE MOVE[34]

On waking, the men who had collected water in a flask or goblet of some kind now drank it. Most did without water, having enough the previous night. Many, having drunk plenty of ale the night before, made water, aye and some even something else where they stood, a depressing experience for those nearby; but orders were orders. A few, a very few, unseen by me at least, probably slunk off to find water and never returned in time. In the dark this would have been difficult; in the half-light near dawn when others would see you: impossible. There was a lot of fear and a lot of tension but our spirits were high; our fears were natural, acceptable. Bruce had arranged that too; all part of his plan.

And then, still in our positions, established days before, we stood and waited for the order to move. It came very quickly, soon after we had been wakened. Not five minutes had been spent in preparation: the time to get a company on its feet. By then, everyone was back in his place. Probably, somewhere, there was a man who never got back to his place, who was too afraid to return. Who went off to shit and crouched down in the brush and remained there in hiding in the gloom before the dawn. For sure, almost everyone returned and did so promptly. Our training had made it so. Anyone who was a problem for the formation—the thing of primary concern, drummed into us over the many days of preparation—would be cut down and thrown aside or trampled just to preserve it. For it was the key to success. Everybody knew that he himself counted for little. The company and the army, they counted above all.

A tap on the shoulder by the marshal sent us on our way. What signal he himself received, I never knew but maybe he just realised that the division was ready. Everybody was standing, pike at the ready. There were no obvious gaps anywhere. The plan, the reason for all these careful arrangements, was to get us down into the Carse and in formation as quickly as possible. There was to be no delay. Suddenly, we were all in motion in single file, treading the well-worn path through the wood. On both sides of me, just a yard or so away, were other men descending the slight slope through the wood just like ourselves. In the wood, under the great canopies of the big trees that stood there, the light was less but it troubled us little for we were used to it by now. Just in case, rags had been left in the centre to aid our descent.

Behind me I could hear Seaton's heavy breathing, for the man was nervous. He had a right to be. Moving in the dark was difficult and his eyes took a while to adjust, though the presence of the moon and stars above the tree tops made it easier for him. We had stripped him of his armour, of course. It would have been no help to him or us.

I was aware of a great tension throughout my body, as if I were about to be given the greatest test of my life and about half way down I was just beginning to think everything was going along smoothly, when I unthinkingly put my foot down into a depression in the path that had been caused by a branch, cut down to make it easier for pikes to pass. It had fallen and crushed the soft earth so much that there was a hole there of almost a foot deep. I had forgotten it, of course, despite the recent day of practice, but knew it by instinct and was just about to mention it to Seaton behind me, when he stumbled and cried out, swearing, and fell upon me, so that I fell full length and hit Magonigal in front of me.

Behind Seaton, MacFee also fell and only Kincaid kept his footing and stopped, managing with a whisper to stop the rest following behind him. Magonigal tried to rise and cursed: 'Haw Sur! Haw Sur! Bae the Christ, keep yer fucken haun aff thet pike. It's stuck in ma erse!'

It was not my pike which I had somehow managed to keep mostly vertical, despite my fall, but Seaton's who, without training had little idea how to control it, especially in the dark. There was a sudden acrid stench of pish and I knew Seaton was so afraid of being dispatched on the spot that he had wet himself. 'Move very slowly,' I cautioned them, quietly. 'There's no real harm done, so long as there is no more stupidity.' On either side, the men continued, as they were supposed to. So the damage was to our company's formation alone.

We picked ourselves up very slowly and carefully, arranged our line again and set off again and reached the Carse at the edge of the wood in due course, a little later than planned but in good enough order. The only defect was that Magonigal now had a bloody hole in his backside.

'See you, sur!' he told me quietly, 'efter this is ower? Ah'm gonny fucken do ye in, ya fucken stupit young cunt.'

'It wisnae me,' I replied. 'It was Seaton's pike stuck ye. Mine was straight up all the time.'

I don't think he believed me. It crossed my mind that perhaps I should watch myself henceforth in case he slipped a dagger into me during the next hour. Surely, no one would notice in these circumstances? The one certainty was that he was very angry and in great pain. But it never occurred to him to stand out of it. None of us would have. We had come there to fight and that we would do before anything. I even felt sorry for the men who had been culled and told to remain in safety around Gillies Hill, moping about or asleep, wondering what was going on, but under guard so that they remained where Bruce wanted them: out of it. There were too many Scotsmen in the battle area and complete control was so essential for success.

By the time we reached the Carse we could see quite well, for the dawn was close. And yet I knew we ourselves would not be seen, because of the backdrop of the dark wood on its sixty foot slope. Ahead, well out of bowshot of our wood, about 500 yards away, as we were marshalled into our places, the sky and the whole area on and around the Knoll was lit by ten thousand points of light and I smiled and marvelled. For sure, the English would be even less likely to notice us forming up when looking out of so much light to our darkness. Every tent had its campfire. Many, inside had candles, oil lamps and even lanterns (lamps with glass sides, a novel feature I had never seen before) which cast an eerie glow around. Up on the Hillock, where the King's encampment would be, were very large tents, we could now see, because of the increasing light and many, many lanterns, every one of which would make it far harder for them to see us, even from their height above the Carse. In the distance, on the walls of the tents, the shadows of giants could be seen, in no hurry, men stretching their bodies, newly awake after sleep, raising their arms to heaven as if they were preparing to meet another heaven-sent day. Everything was calmness and harmony, so it seemed.

In the second column on the right of centre, I descended the wooded slope. I was at the end of a column of 200 made up of two companies, Boyd's being at the rear. At the foot, we were to make a right turn along the front of the wood. On either side, other companies had made the turn before us, but we simply moved in between them and soon caught up to the rest of our company. When I halted, it was to find myself in the centre of the division in the second rank. On my left was the other half of the division which had now joined up and stood right across the centre of the Carse in front of the wood.

And so we waited, as we had waited on so many other mornings just before dawn. But in a few minutes we were ready. All shuffling ceased. The dawn was not yet up! And I knew my eyes were glistening with emotion. Bruce had done it! We were down and we were ready and it had taken no time at all. It was a miracle to cap all the other miracles.

Best of all, there was no noise. There had been a few curses in our company when Seaton fell but nothing much else could I hear. Around me, closer packed now, men shuffled their feet but they said little to each other and that in whispers. Most were too tense for speech. Any that felt like it were dissuaded by those around them, each one in his own yard of space, each one about to tread very carefully so that his footing was secure and he did not trip and fall, for if he did, as we all knew, lines would fall like dominoes and the formation might never recover its shape. Away in the darkness, to right and left, now growing lighter with every minute, were groups of men by the score, the hundred and even the thousand. And there was hardly any noise. Only the faint hush of a zephyr of warm air blowing across the land into our faces from the River Forth a mile away to the north east.

In front of our division, seen dimly in the gloom, was Edward Bruce whom, at first I took to be his brother, the King, because his colours were similar. Gradually, as the light came up, we could see on the right, Douglas's division, slightly ahead of ours far across the Carse and on the other side would be Moray's, also ahead of ours, but also too far away to see, led in each case on foot by the commander out in front. And then as dawn was about to break, there, out in front of the whole army, we beheld Bruce himself, the standard waving gently and the two squires one on either side. And I knew what he intended to do and I gasped in amazement at the daring of it, as did everyone else who could see it: he meant to lead the entire army himself on foot[35] against the greatest army ever seen in these islands! Best of all, what lay ahead of us was their heavy cavalry, who had all taken the best places from which to begin their foxhunt of Scottish rebels the day after making camp, just as Bruce had predicted.—After they had enjoyed a good breakfast and mounted at their leisure, a difficult task in full armour for most, requiring assistance and even a pulley and winch for some very heavy men. Between Bruce and the massed ranks of men were some of our archers, strung out along our lines, maybe 100 in all, maybe less. I could not see more than a few.

Beside me, stood Seaton, stinking like a privy, but he was not alone. Here and there among the massed ranks of men, 35 deep, were a few men who had pissed or shit themselves in fear at the coming conflict. But fearful or not, they were drawn on by the rest and could hardly retreat from within that most carefully arranged phalanx. Most of us were not like that. We had heard Bruce, in the days before, speaking to us in small groups, telling of his fear and his self-belief, his love of his country and its people—of us—and that we would prevail because we were defending our own land, protecting our own families from rapine and because we had a good plan. So despite the fear, admitted, we had heard his confidence. It was in his voice and his bearing. The theatre speech had roused everyone, ignited their ferocity, tempered their anxiety.

Now we had an inkling of what it was, this plan. But not the full brilliance of it. That was still to come and no one knew it. And men who remembered Falkirk—and might have feared that once again, when the fighting became too intense, the commanders, the men on horseback, would ride away and leave the ordinary men, myself and this small company of which I was a member, to be slaughtered for sport by better armed, well-trained and more numerous mounted enemies—had their fears squashed. For we looked out ahead and saw Bruce on foot and knew that would not happen. We were well-trained too and knew it. Bruce was out there in the front and would be in charge making the right decisions. This we knew by now. For a certainty! That was one of his gifts, perhaps the most important: he knew what to do and could decide in an instant and he had brought us to the point where he had arranged that we would do what was required of us. And there were no trumpet calls, no trumpery of any kind. Where he went, we went; where he stopped, we stopped. What he did, we would do. So there we were, standing silently in our ranks, each man with his own thoughts.

Mine were remembering Bruce's attitude to battle. He expected to die. Because of it, he wanted to kill as many enemies as possible. He wanted no foolish death but one that the enemy would suffer loss at his hand before they took his life. And if, by some miracle, he were on the winning side, well then, that was a bonus. And so, by taking his own death as probable, the best thing to do was accept it and die after fighting bravely and sensibly.

Suddenly, my reverie was halted. We were on the move. All the divisions were ready. It was not yet dawn and we were on the move! What a triumph that was. To arrange such a manoeuvre and execute it! Bruce's standard went forward and so did we. And dinned into us, once again, came the message to every mind: step carefully, do not fall, remain in control of yourself, keep the pike vertical. I counted the steps, every one. Counting kept my mind occupied as we marched in the gloom of a new day out of the protection of the dark woods of Balquhiderock. After 407 steps an arrow flew near me, the first I heard. There was a whirr like a swooping hawk in flight and it buried itself in a man, not ten feet behind me. There was a strangled gasp. That was all the reaction. I never knew what became of him, whether he fell or continued. My face was set firmly to the front, undeviating, every nerve tingling at the excitement of the imminent event. There was no slackening of our forward movement, no alteration to our formation. Everyone was marching forward steadily, relentlessly, carefully, and if that man could keep up, he did so, if not, he fell and was trampled over. No one stopped or thought of it. Preserving the formation was everything, as we knew. Others would have died in that deliberate march into the Carse centre but I knew nothing about them. Our approach had been so silent in the dark that few of the enemy had seen us against the backdrop of the wood on the steep slope. Bruce had done it. He had got us off before the dawn. That had been the key.

And then we found ourselves closing up to Bruce's standard. He had stopped. I heard an arrow smack into one of the shields held up to protect him by his squires when he turned round to view us. His hands spread wide as we had seen him do so often and we knew it meant that we would defend this place. And then he took his own pike and gave it a dunt into the soft ground and then turned to face the front and knelt down. And everyone did the same, each with the butt of the pike in the ground beside the last part of the heel, as we had practised. In this way, the pikes were set as required, each butt in the ground, both hands on the shaft four or five feet up and the pike pointing upwards at an angle. And there we waited in silence. A few men crossed themselves and said a prayer. But our kneeling was not about prayer. It was our way of dealing with our enemies. Afterwards, a lot of clergymen thought we were kneeling to pray. They wanted to think that we were asking God for his help and knelt in prayer. Not so. It was not like that at all. By then, our archers had come back through the lines in the gaps between the divisions, to shoot over our heads at knights high on their horses when targets presented themselves. But the order to fill the gaps had not been given yet for Douglas's division was still five yards from ours, as I could see dimly in the gloom, 200 yards away out beyond Boyd on our right edge.

I see now, these many years later, that few men understood what had taken place, only those who had walked over the whole area. Often, not even then. The thing was not easy to see; it took what I dimly recognised as insight, an inner quality of the mind, most men lacked. That I should have loved Euclid was the source of it in my case. But Bruce had it and he had never read that Greek master. So it was not essentially mathematical.

Even the English up on the Hillock in front of us did not understand it and that was because they were too far away from the streams that were the boundaries of the Carse. But I had seen it. Bruce had shown me and I knew that he had just moved the whole Scottish army to a new position off the Dryfield which we had successfully defended the day before (and could have held for a year! That was part of the surprise; that we had chosen to leave it!) down through the wood of Balquhiderock and marched out into the Carse closing off our enemies in their camp: confined them between the two bounding streams, deepened by the recent rain and muddied by the presence of their own army. I suddenly realised that with that move we had already won the battle. What I did not at that time realise was that the tide in the Forth was up[36] and the streams were bigger and deeper than usual.

So there we waited.

Above all things, I believed Bruce would want the gaps between the divisions filled. Were the gaps between the wings and bounding streams filled? I could not tell. There was no sound from those directions. And so we waited and I had no idea what had happened about filling the various gaps. I knew that they should have been filled but were they?

Ahead of us there were a few raised voices in that great army, still awakening from sleep, even a few shouts, but there was no move against us. Even kneeling behind someone else, the great enemy host could be seen clearly now in the increased light. The ground ahead was packed with tents, wagons, men and campfires all of them sensibly well out of bowshot of the wood we had just vacated. The smell of bacon cooking wafted our way in the breeze and even the sound of sizzling as some animal was roasted on a spit and gobbets of hot fat flew among the flames. Horses were everywhere, horses in confusion though mostly tethered, horses neighing and rearing and bucking as ostlers tried to prepare them for the conflict. Tin pans and skillets were rustling, as food was cooked, pewter platters and cutlery tinkling. Sounds of snoring—though we were so very close! Some of them were still asleep from the drunken carouse of arrogant and overconfident men the night before.

And so we waited in silence for them to come to us and it gradually dawned upon us, Bruce especially, who was quicker than anyone, that our enemies were unprepared, in total confusion and without any control worthy of the name.

Far up on the Hillock in front of a large tent, its side emblazoned with 3 lions puissant in bright red and yellow heraldic colours stood a tall man with a crown that shone and glinted in the increasing light and we knew it must be the very King himself, accompanied by a few of his knights. What were they saying to each other? I wondered.[37]

And still we waited and still there was no response. All of a sudden, as if he had experienced a revelation, Bruce stood up and straightened his pike into the vertical. For once, none of us moved. It was so unexpected. Knowing it, he turned and spoke quietly to those nearest him and they rose from their kneeling positions and straightened their pikes and when he moved forward again, they followed him and soon the whole army, all three divisions, was in movement again.[38] But the gap filling group would remain. They had been told to be independent and so they were. They would not move until they were told to do so and that would not happen until we had once again set our pikes and knelt down for the last time.

Ahead, the few English archers still out in their picket line, rushed back behind the tents and wagons, as we strode carefully forward. My heart was in my mouth, for I knew how dangerous this was. "Why do it then? Why take this risk?" My mind shouted to my quivering heart!

Closer and closer to the enemy cavalry lines we marched. On my right, a slight figure detached itself from the small company with the King of England, jumped on the nearest horse and rode like a madman across our front towards Douglas's division on our right. The man wore no colours to identify him. But I would not have known him anyway. He carried no lance; a sword only, which he unsheathed as he came at us, trying and mostly failing to get around the many obstacles in his way, brushing them aside or overturning them: wagons, tents, horses, campfires and men and women. It was a desperate race against time. That race, to him, was the most important of his life and nothing must prevent it! I saw him hit a man out in front of Douglas's division a glancing blow with the horse—the commander himself it must have been—and then, after a further flight forward, it collided with the moving ranks and in a great whoosh, steel points grating on steel, and tumult all around, distinctly heard despite the noises of the camp, the rider was down. There were the sounds of hatchets striking, hitting steel and bone and soon silence descended yet again and the very world stood still. Bruce was awestruck and he stopped. So did we. In the English camp in front of us everybody stopped, even the horses seemed to sense that some dire calamity had occurred, for they were quieted by the eerie silence.

A man, a man alone, a small man in armour without a helmet, on a huge horse also with a highly coloured blue and yellow leather trapper protecting it, had dashed ahead of his whole army and taken us all on singlehanded. He was dead. None of us knew it was the Earl of Gloucester. None of us knew that he had 500 mounted troops behind him in those cavalry lines, none of whom had gone to his support. But we all knew that this was an important man, for had he not just come from conversation with the King of England? The silence continued; the world stopped dead to mourn and reflect. Gradually, we realised that one of the greatest of Englishmen, a man with thousands of followers, many castles and great wealth, had just been slain by a Scottish peasant armed with a small hand-axe. It was as if chivalry itself had been killed.

As if he had just awakened from a sleep, Bruce led us onward. Closer and closer to the English cavalry lines we marched in our silent formation. So close were we that I thought we were being taken to breakfast with our oppressors! The camp seemed paralysed. Whatever men there had been doing, they remained paralysed, staring at us. On the Hillock, the group of knights there were like standing stones, immovable, at the catastrophe they had just witnessed. We could almost tell what they were thinking: 'These are the rebels. They are not supposed to come this close. We are here to chase them in our foxhunt. Not be hunted by them!'

It was mystifying and terrifying, this move of ours. Then they seemed to awaken as if from a sleep. Ahead of me, not twenty yards from me, were men trying to mount horses which were not under proper control. And still we went on. And then, when the English before us were almost close enough for conversation, Bruce stopped, gave the pike a dunt, set it at the angle behind his heel and knelt down beside it and we all followed his example.

Again we waited in silence, almost 35 ranks of men spread out right across the Carse from one side to the other, from one broad, deep, brown, swirling river on our right—the burn—to the same thing on the other side— the Pelstream. But hardly anyone understood it because they could not see the bounding streams unless they were close to them and it was 830 yards from one side to the other. I was in a state of ecstasy! I understood what a miracle I had just taken part in. Tears streamed down my face and Seaton alongside, thinking I was afraid, tried to comfort me. I turned my face and he saw the happiness, the kind that is unmistakable. I even understood now what Bruce had known at our practice: that a second move was possible and that was why the gap-filling ranks at the rear had to act independently under their marshals. Suddenly, I realised that Bruce had given them secret orders. He had foreseen this possibility and had hammered into their heads the idea that gaps would be filled only when the divisions set their pikes and if they ever moved again the gaps would be filled last only once these had been reset. Who would have imagined that there would be no gaps? That we would be taken so close that we had reached the ideal place? The shortest distance between the bounding streams.

The English were silent for a while also. The slaying of the one commander who understood the move we were making had dismayed them. The one man who had tried to divert it, assuming that his men would follow him and obstruct our dangerous move. They understood none of it. They remained in confusion and no one had gone to his aid. That was the reason for their inactivity. The greatest magnate of England had just died, the Earl of Gloucester,[39] one of the richest men in these islands, proud possessor of five earldoms.

No wonder the English were shocked. The noblest man in their country (after their king) whose wealth was uncountable, with a hundred castles, a thousand servants and a private army all his own, a man on a huge destrier which would itself have cost a fortune, had just been brought down and slain by a peasant armed with a hatchet. There was no getting used to such a calamity. It could not be absorbed and understood. The English ahead of us looked at each other with amazement and talked in hushed tones, as if the end of the world was nigh. And so it was, their world, at any rate.

By the time they had recovered, we had set our pikes within ten yards of them—five! And there was nothing they could do to prevent it. Still drunk from a night of carousing, a few—goblets in hand—still sang, unaware of the danger they were now in.

Bruce had put us so close to the English cavalry lines that there was hardly any room in which to charge us. They would never get up speed! I saw it, understood it and nearly wept at the brilliance of it, the daring and the risk. What if someone had tripped and some ranks had gone down like ninepins? So much could have gone wrong. But Bruce sensed it could be done; sensed it would not matter if there were a few failures in our ranks. Getting as close as this was the logical extension of everything he had been trying to do: close off the Carse so that the English could not escape and save Scottish lives in the cavalry charge by getting really close. How could they behave like cavalry when they could not get up speed? They were lost before they had even begun!

Bruce turned and stood up, for it was quite safe for him to do so. He was so close that no one not in their front rank could see him and they were all cavalry, petrified and paralysed by surprise; to a man, unready. Even so, two shields went up behind him, held by the squires. He wanted to see what we looked like and his eye searched for me, I now believe, and found me. I was still weeping tears of ecstasy out of a face shining with delight, despite the discomfort of the pool of water in which I had been obliged to kneel. He saw it and waved with the hand not holding the pike. He knew I understood what he had achieved. He saw us all and was happier than I had ever seen him. His high-complexioned face, with the grey beard, shone as I never saw any face shine. He looked god-like in that early dawn light on that fine summer's day. And everyone who saw his exultation and self-confidence was turned into a confident, cold-raged, killing machine. Those who had pished or shit themselves were reborn, those who had feared death now felt themselves immortal. Why? Because Bruce knew we were going to win. It was now as inevitable as day following night. He had told us with that look. We might not understand it, but he did. That was the message of that look. To Bruce's audacity, we would add ferocity. He turned and knelt down again and there was a palpable, collective, sigh of relief to see him safe.

13

THE BATTLE

We waited and watched the preparations of the enemy. Tall men, short men, fat men, some half asleep or still drunk with an evening's wine women and song, in suits of shining armour, being hoisted aboard huge destriers caparisoned with all the heraldic symbols of England, drawn in all the colours of the rainbow. We thought them beautiful, envied their wealth and style of life, marvelled at it. And thought of our own and how different it was. Dressed in drab homespun, ragged in places, some of us without shoes—things unknown to many, too many—but not an ounce of fat upon us. Any we began with—and there was little—had sweated off during these many days of training and the meagre food that was our usual fare: porridge and bannocks with an occasional rabbit, hare, deer, fish or sheep—skinned and thrown into the pot.

There was no trumpet call to action, it would not have been heard in that confusion of this most disordered camp; no control was exercised. The Scots were here where they were never expected to be. The greatest magnate of England, aside from the King, had been slain by a Scottish peasant. What need of control? Of a command to charge?[40] Thus, when a knight was horsed, he dug in his spurs and moved towards us, lance at the ready, expecting to skewer a few Scots before breakfast. What a favour the Scots had done him by presenting themselves at his tent door where he could perform his ceremonies without the labour of pursuit and discovery from hiding. Some of them actually grinned as they took a last look at us before lowering the visors. Besides, the King was on his Hillock, overseeing the army. Who would not make haste to do his business when that royal eye was upon him?

I saw it all, understood it all and marvelled at the difference in the level of thinking. Not for them, the brilliance of Bruce's tactics. Or his second move which made everything so much easier. Gloucester had understood that and alone had ridden to try to prevent it. But no one else did. So no one supported him as he had every right to expect after paying them, the 500 fighting men he had brought, among a regiment of servants and support for the troops.

And so, in ones and twos, having first tried and sometimes failed to get around tents and wagons without knocking them over, careless of the occupants, they charged our pikes and hardly got up to a trot. Even their horses were half-asleep, overfed, overwatered, as well as badly ridden. The collisions when they came were very different from what all chivalric training had supposed, imagined or expected. The knight or his horse collided with at least a dozen pike points, whose butts were buried in the ground and when the pikes broke, in a shattering crescendo of impacts, he was left on a stationary horse with his lance not even engaged because it was so much shorter than the pikes. Around me, the Scots were shocked at this. They stood, holding the broken-shafted pikes, unmoving, as if it had nothing to do with them and there was no consequence: the ground had done it, the pikes took the strain; not them. Then did Bruce utter a great shout and they awoke as from a sleep, dropped the broken pikes, pulled down the knights from the horses, opened the visors and smashed down with the hatchets that swung on the right wrist. Other men lifted the trappers and slashed the throats of the horses to prevent them thrashing about and destroying our most excellent formation.

Behind those we had killed, other knights rode at us and did even less damage for they ran into the backs of the horses and knights already present, in the course of being killed and, when stationary, were soon pulled down and killed themselves in their turn. Another confused group of cavalry and then another charged into the rear of the first and as we slew them, more and more. Just as there was no command to begin the charge there was none to end it. Every man with a horse mounted and charged as soon as he was ready because he was under the eye of the King and all the best men of the realm. Unthinkable not to join in. And the horses would not for the most part charge over the horses lying in their path, those still alive and kicking but even those newly slaughtered.

A few horsemen, seeing the difficulty, found a gap in their own stationary horsemen and rode into it, even trying to jump over the first few lines of pikemen, but these pikes were unbroken and they took the horses in the belly and they fell just the same. It was like a fence of steel. It could not be breached by horse or man. A few of our men were wounded in these exploits but mercifully few. Some riders tried to leap over the horses lying on the ground, some horses fearing to damage another horse, shuddered to a halt; others were piked and stopped just as surely.

Soon, their cavalry was all engaged. Then there was the killing time proper. Knights were pulled down from their stationary steeds and slain and their horses too and while it happened, almost as if the divine hand ordained it, the position of the English was made far worse: the space vacated by all the cavalry who had occupied the leading position for the sake of first blood at the fleeing Scottish rebels—what they expected!—was soon filled with infantry, eager to get into the fight. Archers ran in, crammed together and were squashed by other soldiery from behind. Even the servants and the support tradesmen and the monks and the women of the army struggled to see what deeds of valour would be done, never realising the danger and that their very action in cutting off a retreat made manoeuvre of the horsemen to the rear impossible.

Thus, movement to the front was impossible because we were there in great force. Movement to the side was impossible because of the swollen streams at either side of the Carse (which none in the centre could see, even from the Knoll, for they were too far away: 400 yards) and now, because of the space behind the cavalry filling up with infantry and onlookers, movement was impossible in any direction whatever. Even their own space was an impossible confusion of wagons and tents, spare horses and camp fires, everything being overturned into a worse mix-up which made clear sight to the front even more difficult for them. A few tents and wagons were actually set on fire by the confusion of people and animals moving among them. For many of them, why they were unable to manoeuvre, why they were hemmed in, remained a mystery they never understood.

Arrows began to fly from the English archers who were massed there in thousands and a few found Scottish billets but the increasingly dense assemblage of horsemen on six foot high horses, tight-packed, made the Scottish targets impossible to hit. An archer might try and shoot through a gap but, as often as not, the gap was filled by another Englishman while the bolt was in flight. The horse and rider to the front presented an obstacle nine feet high. Impossible to hit a Scotsman under six feet tall, especially, when kneeling, he was transformed into a dwarf three or four feet tall. Arrows were fired skywards in a parabola to get over the horses, a move never practised and difficult to judge, and most fell on Scottish helmets and in many cases bounced off.[41] At such close range, shooting accurately in this way was impossible. Unless the arrow hit the steel directly, it would not penetrate. But by the time all the cavalry had charged, the ground behind them was densely packed with foot and hangers-on, eager to see the battle close to, and this made shooting even more difficult because there was not the space to load the arrows and draw and fire. Everybody was getting in everybody else's way, jostling elbows and interfering with their performance. The noise of disagreements and the shouting of insults carried over the helms of the knights. And it all took place amid a confusion of tents, wagons, campfires, kit, spare horses and people not involved: servants, cooks, tradesmen—monks even.

Some archers, over-excited, stupidly insisted on firing directly as usual and a whole salvo ended up in the backs of mounted knights high on their horses. There were calls from the front then to stop shooting and mostly this was obeyed. So the archers could play no further part in the battle and had had little effect until then. Worst of all, they were unable to move to the rear for the press of others behind them and themselves prevented the stationary cavalry from retreating to regroup.

What was it like around me? I saw a knight detach himself from the confusion of wagons, tents—horses being mounted in alarm now—and this one came right at me and the man in front of me. The lance had a pennant with the red cross on white ground, and it fluttered, feebly in the gradual warmth of the summer morning. There was the sound of the hooves and even the whirr of rowels as he tried to spur his horse into a trot but it wasn't possible—there was no space—and soon the horse's head was breathing at me—I could even see the nostrils dilating and steaming with the effort—the eyes under the blinkers racked with fear, but I aimed my pike and with a sudden jerk the point struck between the saddle and the thigh of the rider high on his steed, shining and brilliant in the armoured coat of plates he wore, emblazoned with his own design: a red deer with an arrow through it on blue ground. The pike in my hands bent like a bow, I could feel it drive into the ground by my right heel and then it snapped. Other pikes had hit the enemy and they snapped at almost the same time, though not all that might: several bounced off or were inadequately aimed.

In the blink of an eye, kneeling on the ground in the second rank, I found myself staring up at the knight in all his mailed finery. And the surprising thing was that he no longer moved! He had been hit by about ten pikes from two sides and that was like driving into a sharp pointed tree trunk, twenty inches wide, stuck in the ground. No contest! He was stopped dead in his tracks about eight feet from me and I could see the pennon, waving futilely, the only thing of his that could move. At first he did nothing, surprised like all of us by the alteration to his circumstances. Then he was trying to thrust at the man kneeling in front of me with his lance. But he could not reach him for the pikes, others coming onto him from both sides to replace those broken. Then a pike to one side of me, Magonigal's, caught him on the chest and pushed him and he fell off the back of the horse. It was then that little Crosby came into his own. With a cry of excitement, this fierce little man dropped his broken pike and ran forward, others soon joining him despite the struggles of the horse, grabbing its rein futilely to quiet and calm it. The knight's visor was lifted, a hatchet smashed down and for good measure another and another. The horse was incensed, crazy with fright at being confined and was soon dispatched with a stroke to the throat under the trapper and a gush of blood spattered everyone. By then other riders had suffered a similar fate further away, as we could hear from the sounds of splintering wood. Others yet, were heading for our group after the first, but our formation was quickly restored.

Some of those with broken pikes knelt with the shattered remnant, knowing no better, but soon, pikes were handed forward from the rear and reset even while we were just about to experience another attack. Bruce had never foreseen this and had not trained us for it. We reacted as circumstances dictated. In that next attack, the riders went straight into the back of the slain horse, one trying and failing to leap over it, only to be hit by several pikes at once which stopped the horse dead in the air and caused the rider to pitch over its head and fall right in front of our front row. Two dead horses soon lay in front of us, and their riders. Then, the men with broken pikes set forth and slew the second rider. And as more and more riders attacked, ready now and with room to reach our lines—so they mistakenly believed—they too were knocked flat with pikes and the men, small men like Crosby, some of them, ran beneath the horses legs which, increasingly hemmed-in, could not move, to get at the fallen knight and dispatch him or heave him off the horse and then kill him when he hit the ground.

Everywhere across the field our lines of men were adapting to the situation, pikes were handed forward to replace those broken and reset at the front and where this did not happen men with broken pikes used hatchets to get among fallen men and horses and deal with them, which, without armour and light on their feet, they were easily able to do. The knights, weighed down with sixty pounds of armour, were slow and incapable of decent response. Worst of all they were often on the ground and without weapons. What chance had they then?

Not all the field was like this, of course. On the north, as I learned later, the attack of the knights was more concentrated, a hundred, arriving at once in a small area, saddle to saddle, many yards wide. This was the group that had failed to penetrate the pikes the day before and they had worked out why it was: individuals charging had little effect. That was why they charged mostly together. Even so they were unready also and had to circumvent tents, wagons and campfires. So their effort at concerted attack failed, could not act as one. Then the later lines just smashed into those in front and when all were halted, the killing began as soon as the pikemen recovered from their surprise. Mainly, elsewhere, it was a sporadic attack by individuals who piled in behind each other at different times.

At the south, the men with Douglas responded differently: they were attacked by a mass of Gloucester's division, hundreds of them on horseback, furious at his death, embarrassed by their failure to help him, jammed together and behind each other in many ranks, but starting from so close, that even a combined charge achieved nothing. Here, quite unexpectedly, for once there was no thunder of hooves because Douglas had stolen so much ground, having reached the ideal position: the Great Bend in the burn. They crashed into the pikes almost immediately at walking pace, amid a tremendous roar of shouts quite overwhelming the sound of splintering shafts, shards of wood flying everywhere, hitting men like miniature arrows. Then there was a dead silence which lasted a very long time, as it seemed. Everyone there seemed shocked by the change in their circumstances. The violent tumult stilled. Every horse had halted by this time, almost all were saddle to saddle, every space filled. Between the cavalry and the pikemen of the Scots was a narrow gap filled with the remaining pikes which had not broken and which prevented the horses and their riders from further progress. There was a lull. Then, suddenly, everyone seemed to awaken from a sleep. Some knights tried to push forward into the pikes and were immediately pushed over the back and unhorsed. Those in the rear ranks could not even get their lances into the horizontal for the press of their own men in front of them. A few at the very back tried to turn and reverse their path to regroup and were soon engulfed by a horde of people running into the space vacated from behind: archers, men-at-arms, servants, cooks, women, even children, all struggling to see the deeds of chivalry about to occur. But all they did was fill the space and prevent the retreat of their cavalry.

As if by magic, here too, men at the back of the pike lines already engaged, passed their good pikes, still in the vertical, forward to those in front and the broken pikes were soon replaced in case of further charges. They need not have bothered. The front line of cavalry could not move at all. Knights began to be pushed down and slain by pikes and dispatched by small Scots who crawled between the legs of horses and brought down the hatchets on faces lying supine with opened visors and the horses too were killed with a quick slash to the neck.

Thus, what Bruce had never trained us for, we adapted to as seemed best and this was possible because of the training we had received which had prepared us so well. Everything we did was sensible, orderly, harmonious and deliberate. This was no lordly group of individuals out for their own personal fame but a team, working for each other and Scotland, led by the finest king we ever knew or imagined—that much was now as clear as the blessed day that lay before us. A king who had put his own body in front of everyone else and why? Because it was the way to keep control, the way to lead, the way to inspire confidence and the way to win and that came before anything. What a marvel that was! What a miracle, a thing never seen before. Such courage, such command and such insight, in one person.

The aim of the move, as all knew, was to halt the cavalry and we did everything we could to achieve it and succeeded. Once halted the riders were easily slain, some shot by our archers who were behind us now and had easy targets: Englishmen sitting high on great horses who were so close that our arrows easily penetrated the armour, mainly mail shirts but many with coats of plates, like the Romans. Most were pulled down or fell down and slain with hatchets. The most troublesome were those whose horses were stopped so suddenly that their riders pitched over the horse's heads and landed among us which injured many a pikeman because of the sheer weight landing on us or hitting us as they fell to earth, our pikes and his momentum acting upon him like a stone thrown by a two-part mangonel. Even a glancing blow from a man in armour in the act of falling was painful to men without it. The very weight was crushing. Ribs were stove in, limbs broken, so that for the rest of the battle, some men took no further active part, just stood and watched. Even then, the pain was easily forgotten because of the prospect, the fact, of seeing Englishmen killed with impunity in such large numbers, and these of the most dreaded and arrogant type from which all had suffered or heard of the suffering of relatives and friends. This was vengeance, the day of reckoning. The wounded Scots fought, some of them, mindless of their own hurts, one-handed in some cases, the broken arm hanging uselessly, some gasping for breath at the pain in the broken ribs. Most were active, hurts and wounds or not, clutching the sore bit with one hand while dealing out blows with the other.

In the first few moments after the first line of cavalry hit us, these circumstances were adapted to and decided as each group deemed best, but the killing proper did not begin in earnest until all the cavalry had charged and all been halted. A few knights seeing there was no way forward, tried to turn and ride back the way they had come, in vain: they were engulfed by other knights coming forward into them and merely impeded the speed of their attack or were engulfed by archers unable to see the men in our lines for their own men in front on horseback and too tight-packed to be able to shoot accurately. Many Scots, whose pikes had broken, and were anxious to play their part even without it, crawled under horses legs and were kicked or trampled by the frightened horse. Some fell and never rose again. Horses invariably fell in the collision and could not rise for broken legs, fell on our men even. Men fought around them and over them but the smooth curved surface was uncertain footing. Until killed, when at least they did not thrash around under foot, we fought between them, filling the spaces, though soon there were few of these. Of course, horses piled on top of each other, as their riders were pitched forward over the heads of their steeds, so sudden was the collision and soon died, when all thrashing ceased.

When the mounted knights stopped coming, by which time I had broken another pike on a different horse on the other side, handed up from behind me at my frantic call, I myself pushed forward from my kneeling position on my knees, axe in hand, and smashed every armoured foot I came across and when the man fell as he often did I got his visor up and sent him and his thrashing horse to hell. Me he could not hit at all, having no weapon to hand, lost in the fall, and pressed on all sides, especially from behind which quickly gave him no space to do anything. All the available space was at ground level up to the waist. That was where Crosby and men of his size operated with impunity, once the horses were killed, and to great effect. There soon came a time when to stand up was to achieve nothing for the press of men in front. They were too close to hit. All you could do was look them in the eye. The press was too strong to even punch them on the nose. Then, realising it, we would bend down and find space and aim our blows at feet, or crotch and, when the man fell, leave him to others or dispatch him as seemed best and then advance into the press of enemies and attack another.

When I was learning this, I stood eye to eye with one tall knight who spoke to me in a language I had never heard before. His helmet had come off or was never even put on, such was the surprise of our attack. He had blonde hair that shone in the sun and blue eyes in a lightly-tanned, golden face. A very handsome man, a god-like man. I had no idea what he was saying. I believe now that he was speaking German,[42] but not French where King Edward owned lands in Aquitaine and would have recruited from. This man must have heard about the battle and travelled far in the hope of being able to exercise his knightly training: some people always have to go where the action is. Probably, he had hopes of some distinguished act which would bring him to the attention of King Edward who might even reward him or employ him. Maybe he just wanted to refine his skills. His horse was flat on the ground, killed stone dead by the collision with a dozen pike-shafts, like hitting a tree; and he was standing near it, hemmed in by many others behind him, unable to reach their weapons, just as I was hemmed in behind me, the man ahead of me being down—how I know not, knocked down probably and trampled to death, maybe even by myself. God knows, I spent an hour trampling bodies, alive and dead. The man and I were chest to chest and he was speaking to me urgently, insistently and I expect it was an encouragement to me to make him my prisoner or the reverse. He wore a coat of plates, like the Romans, and a fine surplice—with his own colours I suppose: a golden eagle on azure ground, it was; and a red cross on a white band on his arm. He was holding a sword but was unable to raise it to strike for the press of men, me included. I could not raise my axe to strike because his mailed hand prevented it. For a few moments I was in a state of shock, paralysed by fear. I couldn't move in any direction, it seemed! I must be killed! I was hemmed-in. Men pressed me on every side: Englishmen to the front, Scots to the rear and the side. The noise everywhere around was deafening. But it was nearly all in English. English knights calling to each other and those behind, complaining, ordering, commanding, and being ignored mostly. There was the whirr of arrows, the clash of weapons, the screams all around that stopped suddenly in death and the sough as a pike, already stuck in, was withdrawn, often in a spray of blood, even a whoosh as a great artery was severed when it shot into the air. The stink of it and the shit and piss emerging from the terrified, in the process of dying, was nauseating, sickening, made some of us puke. Some of it was horses dying: their bellies erupted clouds of gases, foul smelling and noxious: you could collapse from the stench alone or slip in the blood, which was to court disaster: for you were unlikely to find your feet again in that crush, that intense pushing on both sides, as the Scots advanced into the English cavalry and their infantry advanced into the backs of their mounted knights.

But there was little noise from the Scots. Schooled for weeks in the virtue of silence, we were content to do our talking with our axes and pikes and hands and feet, anything that would do the job of ridding us of the usurpers, the invaders who had arrogantly laid claim to us and our lands and women and children, to our country—the country we had become under the most charismatic king it ever knew. Only later, did the Scots make any noise and it was a low rumble at first, which eventually grew to a roaring, as if a great torrent of force had just been unleashed all across the battle field, by twenty thousand Scottish lungs. No, our comments were minimal, quiet even: simple directions to each other to improve the efficiency of our joint killing: 'Get his visor up!' or 'Kill that fucken horse afore it kicks me!' or 'Haud his airm, so ah kin get my axe in!' or 'Puush him doon wi' thet pike!' Just occasionally, 'Use yer dagger!' but the hand axe was usually enough, blade or spike as seemed best.

And so the German and I stared at each other, not understanding. I had nothing to say. He was entreating, as if I could do anything to please him. Neither of us could move forward or back and we were both perplexed. It was a situation he had never trained for or experienced. I was the same, but my training had been a little different from his. I had learned to use my mind and that was what I did.

I could move up and down easily and he could not for his leg armour which made him stiff and unmanoeuvrable. I ducked down, spun my axe and lifted the spike right into his groin. I stood up and saw the man's eyes turn the colour of lead and fear travel across his whitening face as quick as a predatory eagle falling from the sky. I ducked again and hit him again in the same place, driving the spike in as far it would go and heard it crack a bone. Then, as I looked, he screamed and to my amazement it was not blood that poured forth but pish. The stench of it filled the air around. He had wet himself. Or my spike had punctured his bladder, I know not. A moment later he fell and disappeared. I knew I need trouble myself no further with him and went on to the next, trampling him as I went.

But the men we slew were all armoured men. Had they been without armour we would have fared less well, being on an equal footing. Horses had helped them not at all because they could not get up speed and were quickly and effectively halted. Armour was even less helpful, for without weapons which they lost in falling or could not use for the weight and the press of men, it was a great hindrance. They tired very quickly because of the difficulty of moving in any direction in that press. We could easily kill them because we alone could move, especially up and down. In the spaces we found there, we slew them. All they could do was stand and face us, held up as often as not by the very implacable stiffness of the metal protecting them, if they could stand at all. Most were on their backs soon after their horses were stopped. Few managed to rise after that shock. Those that were catapulted over the saddle into our ranks often landed on other pikes set behind the front ranks that brought them down in the first place. Some caused injuries to our men but these knights were easily killed by those of us close to them. Pikes were still useful, even the broken bits of pikes some still wielded. The point in the chest knocked the armoured man over and then his death was swift. Another Scot would move in with the hatchet and lift the visor. And so our men often worked in pairs, so close-packed that the pairs selected themselves.

We took full advantage of our manoeuvrability, becoming very red with blood not our own. Once, after a spate of killing and the sound of killing all around me, all of them English dead, I managed to stand up to see. On the Hillock just across the pond which I had reached, between the heads in front of me, I could just make out the English King in armour and crown sitting on a huge white horse with the reins in another knight's hands[43] and other knights, similarly mounted, remonstrating with him. Then I ducked down again and continued my grisly work, in a high glee of passionate cold rage.

Bruce led us all around both sides of the pond, knowing it was too deep to venture into, but into which a great press of Englishmen had been forced. For men in armour it was a death trap. The weight of armoured bodies made them sink into the deep mud that lay beneath the surface. Here again the pikes were useful. From the dry ground at the edge, the pikes were thrust into the throng struggling in the pond, each knight thinking of himself alone, as before on both days, so that many were knocked down into the mud never to rise again, unable to gain a footing there. There they would splash and struggle, kept there by the pikes which pricked any attempt to get out and then tire and succumb and drown in the waters which were soon full of dead knights. By the time the killing in the pond had ceased and I looked up, the King of England had vanished, leaving his tent flap wafting impotently in the slight warm wind of the midsummer morning, the most glorious any of us had ever experienced or would see again, he and all his personal guard of the best knights in Europe along with him.

A flood of folk was now in progress in every direction but towards us, for no Englishman had any stomach to remain and fight when their King had fled. All over the Carse, Englishmen presented their backs to us and we were soon chasing them, whooping with glee as hatchets were driven into the backs of helmets. The spike went through the metal like butter. It was a matter of getting really close, dancing up quickly and striking with the hatchet, a question of timing mainly. There was often little blood but if your stroke was short you would hit him in the back of the neck and you heard the crunch of steel on bone, smashing the vertebrae, even if he wore mail or not. That two inch spike on the hatchet, with force behind it, cut through anything.

Small groups, seeing the danger of their flight, stopped and tried to defend themselves but our archers then appeared and shot them down and we attacked and finished them off. Of the thousands of English archers there was no sign, all having moved towards the burn to attempt a crossing, the cause being hopeless as the King's guards had seen. Imagine if we had captured him? What a chest of treasure then we would have got in ransom! It would have fed the whole of Scotland for a century.

No orders from Bruce were necessary. Every Scot raced after an Englishman and often killed him easily because he was at such a disadvantage and then, not stopping for loot, chased another. A few Scots did stop of course, seeing the rich accoutrements which they coveted. Some men were too easily diverted from the first task: to defeat the enemy. There were, however, enough of us to carry on the slaughter, counting every man slain for his personal history of the event.

One man I saw, with an expression of gleeful savagery, came upon a woman, a beauty, still half naked from sleep and promptly entered the tent and her a few moments later, so fired up was he. But there was little of that. We were sweating under a warm sun now and in the midst of an exercise the like of which we had never imagined in our wildest dreams. Between the pond and the burn I slew nine[44] Englishmen, only two of whom put up any resistance. Once you got the hang of it, the killing was routine. The easier was a grey haired man-at-arms in mail, wearing a great helm, once shining, now spotted with rust by the rain and the damp. He heard my feet running towards him and he turned to meet me, sword in hand. There was a rage in him, an arrogance, a presumption that I had no business with him, for he knew what to do and I was too young to know and, clad like a peasant without armour, what could I achieve against the likes of him? I saw it all in his face, in his look of disdain, in an instant, as he swore at me to leave him or he would slay me where I stood. The blade came swinging in a great arc and I leapt to one side and it missed me by a foot. The effort of the stroke made the man slip and lose his balance, going down on one leg in a pool of water. That was when I moved behind him, like a whippet out of a trap. I brought the spike down on his back below the helm and heard the crack as it broke right through the back bone. There was one who would trouble Scotsmen no longer.

There was no exultation this time. I had just killed an old man who was in the wrong place at the wrong time. He had no chance to live. Without pausing even for breath I ran on across the south Carse which was strewn with tents, wagons, campfires, weapons, tables and all the appurtenances of campaign—all in increasing confusion as they fled and we trampled everything just to get at them—heading for the burn where archers by the hundred were throwing themselves into the brown swirling waters. I saw tents go on fire because they were stamped down in the stampede of people, the canvas falling into the fires. I saw a fat Englishman with a purple face sitting on a stool with his back to a wagon and his head slumped forward onto his chest. He was snoring! He had consumed a barrelful of wine, judging by the size of the pitcher overturned beside him, had got utterly drunk and fallen asleep; and despite all that noise and tumult nothing would wake him. I halted only long enough to hit him on the flat of his bald head with the spike of the hatchet, en passant, and heard his skull crack like an egg.

The last man I slew heard my steps and turned. He was carrying a bow unstrung and a short sword. He was very tall, taller than me by half a foot and yet light on his feet. As he moved to stab me with the sword, I stepped back a pace, detached the string, turned the handle of the axe in my hand and then threw it with all my might. It travelled barely a yard, for he was advancing. The blade bit into his forehead with a dull crack and he went down like a fallen tree with my axe sticking out of his head. None of his companions came to his rescue. If they had, unarmed, I was helpless. I pulled on the axe and could not shift it out of his forehead. It seemed to be permanently fixed there. I could pull his head up with the axe but I could not get the axe out. It was the only weapon that remained to me.

In little over an hour[45] from our march out into the Carse, I had reached clear across to the north bank of the Bannock burn which swirled down to the Forth in a wide brown torrent. As usual in such conditions after heavy rain, the burn had become two streams, and the entire salient after the Great Bend was awash and muddy. The sound of men screaming in death, the smell of pish and shit as they involuntarily opened their bowels and the fright in their faces as they suffered the process of dying, will live with me all the days of my life. I never saw anything like it before or since or ever heard of such a catastrophe. The heavily armoured Englishmen, even the foot soldiers, were struggling everywhere to cross the burn, falling in it, unable to rise for the mud and being swept along by the force of the water which, though held up by the tide, was deeper than usual at such times of heavy rain but still had some power. Bodies were everywhere around, and many, so many, already underwater, because of the weight of armour and weapons. Only the lightly armed, the archers, had any chance of escape. They could cross over and many of them did, often on the bodies of their comrades and when they reached the other side they set off for home as fast as their legs would carry them, running to escape the chasing Scots.

Englishmen in mail or other armour with all the heavy bits to cover vital organs and joints suffered in that crossing and most never made it at all. Some of the armour was plates of steel held in pockets of the tunic which was fixed on by leather straps. Many had parts of a full suit of armour and some, the wealthiest, entire suits of armour, including greaves and arm braces. Every knight had a helmet and that was heavy. With the sword and the other weapons the task of crossing was too dangerous for most and they were too attached to their weapons to discard them. A few tried to ride across but the weight of the rider and his armour and the horse armour, even if it were only a leather covering, was too great even for these great horses to bear in such slippery, deep-water conditions. Because the press of infantry and hangers-on had been released on their fleeing the field, many knights were able to detach themselves from the press being slaughtered by us, the Scots, and ride for the burn where, because of the power of the horse, they were often successful in crossing, provided they chose a place which was not too broad, even in those conditions of great width and mud and force of water pouring down from all the hills in the hinterland. But some did not, the horse fell or tripped on other bodies in the burn or just lying on the ground or other dead horses in heaps that presented an even greater obstacle. Some horses were carrying wounds, lacked the strength to get out of the swirling waters of the burn and died there.

The entire south Carse, especially around the burn, was a scene from hell; every sort of atrocity on view. A man with his foot on the chest of an Englishman smashing down with the sharp end of a splintered pike. The sound of roaring and bleating as the man was being killed like a sheep but slowly, the killer enjoying his screams. A woman, naked, running for the burn and a lad, no older than myself, in hot pursuit. He had picked up a sword newly sharpened with a razor edge and had swung it experimentally, horizontally, just as she, hearing his footsteps approach, turned to plead for her life. Her head sailed through the air, rotating, the eyes full of wonder, to join the hundreds of dead ones already floating downstream and what remained of her subsided to the ground amid a fountain of bright red blood. A child, a girl with fair hair who could not have been more than ten years old, was standing by a man who lay so covered in his own blood that death was happening before her eyes. The child, standing knee deep in a pool of water, mindless of it, wailing as if the world had come to an end. And for her, that day, it did. What overconfidence had so possessed that man that he had allowed his lovely child to come and watch him die?

Across the burn I could see another low rise in the ground[46] made by an embankment on which a group of Englishmen had gathered to defend themselves and there they fought with swords and axes and even arrows for a while. But they were eventually overcome and slain by far more numerous Scots attacking from all sides. A few hundred Englishmen there were, all of them infantry and they made a better fight than any others.

The men of my own company were all around me, all of them exultant at the killing. Seaton was laughing at my bloody face and yet his own was just as red, and none of it was ours. Turning to look to my left, the Carse was a scene of slaughter with fleeing Englishmen trying to surrender, falling over fires, tents, tables, stools, wagons and each other and in many cases being slain for sport. Some with wealth obvious in their clothing or weapons were spared for ransom but anyone who looked too poor for that was fair game. Bodies lay everywhere around, in every condition from shock to awful wounds, having lost arms and legs, hands, ears, noses and heads—worst of all—and death in all its stages of completion. Many non-combatants, men, women and even children who had come along for the pleasure or were brought for the experience, were killed outright. Capturing took up too much time. We were in a high fury to expel them altogether. Most of us were possessed by a quality of controlled rage that turned us into assassins, killing machines, mindless of the screams and entreaties of those whose lives we ended. For twenty years we had been shamelessly exploited and mercilessly treated. We remembered Wallace and what they had done to him—castrated him, tore his entrails out, beheaded him and quartered him—and it never occurred to any of us to do anything but avenge him and all those who suffered like him. He had been guilty of nothing but a spirited defence of his own people and his own country. For once, at long last, we were dominant, in control of our own destiny!

Tents and wagons full of produce that seemed to us like riches were scattered everywhere. Behind me, when I turned to face the north, I could see Bruce on the Hillock in the Carse centre, beside the tent that had so recently belonged to King Edward, other tents in profusion all around, gaping empty, or half collapsed, the trees on the Knoll having been cut first for firewood before the tent pegs were driven in. Tired out, some of my companions like Crosby who had killed more than anyone, lay down in the blood-soaked grass between the pools and immediately fell asleep, having failed to sleep the night before.

Exhausted myself, I decided not to cross the burn and pursue the fleeing enemies. I could have found a weapon easily but was too tired to move another foot. As I looked eastward, smiling to myself at Crosby's snores, I observed an English archer with a green hat and a fine yellow gambeson with a red cross on the chest. He was walking calmly along the bank from the direction of the confluence on the east side of the burn beyond the salient at the Great Bend, still flowing and swirling with brown spate water which had burst the banks and taken the shorter route, slowed by the tide but deeper and wider because of it. The man seemed cocky, untroubled by the fighting going on near him. Seeing me, and drawing level, he loaded an arrow into his bow and aimed at me. There was nothing I could do to defend myself. I was in open ground on a slight grassy slope with no trees near to shelter behind and too tired to run, too slowed by weariness to dodge even. He was not sixty yards away. He fired and as he did so, I heard the arrow as it approached whirring through the air.

Below me and close by, restored after his short rest, Crosby sprang up and faced me with a face shining at the excitement of victory. His hands, hair, face and clothing were spattered with blood but his eyes were lit by triumph. From his mouth came the beginnings of a sentence he never finished, for out of his chest appeared the harsh, steel, wedge of an arrow which thumped into him and he fell forward on his face, pinned to the ground by it right at my feet. For a few moments I was paralysed by the shock. He needed to be turned face up. I pulled his shoulders and he would not move. I screamed with anguish. What was I to do? I broke the arrow near his back and threw the flight away. Then I heaved him up off the ground by the shoulders so that the arrow remained in the ground and I laid him on his back, face up, but as I did so, a surge of blood spurted forth and soaked the grass. I tried to comfort him.

It was a waste of time. He was already dead. And so died one of the best men of the company, who had killed many an Englishman that day. Myself, I could not comfort. It was all too much for words, or feeling. I think a part of me died that day at that moment.

When I looked across the bank at the archer, he had run off towards the bog far to the east. I cursed him aloud amid my tears of rage and prayed that he would sink and drown in that bog. I was now too exhausted by this additional shock to be of further use. So I decided to go and see our King and congratulate him on our victory which, to me, at least, was a marvel of the mind of man.

As I wearily trudged up the side of the Hillock in the Carse centre, the full extent of the rout lay spread out before me, sixty feet below. Many Englishmen, cut off from the route across the Bannock burn to the east which led to England and home, were escaping across the confluence of the burn and the Pelstream, not realising that half a mile further on was the River Forth which was deep and even more treacherous to armoured men, for the banks were covered in a thick layer of black mud at the best of times, and these were the worst. The river, I knew, because of the recent rain, would be high, five or ten feet higher than usual. Men who tried to cross there would drown even without armour.

The scene around the pond to the west of the Hillock was a charnel house of dead horses and dead knights, some being stripped of their armour even as I watched. Thousands of bodies littered the line from the burn to the Pelstream but in and around the pond which was the centre, the place where Bruce himself had led the army and fought furiously for so long, was full of bodies, some still in the process of dying, some piled high on dead horses or each other. All this, amid the shambles of a tented camp with wagons upside down and goods of every kind spread all around in confusion with scavengers, men, women, children, dogs and birds beginning their work everywhere. I saw a dog begin to lick the blood on the face of a seated man who had lost his nose while trying, and about to fail, to save his own life.

As I arrived on top of the Hillock it was to find Bruce sitting in King Edward's chair—or what had been his chair, a padded, jewel-encrusted throne, indeed—looking very weary, his yellow tunic blood-stained and bearing many scars, mostly minor, I judged. Gloag arrived from the tent inside bearing a golden chalice full of dark red wine. 'Wull ye drink this doon, the noo, Rab?' said he, one of the few to take such liberties because of his status as a tutor of the boy, now the man, now, indeed, the great man, after such a day's performance. Bruce said nothing but took the wine and sipped it thoughtfully. Tears fell down my face and I knelt to touch the his knee, once brown and undistinguished, but sufficient for such desperate work, now torn, slashed, holed, stained with the blood of dozens, some it his own, and the mud and even the shit of his dying enemies, in which he had wrestled and struggled. Words failed me. The exultation of such a set of moves as we had made under his inventive direction was too much.

'I know,' he said, turning his weary eyes upon me. 'It is all too much for speech,' and after further reflection: 'I feel more humble than at any time in my life. God has been kind to me.'

'He has been kinder still to all of us,' I said. He knew what I meant, smiled weakly, leaned forward and clapped me on the shoulders as he was wont to do in times of high emotion.

People soon arrived from all over, full of excitement, congratulations, questions and suggestions about things that needed doing. Every one of them wore clothing filthy with blood and mud and stank to high heaven. And no one minded. We were all the same and all desperately astonished to be alive. To all of them Bruce was humbly grateful and gave his orders. We were to be generous in victory but firm. All the captured knights would be stripped of armour and weapons and taken to the Castle where they would be well treated until ransoms were set and paid. Any infantry would be spared, disarmed and held under guard, meantime, until they could be tied up and collected in an enclosure that would be closely guarded, night and day, until their release was paid for. Anyone not a soldier was told to return to England, as we did not want the trouble of feeding them. All armour, weapons, treasure and goods of any kind would be collected in two places, one in each part of the Carse and distributed as seemed best at the discretion of the commanders of companies. Bruce was not much interested in these. He knew he would profit hugely from ransoms. He would, for one thing, be able to get back his wife Elizabeth and a few others like Bishop Wishart who had been captured.

Until these things were settled, and the prisoners all under proper guard, there would be no jollification. Douglas received permission to chase the King of England who must be presumed to be headed for the border. Knowing the border country better than anyone, Douglas was assigned to track him. As soon as he was able, he took off with a large party of riders, using any of the horses available in the English camp which he now had full control of. His own horses were far away beyond the Dryfield at our camp near Gillies Hill. Edward Bruce also set off chasing

Englishmen. The Earl of Hereford had been seen crossing the Pelstream, heading for the Castle. 'They'll never admit him,' said Bruce. 'They must give up the Castle now. What would be the point? You will have to chase him to the western border.' Time would tell that Hereford had been stupid a second time. He sought sanctuary in Bothwell Castle, where he was eventually tracked and captured. A company of his size with a hundred knights, all mounted, was easy to follow.

Bruce then rose from his chair to go and count the dead, whom he ordered laid out in a line west of the pond where they would soon be buried when we had recovered our strength after feasting and celebrating. By then, the English had left the Carse, those that could, still pursued by hot-blooded Scots with energy left for killing. Those that remained alive, stripped of all that mattered to us, were being tied to each other with rope and marched off to captivity at a guarded enclosure already being designed, materials for which had been ordered. From every corner of Balquhiderock Wood and its environs north and south, the Scots who had been kept out of it by the orders of Bruce, streamed onto the Carse now that it was safe to do so and were scavenging among the dead; and few stopped them. They deserved their share of plunder after such a victory.

14

THE GOLDEN AGE

Rejoicing among the Scots, once the prisoners were safely held and guarded, was prolonged and intense. The English had brought wagon-loads of provisions for a campaign of months. Now they were ours: barrels of flour, salt-herring, other fish, preserved meat of every kind, most of it ready cooked to last longer, barrels of ale and wine—barrels of the finest wines, galore! Along with the wagons and the tents. And every kind of useful tool and article of furniture that might be helpful to a wealthy person: several small forges used by armourers, several portable bakeries, many artifacts that we had never known in our relatively impoverished style of life. The riches of that camp were a treasure trove never seen before and were now the property of the Scots, along with the prisoners. Everyone in the Scottish army came away with a souvenir: a weapon, or weapons as often as not; a horse, a wagon, a mail shirt, a shield, a pair of shoes, a carpet, a tunic—the highly coloured trapper of a horse, soon to regale his own—a great helm, a sword, dagger or halberd or a pennant or surplice or highly coloured standard. Even bows and arrows, though they were less durable. They fared less well in that season of rain that lasted several years, the wood soon warped, twisted and lost its power.

King Edward boarded ship at Dunbar and escaped. The shame of his defeat affected him badly and the trouble with his barons before the battle was nothing to his difficulties afterwards. On several occasions in the years that followed, English armies returned but in every case they soon went home again having achieved nothing. Partly it was the bad weather which ruined the crops and made food hard to find north of the border but partly it was lack of resolution and that was due to lack of understanding. They never did understand why they had lost at Bannockburn. No one person was in a position to see both sides of the field where the bounding streams were an effective and even lethal obstacle. Like many since, visits afterwards were made on fine sunny days in periods of good weather when the problems presented by these streams after heavy rain were disguised. The very presence of the Knoll in the centre meant that no one had a view of the entire battlefield, except those of the King's party and too many large tents obscured the view. This much was learned: that archers must deploy on high ground so that they can see their targets and they must be in fierce formation: spaced out like the tines of a harrow, so that each man can not only see to aim properly but load and fire without interference from his fellows. The very press of people around the archers themselves and others not archers, had been instrumental in the failure of the archers that day. And so, at Crécy, Poitiers, Agincourt and a hundred lesser engagements, the English often thereafter had two wings of archers on high ground with dismounted heavily armoured knights on foot between; and, between them and their enemies, thick wooden stakes hammered into the turf and then pointed to deal with attacking cavalry. Even the lesson of the pikes was not understood. Kneeling was taken to mean praying by too many and so the effectiveness of kneeling as a means of aiming the pike over the head of the men in front, of the great number of pikes that would strike an attacking knight before his lance hit anyone, were never understood. And the main reason for kneeling, not because the pikeman was harder to hit with arrows but because then and only then the ground bore the pressure of the attacker on the pike which was expected to break and often did so. Nor did any Englishmen understand that setting the pikes within a few yards of the English cavalry lines was the key to resisting the cavalry charge which could not get up speed because of it.

Bruce never again met these invasions at Bannockburn, knowing that the English would not fall into the same trap within a single lifetime. To me and the few others like Magonigal, who understood the plan in all its genius, he cautioned silence and we were by then too much in awe of his majesty to disobey. So the secret of that brilliant strategy, that plan he had devised, was allowed to remain concealed, a source of much confusion among historians in later centuries, no doubt. No, Bruce's next tactic was to lay waste the countryside ahead of the advancing English army and deprive it of the means of sustenance. Everything of the slightest use was removed and taken north of the River Forth where it was hidden, the same for every mortal soul among the Scots. No one was allowed to remain. So the English when they came again found a desolate landscape in which they were unable to live in any comfort and forced to leave when the forty days that was usual for knights and yeoman service were exhausted.

Bruce's troubles were not over, however. There was incessant pressure to get the English to accept his right to rule Scotland, letters being sent in every direction to drum up support, in the Vatican, for one and later, when the pope changed his domicile to France. But Edward, King of England, was just as hard-headed as his father and would not yield on this, despite his disastrous defeat.

By October, Queen Elizabeth, who had been a prisoner in England for seven years, was returned to her husband; and others like Bishop Wishart, now old and enfeebled by his years of incarceration. Within two years, Edward Bruce had been persuaded to become the King of Ireland and a force was sent from Scotland to help him win it back from the English, who garrisoned several castles there and had exercised a certain amount of control. Robert our King even joined him there for a time, leaving Scotland in the hands of Moray and Douglas. But Irish support for the Bruces was fragmentary. They did not really want him as king. What they did want was that he would expel the English from their land. This was impossible, for lack of siege engines but mainly the incessant rain that fell which blighted all the crops; and made surviving there for the Scots just as difficult as it would be several years later, for the English in Scotland, suffering the same appalling weather and the deliberate destruction of the means of sustaining life on later invasions.

The Irish were not much help to Edward Bruce, their loyalty could not be counted upon and as soon as his abler brother left to return to his native land, Edward was killed in a battle facing odds of 20 to one, a fitting end to the bravest, but not the brightest, of Bruce's brothers. Niel, killed in 1306 after capture at Kildrummy when escorting the chief women of Scotland. They were held in England at the orders of Edward I, some of them in conditions of utmost depravity as an inducement to compel Bruce to go and release them. The young countess who had presided at Bruce's coronation in lieu of her husband and the stone of Destiny, both absent in England, had been kept on public view in a cage on the castle wall, there to pish and shit in public in all weathers. And she was not alone: other noble Scotswomen endured the same privation: to suffer the gibes of the malicious and even stones thrown and arrows fired in what would have been called 'fun'. Thomas and Alexander, the brightest star at Cambridge

University, beheaded at Carlisle. And then Edward pursuing fame and fortune in Ireland. All dead.

Not until the last years of Robert Bruce's life was the problem with England resolved. The autonomy of the Scots was bought for twenty thousand pounds. But when Bruce died, that treaty died with him. Perhaps the main useful outcome of the victory at Bannockburn was that thereafter, Scotsmen were much feared for their warlike prowess, all the more since no foreigner understood it. A Scottish force had only to cross the border and Englishmen fled in fear.

THE END

THE PLAN: **Maps showing the stages in the battle**.
These are the work of more than 3 years full time, the latest and best of three versions in earlier books of this research. In 1999, The Roy maps of Stirlingshire (1750), recently released from the Queen's library to the British Library, were copied, joined and taken as the base from which everything added after 1314 was removed. The explanation of every detail, based on charters, old maps and the ground, is written up in the works of this research, occupying about 150,000 words for the map of the area alone. It has been confirmed independently. These are triangulated maps, more accurate geometrically than Roy's, but the scale is different than stated here in this smaller book.

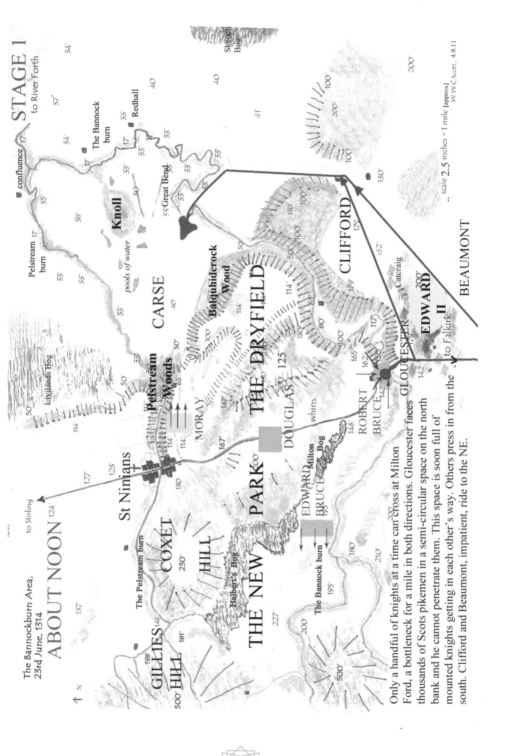

STAGE 1
to River Forth

The Bannock burn Area,
23rd June, 1314

ABOUT NOON

scale 2.5 inches = 1 mile (approx)
W.W.C.Scott. 4.9.11

confluence

Redhall

The Bannock burn

Knoll

Great Bend

Pelstream burn

pools of water

Linxlands Bog

CARSE

Skeoch Bog

CLIFFORD

Balquhiderock Wood

THE DRYFIELD

Caecraig

EDWARD II

BEAUMONT

to Falkirk

GLOUCESTER

ROBERT BRUCE

DOUGLAS

whins

MORAY

Pelstream Woods

St Ninians

to Stirling

COXET HILL

The Pelstream burn

THE NEW PARK

Halbert's Bog

Milton Bog

EDWARD BRUCE

The Bannock burn

GILLIES HILL

N

Only a handful of knights at a time can cross at Milton Ford, a bottleneck for a mile in both directions. Gloucester faces thousands of Scots pikemen in a semi-circular space on the north bank and he cannot penetrate them. This space is soon full of mounted knights getting in each other's way. Others press in from the south. Clifford and Beaumont, impatient, ride to the NE.

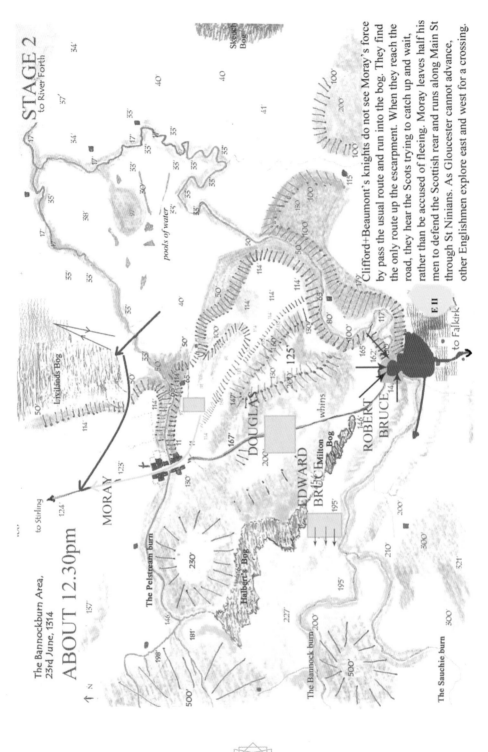

STAGE 2

The Bannockburn Area,
23rd June, 1314

ABOUT 12.30pm

to River Forth

to Stirling

Sketch Bog

Livilands Bog

pools of water

MORAY

DOUGLAS

EDWARD BRUCE Milton

whins

Milton Bog

ROBERT BRUCE

E II

to Falkirk

The Pelstream burn

Halbert's Bog

The Bannock burn

The Sauchie burn

Clifford+Beaumont's knights do not see Moray's force by pass the usual route and run into the bog. They find the only route up the escarpment. When they reach the road, they hear the Scots trying to catch up and wait, rather than be accused of fleeing. Moray leaves half his men to defend the Scottish rear and runs along Main St through St Ninians. As Gloucester cannot advance, other Englishmen explore east and west for a crossing.

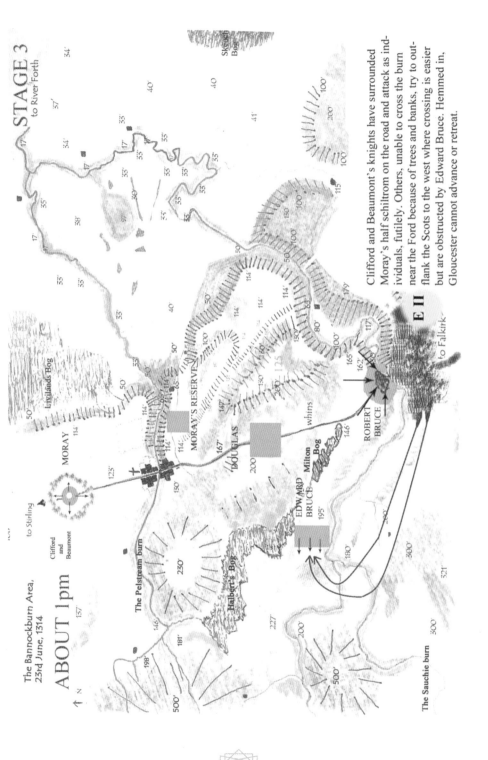

STAGE 3

The Bannockburn Area,
23rd June, 1314

ABOUT 1pm

Clifford and Beaumont's knights have surrounded Moray's half schiltrom on the road and attack as individuals, futilely. Others, unable to cross the burn near the Ford because of trees and banks, try to outflank the Scots to the west where crossing is easier but are obstructed by Edward Bruce. Hemmed in, Gloucester cannot advance or retreat.

to River Forth

to Stirling

Clifford and Beaumont

MORAY

MORAY'S RESERVE

DOUGLAS

EDWARD BRUCE

ROBERT BRUCE

E II

to Falkirk

The Pelstream burn

The Sauchie burn

Livilands Bog

Halbert's Bog

Milton Bog

whims

Skeoch Bog

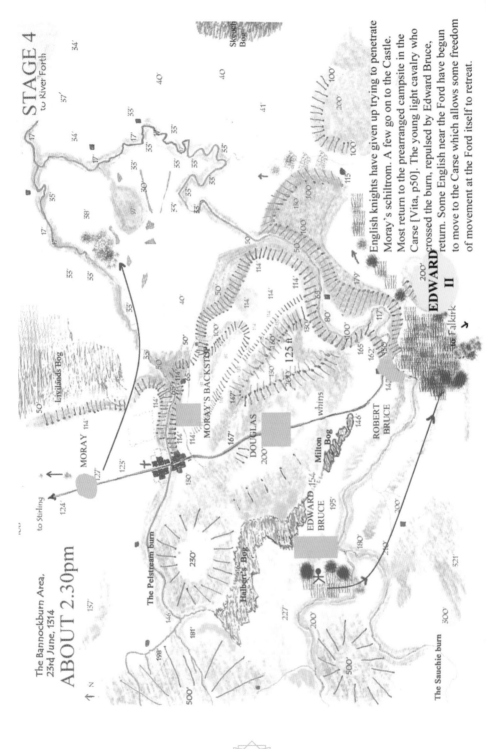

STAGE 4
to River Forth

The Bannockburn Area,
23rd June, 1314
ABOUT 2.30pm

English knights have given up trying to penetrate Moray's schiltrom. A few go on to the Castle. Most return to the prearranged campsite in the Carse [Vita, p50]. The young light cavalry who crossed the burn, repulsed by Edward Bruce, return. Some English near the Ford have begun to move to the Carse which allows some freedom of movement at the Ford itself to retreat.

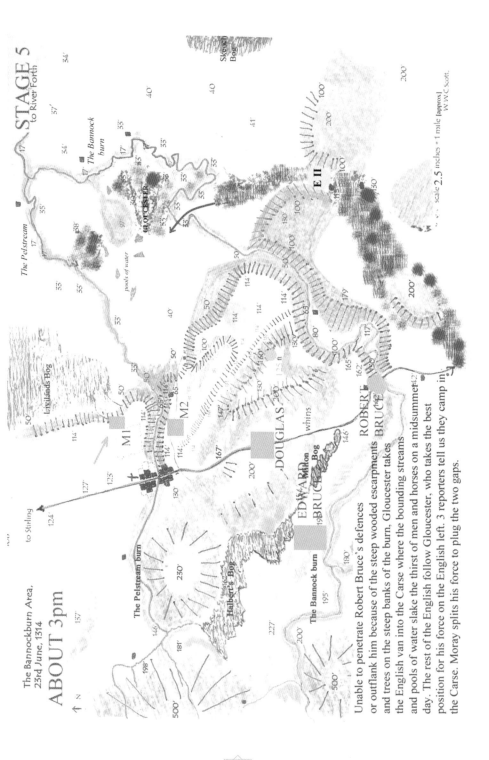

The Bannockburn Area,
23rd June, 1314

ABOUT 3pm

STAGE 5
to River Forth

Unable to penetrate Robert Bruce's defences or outflank him because of the steep wooded escarpments and trees on the steep banks of the burn, Gloucester takes the English van into the Carse where the bounding streams and pools of water slake the thirst of men and horses on a midsummer day. The rest of the English follow Gloucester, who takes the best position for his force on the English left. 3 reporters tell us they camp in the Carse. Moray splits his force to plug the two gaps.

scale 2.5 inches = 1 mile (approx)
W W C Scott.

157

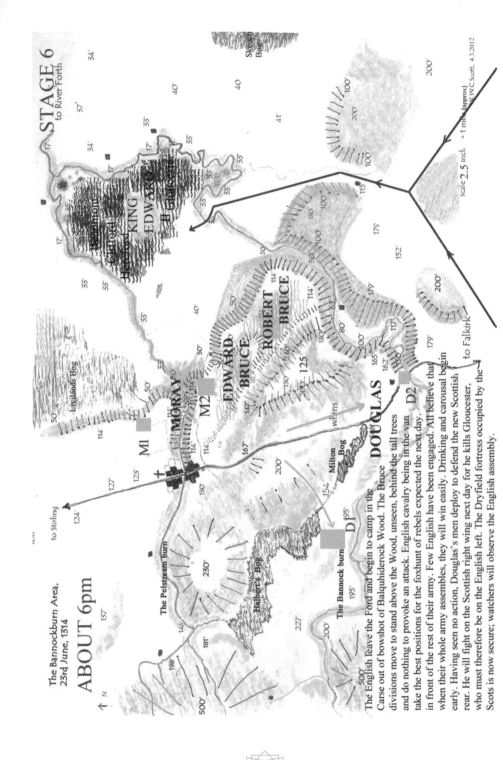

The Bannockburn Area,
23rd June, 1314

ABOUT 6pm

STAGE 6
to River Forth

The English leave the Ford and begin to camp in the Carse out of bowshot of Balquhiderock Wood. The Bruce divisions move to stand above the Wood, unseen, behind the tall trees and do nothing to provoke an attack. English cavalry being in the van take the best positions for the foxhunt of rebels expected the next day. Few English have been engaged. All believe that when their whole army assembles, they will win easily. Having seen no action, Douglas's men deploy to defend the new Scottish rear. He will fight on the Scottish right wing next day for he kills Gloucester, who must therefore be on the English left. The Dryfield fortress occupied by the Scots is now secure; watchers will observe the English assembly.

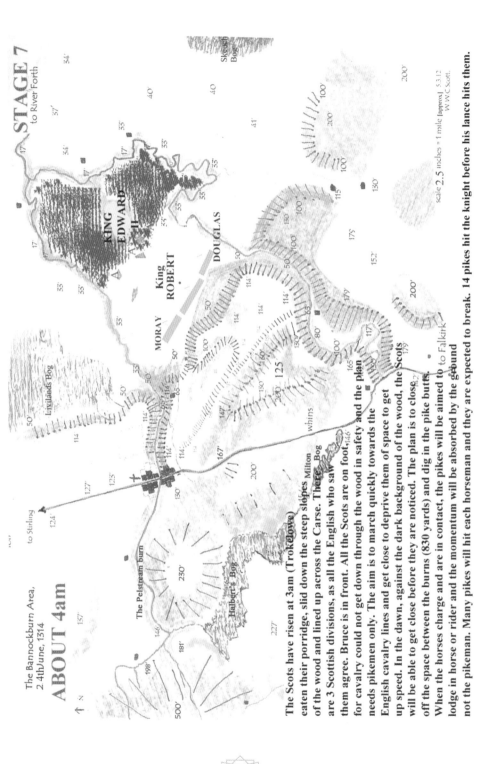

STAGE 7

to River Forth

The Bannockburn Area,
24th June, 1314

ABOUT 4am

↑ N

to Stirling

The Pelstream burn

The Pelstream burn

Livilands Bog

MORAY

King ROBERT

DOUGLAS

KING EDWARD II

Milton

Bog

whins

to Falkirk

to Stirling

Halbert's Bog

Skeoch Bog

scale 2.5 inches = 1 mile [approx] 5.3.12 W.W.C.Scott

The Scots have risen at 3am (Trokelowe) eaten their porridge, slid down the steep slopes of the wood and lined up across the Carse. There are 3 Scottish divisions, as all the English who saw them agree. Bruce is in front. All the Scots are on foot, for cavalry could not get down through the wood in safety and the plan needs pikemen only. The aim is to march quickly towards the English cavalry lines and get close to deprive them of space to get up speed. In the dawn, against the dark background of the wood, the Scots will be able to get close before they are noticed. The plan is to close off the space between the burns (830 yards) and dig in the pike butts. When the horses charge and are in contact, the pikes will be aimed to lodge in horse or rider and the momentum will be absorbed by the ground not the pikeman. Many pikes will hit each horseman and they are expected to break. 14 pikes hit the knight before his lance hits them.

159

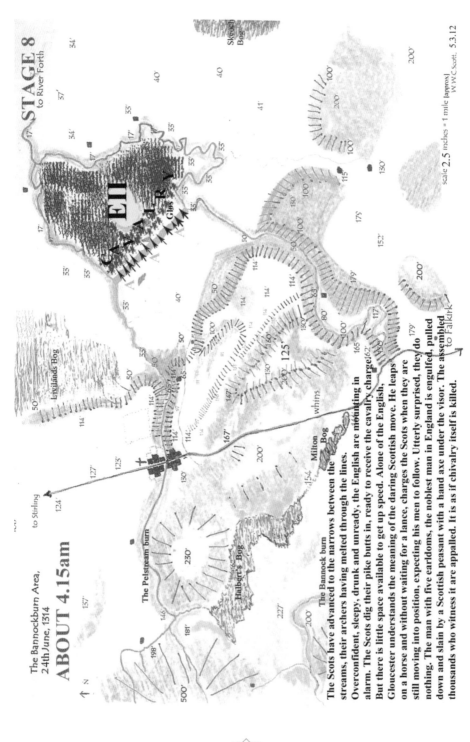

scale 2.5 inches = 1 mile (approx)
W.W.C.Scott. 5.3.12

The Bannock burn

The Scots have advanced to the narrows between the streams, their archers having melted through the lines. Overconfident, sleepy, drunk and unready, the English are mounting in alarm. The Scots dig their pike butts in, ready to receive the cavalry charge. But there is little space available to get up speed. Alone of the English, Gloucester understands the meaning of the daring Scottish move. He leaps on a horse and without waiting for a lance, charges the Scots when they are still moving into position, expecting his men to follow. Utterly surprised, they do nothing. The man with five earldoms, the noblest man in England is engulfed, pulled down and slain by a Scottish peasant with a hand axe under the visor. The assembled thousands who witness it are appalled. It is as if chivalry itself is killed.

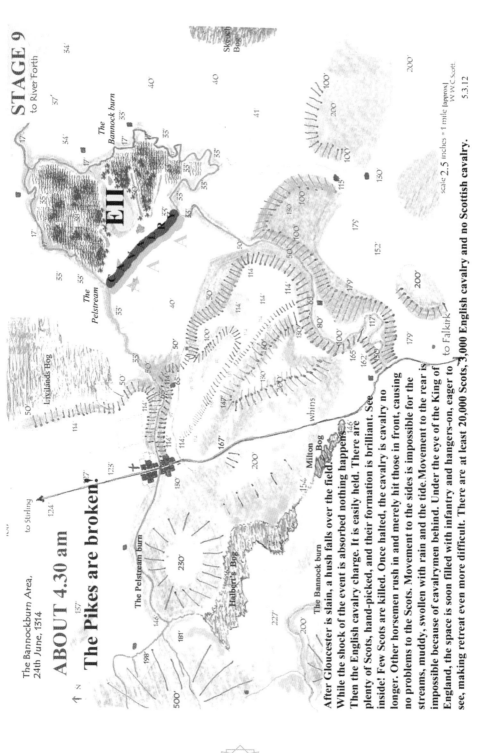

STAGE 9
to River Forth

The Bannockburn Area,
24th June, 1514

ABOUT 4.30 am
The Pikes are broken!

to Stirling

↑ N

scale 2.5 inches = 1 mile (approx)
W.W.C.Scott.
5.3.12

After Gloucester is slain, a hush falls over the field. While the shock of the event is absorbed nothing happens. Then the English cavalry charge. It is easily held. There are plenty of Scots, hand-picked, and their formation is brilliant. See inside! Few Scots are killed. Once halted, the cavalry is cavalry no longer. Other horsemen rush in and merely hit those in front, causing no problems to the Scots. Movement to the sides is impossible for the streams, muddy, swollen with rain and the tide. Movement to the rear is impossible because of cavalrymen behind. Under the eye of the King of England, the space is soon filled with infantry and hangers-on, eager to see, making retreat even more difficult. There are at least 20,000 Scots, 3,000 English cavalry and no Scottish cavalry.

The Pelstream

The Bannock burn

Livilands Bog

Skruch Bog

Milton Bog

Halbert's Bog

whins

to Falkirk

The Pelstream burn

The Bannock burn

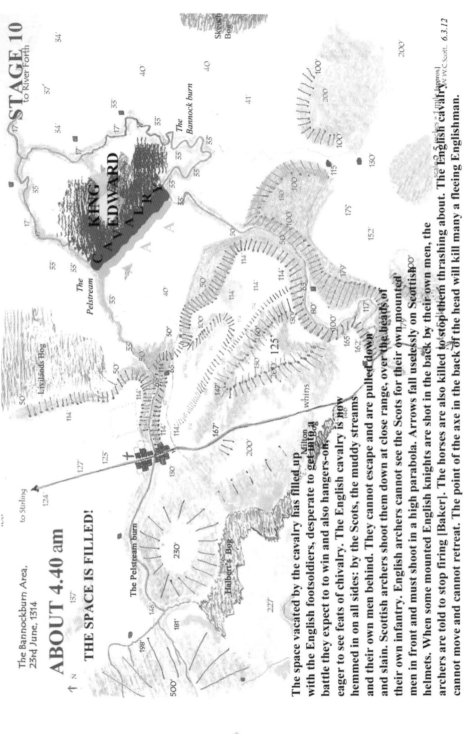

STAGE 10

The Bannockburn Area,
23rd June, 1314

ABOUT 4.40 am

THE SPACE IS FILLED!

The space vacated by the cavalry has filled up with the English footsoldiers, desperate to get into a battle they expect to to win and also hangers-on, eager to see feats of chivalry. The English cavalry is now hemmed in on all sides: by the Scots, the muddy streams and their own men behind. They cannot escape and are pulled down and slain. Scottish archers shoot them down at close range, over the heads of their own infantry. English archers cannot see the Scots for their own mounted men in front and must shoot in a high parabola. Arrows fall uselessly on Scottish helmets. When some mounted English knights are shot in the back by their own men, the archers are told to stop firing [Baker]. The horses are also killed to stop them thrashing about. The English cavalry cannot move and cannot retreat. The point of the axe in the back of the head will kill many a fleeing Englishman.

WWC Scott. 6.3.12

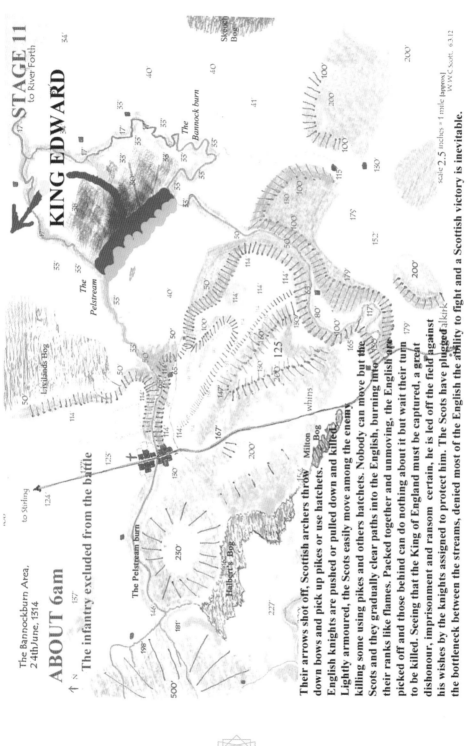

STAGE 11
KING EDWARD

to River Forth

The Bannockburn Area,
24th/June, 1314

ABOUT 6am

↑ N

to Stirling

The infantry excluded from the battle

The Pelstream

The Bannock burn

Linzlands Bog

The Pelstream burn

Halbert's Bog

Skeoch Bog

Milton Bog

whins

Falkirk

scale 2.5 inches = 1 mile (approx)
W.W.C.Scott. 6.3.12

Their arrows shot off, Scottish archers throw down bows and pick up pikes or use hatchets. English knights are pushed or pulled down and killed. Lightly armoured, the Scots easily move among the enemy, killing some using pikes and others hatchets. Nobody can move but the Scots and they gradually clear paths into the English, burning into their ranks like flames. Packed together and unmoving, the English are picked off and those behind can do nothing about it but wait their turn to be killed. Seeing that the King of England must be captured, a great dishonour, imprisonment and ransom certain, he is led off the field against his wishes by the knights assigned to protect him. The Scots have plugged the bottleneck between the streams, denied most of the English the ability to fight and a Scottish victory is inevitable.

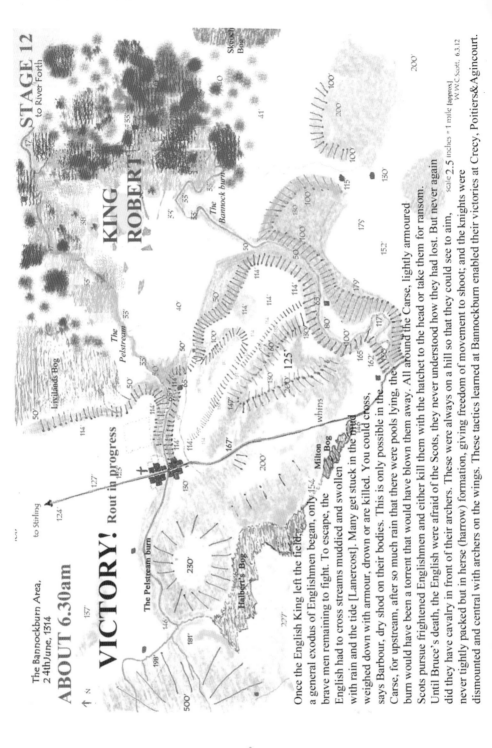

The Bannockburn Area,
24th June, 1314

ABOUT 6.30am

VICTORY! Rout in progress

KING ROBERT

to River Forth

to Stirling

Skeoch Bog

Livilands Bog

The Pelstream

The Pelstream burn

Halbert's Bog

Milton Bog

The Bannock burn

whins

scale 2.5 inches = 1 mile [approx]
WW.C.Scott. 6.3.12

Once the English King left the field, a general exodus of Englishmen began, only brave men remaining to fight. To escape, the English had to cross streams muddied and swollen with rain and the tide [Lanercost]. Many get stuck in the mud, weighed down with armour, drown or are killed. You could cross, says Barbour, dry shod on their bodies. This is only possible in the Carse, for upstream, after so much rain that there were pools lying, the burn would have been a torrent that would have blown them away. All around the Carse, lightly armoured Scots pursue frightened Englishmen and either kill them with the hatchet to the head or take them for ransom. Until Bruce's death, the English were afraid of the Scots, they never understood how they had lost. But never again did they have cavalry in front of their archers. These were always on a hill so that they could see to aim, never tightly packed but in herse (harrow) formation, giving freedom of movement to shoot; and the knights were dismounted and central with archers on the wings. These tactics learned at Bannockburn enabled their victories at Crecy, Poitiers&Agincourt.

Pool in the South Carse of Balquiderock, showing the Knoll. Facing north

Below: a pool in the North Carse looking west to St Ninians. The road (Millhall Road) has had to zigzag to get around this pool, at extra expense, confirmed on every map. So the pools are of great antiquity, a factor in 1314 as the reports, such as Barbour's Bruce and the Brut y Tywysogyon, confirm they were present at the time of the battle.

Another pool in the North Carse, causing the zigzag in the road (beside the telephone poles). After wet weather there is always a pool here and in the other places in the Carse where the undulation in the ground allows it.

The permanent pond in the Carse with the Knoll rising on the right. The burial pits will be under this area, within a 4 acre square with the pond as centre, for this is the Carse centre. **Bruce fought here.** Under the pond is a likely place or even under the rise to the Knoll, because of the effect of water underground from the Dryfield over the centuries driving the bones in the direction of the River Forth. Because the bones will offer resistance to the movement of underground water seeping towards the Forth, they will move in that direction being stopped only by the Knoll.

Wallace Monument

Are the pools a permanent feature? Yes. Millhall Rd has had to be built with a **ZIG ZAG** just get around them. Here it is in a modern map with some features (omitted!) added

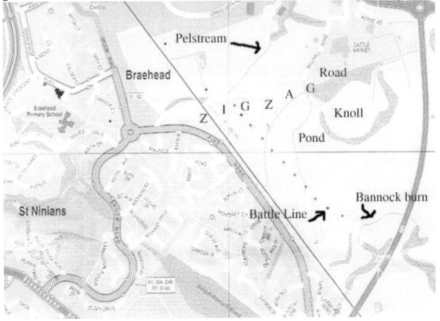

The ZIG ZAG Road (Millhall Rd) in the first OS Map (part) surveyed 1860, pub 1865. Imagine the expense of building and maintaining a Zig Zag in a road, if it were not necessary: Why was it necessary? Because of the pools which occurred regularly.

Here is the Zig Zag Road in Roy's map c1750. The Knoll is also shown by parallel lines and the mill lade to Kersemills having kinks to get around it.

This is the earliest map with reliable details. [Pont's, a rough sketch, made by one man, is useless]

WHY THE CARSE OF BALQUHIDEROCK IS UNIQUE IN SHOWING POOLS OF WATER REGULARLY AFTER PROLONGED HEAVY RAIN.

1. The Carses of Stirling, Balquhiderock and Skeoch in 1314 (same as 1750, Roy's maps)

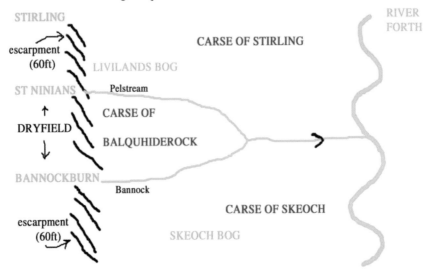

2. The Carses of Stirling and Skeoch only. Section showing the water table (level of saturation) which falls uniformly towards the River Forth, 30 ft below the ground surface. Rainwater falling on the carse is easily absorbed because the water table is low.

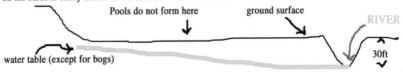

3. This is not true of the Carse of Balquhiderock which is an ENCLOSED carse, ending at the confluence of the Pelstream and Bannock which means the water table is uniformly near the ground surface. Prolonged rain brings the water table to the ground surface which means rain falling on this Carse cannot be absorbed. It lies within the natural undulations, forming pools which do not drain until after the water table has fallen again. The pools are the last things to drain.

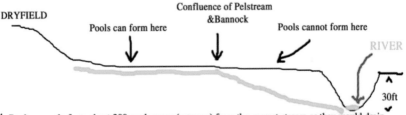

4. Pools can only form about 200 yards away (or more) from the nearest stream or they would drain into it as soon as the water level in the stream falls below ground level. 34 pools some 100yds long and a yard deep have been seen in Balquhiderock Carse. Cockspow (pool), a permanent pool, was 911 yds from the Forth. Drypow, a semi permanent pool, was only 264 yds from the Forth, with a water table often too low to support the pool which was absorbed. Rain falling on half the Dryfield is absorbed and comes down under the Carse from all along the escarpment, raising the water table to ground level but only in Balquhiderock Carse, because it is enclosed. WWC Scott, 14.1.2009

The Battle was fought among pools of water: A page from the Brut y Tywysogyon Ms20. Where was the earl of Clare (Gloucester) killed and many men of England and the King of England fled the field in 1314? **At BANNOCKBURN!**

[1306–**1306**]. Anno. vj. There was a breach between the men of Scotland and the king of England.

[1307–**1307**]. Anno. vij. Edward, king of England, went to subdue Scotland. And coming thence, at the town called Burgh-on-Sands the eminent king died on the seventh day of July.

In the same year, on the feast-day of Matthew the Apostle, the sixth day from the Calends of March, Edward Caernarvon, his son, was crowned.

[1308–**1308**]. Anno. viij. Piers Gaveston began to govern the realm at his pleasure. And the other leaders took that ill.

[1309–   ]. Anno. ix.†

[1310–   ]. Anno dm̄. m. cccx.

[1311–**1312**]. Anno. j. Edward the Third was born.†

[1312–**1312**]. Anno. ij. Piers Gaveston was slain on the feast-day of Stt. Gervasius and Protasius,† near Warwick, after he had been lured out of the castle.

[1313–**1314**]. Anno. iij. Llywelyn, bishop of St. Asaph, died, and Dafydd ap Bleddyn was elected in his place on the eve of the feast of John at Midsummer. And on that day occurred the encounter in the Pools,† and Gilbert the Younger, earl of Clare, and many of the men of England besides, were slain by the Scots. And the king of England ignominiously fled from that encounter.

[1314–**1315**]. Anno. iiij. Dafydd,† bishop of St. Asaph, was consecrated.

[1315–   ]. Anno. v.

[1316–   ]. Anno. vi.

[1317–**1315**]. Anno. vij. The war of Llywelyn Bren took place.

[1318–**1316**]. Anno. viij. Llywelyn Bren was seized.†

[1319–**1317**]. Anno. ix. There was discord between the king and the barons.

[1320–**1320**]. Anno dm̄. ṁ. ccc°. xix°. The barons came fully armed to the council at London, and they wanted to seize the king and Sir Hugh the Younger, unless he placed his seal to the letters of the barons. And he wept and did their will.

Where did Bruce kill de Bohun? The road from Falkirk to Stirling in 1314 went across the Bannock burn at Milton Ford because the first bridge was not erected until 1516 (downstream). The road from the Ford goes along St Ninians Main St, beside which the Kirk was built in 1242. So this is the road of 1242. [Note: even after the bridge, the Ford was still the preferred route across till after 1750] The ford is a bottleneck. Scotland's Thermopylae.
Below: Milton Ford, north bank, 2005, before recent building. The burn is impassable up and down stream for a mile. The escarpment here is just low enough on both sides to allow a horse and cart to pass in safety. Looking north to Stirling. The road has to bend and straighten to reach the flat ground of the Dryfield. Donald Morrison and Roger Graham, two very helpful supporters who have confirmed everything, are in the picture. De Bohun was slain about 10 ft right of the telephone pole.

The Bannockburn at Milton Ford after some rain. Looking upstream, NW Note the black seat.

General Roy's map of Stirlingshire c1750. The road is essentially straight, even on to the Castle and south, off picture: it curves only to reach the ford and then curves back again. Note: only one road went through St Ninians, North to South, in 1750. There was still only one until 1930 when a crescent was built to the west of it. The curve near Milton farm is necessary to ascend the escarpment. The curve below Milton Ford is necessary to reach the Ford. Charter's Hall is post 1314, and the road there. A Bruce knight, Sir Thos Longueville, married an heiress of Kinfauns and took her name: Charteris. BR p446.

Milton Ford, looking to the south side. Note the black seat right of the Telegraph pole. De Bohun was slain 10ft left of the pole. This is a bottleneck: impassable for a mile up and downstream, due to trees on the banks, the height of the banks but mainly the escarpment on both sides which a horse and cart could not manage. Scotland's Thermopylae: where a very large invading army cannot pass because it can only deploy a few men at one time.

Milton Ford, north bank, looking south 2004. The Killing ground. Surrounded by Scottish pikemen, English knights filled this space, were defeated and repelled. The hill in the background is the one the road of 1314 had to curve around to get to the Ford: it was too steep for a horse and cart. Note the palisade of trees to the right, continued for a mile plus

Milton Ford, the 1314 road approaching from the south. De Bohun rode down here to the Ford ten yds below the camera. The curve is to get round the hill on the right. Why is the ground higher on the right? Because of the passage of millions of feet over centuries: they have worn down the path, a feature often seen in old roads in Ireland. The road swung to the right after this and went in front of Catcraig, on through the farm to straighten.

Milton Ford on a modern map [Harvey's]. Note the amount of woodland even today.

The Road of 1314 went across Milton Ford

The road to Falkirk from the Castle in 1314 went directly along St Ninians Main St. Why? Because The Kirk was built beside Main St in 1242. It then went straight across the Dryfield to cross the burn. But there was no bridge then (until 1516) so it had to curve to the Ford and then having crossed, curve back onto the straight. Notice the pond in the Carse which is missing, like a lot of woodland, from modern maps, even OS maps. Notice the amount of woodland around the burnside, even today. The Bannock burn is impassable up and downstream for a mile because of this woodland but mainly because of the escarpment. This means that in 1314 the Ford was the only way across. Bruce defended the bottleneck there. Two sources confirm this: Barbour and Scalacronica. See p198.

Looking west to St Ninians. Note the Bannock burn, Balquhiderock Wood, the pond, Knoll, Zig Zag Rd, the Pelstream.

Looking East to Edinburgh. Note the Bannock burn, Balquhiderock Wood, the pond, Knoll, Zig Zag Rd, the Great Bend in the burn. The River Forth is also on the left, off picture. St Ninians is on the right, the Pelstream foreground.

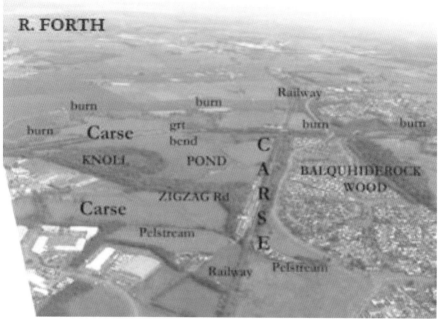

The Great Bend in the Bannock burn, looking east. If Douglas, moving from right to left, could reach the bend, he would have less width to defend. The point he wanted to reach is obvious.The Carse is all the ground left of the burn. Balquhiderock Wood is lower right & off picture right. The Knoll is off picture left and down.

Part of an Ordnance Survey map of 1923 used by Rev Thomas Miller. The red shows the likely size of Livilands Bog before drainage took place, though in wet weather, the ground being so flat and springs into the bog off the escarpment carrying more water, the bog might have reached right across to the River Forth. Notice also the line of the Pelstream in 1314 which is determined by the direction of the huge deep wedge cut out by the stream originally. Go and look. Some early OS maps confirm this. Notice also 'swimming pond' near Kersepatrick. That pond is on Roy's map, the first map and every good map since. See p166. Though I have been seeing it for 23 years it is not shown on some modern maps [eg Harvey's]

The Pelstream wedge looking north. The houses are about 100ft above the Pelstream.The wedge cut by the original stream is about 100 yds wide. Its direction entering the Carse gives the original line, correctly shown on some older OS maps and known to the locals. See the line on p172. Go and look on the ground.

Bannock burn in the Carse after rain at the Great Bend. Looking N towards St Ninians. Stirling Castle is to the right, off picture.

Milton Ford, north bank on a post card dated 1917. [supplied by DL Torrie] Note the escarpment between the houses, which a horse and cart could only ascend by the road curving right and then left. Elsewhere the escarpment is more severe. No bridge in 1314.

Milton Ford, looking upstream. Palisaded with trees and also steep banks. The Ford is a bottleneck. Note the black seat on the right.

The Amphitheatre: SE of St Ninians. See it on the battle maps p153-164.

The building is Bannockburn High School, Balquhiderock Wood is on the left, top

South bank of the Bannock burn 500 yds downstream from the Ford. Impassable to cavalry and even foot.

Looking north from the Great Bend in the Bannock burn. Stirling Castle, background, left centre and the Knoll, right. Gloucester was killed about 100 yards north of here near the hedge, the center of Douglas's schiltrom. Close to the battle line. Shown on p166. Almost the line from the Castle to this point.

The Bannock burn on Roy's map, c1750. There are only 3 houses, 150 yds apart: no village even then! (the two by the burn are down a steep brae, in another world). The village was at Newmarket, ½ mile from the burn where there was drinking water from springs and flat ground for building. The bridge erected 1516 was no good: too steep both sides. SEE the last house on the right at Newmarket on the south. It is <u>off</u> the site line! Only a genius would show it that way. To those who know them, Roy's maps are brilliant! 'Bannock burn', refers to the burn not the place. There is no place then. Not till 1819 when Telford built a bridge spanning the heights on both sides; the slopes no problem then.

You doubt Roy's genius? See the curved line below Bipend. What is that? A stream that falls down a hole! Like some others on Gillies Hill, eg near Wallstale, behind Wm Taylor's house (2005), Firpark. Go and look. It is an inch deep and a foot wide in ordinary weather. Though miles from anywhere, Roy got it right in 1750! Modern maps are full of omissions as we have seen. This stream is on the modern OS maps. See GB no 27 and below.

The Disappearing stream near Cambusbarron on a modern map. There are other streams on Gillies Hill. Eg near Wallstale, where one disappears and reappears down the hill.

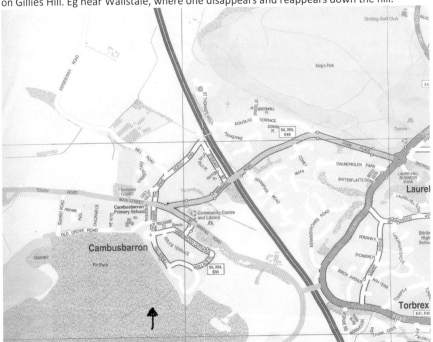

The Balquhiderock Plateau on the NE edge of the Dryfield, looking NE. The Carse is beyond Balquhiderock Wood, the trees in the distance. The flat grassy ground is the valley of the Bannock burn where Douglas's men assembled before dawn on 24th June 1314.

Below: The town on the left is St Ninians through which the Pelstream flows from Gillies Hill out of a dozen springs. The Carse of Balquhiderock is the area south of the Pelstream. In 1314 there would not be any woodland in the Carse except at the edges because it was flat with undulations in which the pools formed as they still do. 34 pools, some 100 yards long and a yard deep, have been counted. The road across the Carse had to zig zag to avoid the pools, otherwise it would have been straight to save effort, time, maintenance and cash. The cost of making and maintaining that Zig Zag Road was twice as much as a straight road. The reason is the pools which form regularly and take days to drain. Because of the Zig Zag Road and its appearance as a zig zag on every map right back to Roy's, the first worthy map of the area in 1750, we know that the pools which regularly form today after heavy rain have been an invariant feature of this ground right back to 1750 and therefore right back to 1314. This discovery is of decisive importance in siting the battle, as will be seen. **Notice the amount of building that there has been, accelerating every year. It is as if Stirling Council were intent upon burying Scotland's greatest triumph under a sea of concrete. Note the great quantity of woodland, about six acres, all of it** <u>missing</u> **on nearly every modern map at the time of writing! And for over forty years.**

6 **Looking NE in the north Carse**. This is Millhall Road, the Zig Zag Road, on the right beside the telegraph poles. One of the pools that made the Zig Zag necessary.

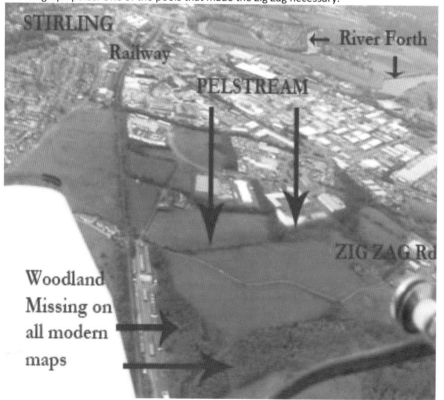

From Roy's map, c1750. The first church of the area was at St Ninians in 1242, on the site of a previous one, the parish church of Eccles or Egglis or Eggles. The first church (the West) in Stirling was 40 years later, the East later still in Cardinal Beaton's time (died 1546) Stat Acct, 1792, p613.

The Kirk built on St Ninians Main Street in 1242 was therefore the first in the district.

Milton Ford, north bank, in 2011. The road is the road of 1314. De Bohun was killed 10ft right of the telephone pole. The matter was shown in BR 2000 and proved in BP 2005. Historians were too arrogant to read it or disliked their errors shown up and the loss of their thunder. The Council took no notice and allowed this desecration of a sacred site: building erected 2010. Arrogance, snobbery, stupidity and self interest are the reason.

ENDNOTES:

Abbreviations: BY: 'The Bannockburn Years' (1998) won Constable Trophy 1997, published by Luath Press, Edinburgh, 1998.

BR: 'Bannockburn Revealed' (2000)
BP: 'Bannockburn Proved' (2005)
GB: 'The Genius of Bannockburn' 16 April (2012)
GS: 'The Genius Summary' 1st June (2012)

[1] This is all worked out in GB p300, 301.

[2] The use of pikes is explained and the logic in GB p295-309. There is no question that this is correct, for four reporters, two of them present, tell us the Scots knelt down to receive the cavalry charge of Englishmen. The four were clergymen. They imagined that the kneeling meant the Scots were praying. Not so! See GB p270. Thus a misunderstanding by 4 reporters has been corrected at a distance of 8 centuries. At least 3 people present actually saw this happen. Barbour mentions two: King Edward and Umphraville. Trokelowe is another. The vividness and detail of Trokelowe tells us he was present, according to the principles established by Professor Bartlett at Cambridge after experiments in psychology. See BR p56-58.

[3] The Battle of Flodden is a case in point. The Scots were on a slope which was very muddy after a lot of rain. When one man slipped, hundreds fell down like dominoes. This is why they lost. How do we know? This comes from 'Falcon: The Autobiography of James IV' by AJ Stewart, a lady playwright and television writer. How is this possible? Because ever since childhood, Stewart had been subject to detailed memories of the life of James IV as if she were a reincarnation. Historians are too arrogant to use such a doubtful source. They are wrong. It is the insight alone that matters; not where it comes from. This makes perfect sense. Nothing else does. On 9.8.13, The Herald carried a piece about experiments performed at Flodden by some historians who concluded that the trouble was that the Scots were using 18 ft pikes for the first time in the use of which they had had no training. The reader should be able to see that this is nonsense. They also said that the pikes at Bannockburn were 8ft. Rubbish. What good would that have been in stopping a cavalry charge? Bruce used pikes of 15ft or so because nothing else would do. They would be about 1.25 inches across, just as important. Then the pressure exerted on the equine tank at contact, though it broke the 14 pikes which were grounded, would stop the horse before the lance reached any of the Scots, even in the front row. Bruce's army at Bannockburn were on flat ground and that was a major factor. James would not have known what Bruce knew. Bruce's attention to detail was crucial to his success.

[4] Lanercost II p201, describes the making of the ladders: 'Now these ladders which they placed against the walls were of wonderful construction, as I myself, who write these lines, beheld with my own eyes. For the Scots had made two strong ropes as long as the height of the wall. Making a knot at one end of each cord. They had made a wooden board also, about two feet and a half long and half a foot broad, strong enough to carry a man, and in the two extremities of the board they had made two holes, through which the two ropes could be passed; then the cords, having been passed through as far as the knots, they had made two other knots in the ropes one foot and a half higher, and above these knots they placed another log or board, and so on to the end of the ropes. They had also made an iron hook, measuring at least one foot along one limb, and this was to lie over the wall; but the other limb, being of the same length, hung downwards towards the ground, having at its

end a round hole wherein the point of a lance could be inserted, and two rings on the two sides wherein the said ropes could be knotted.

'Having fitted them together in this manner, they took a strong spear as long as the height of the wall, placing the point thereof in the iron hole, and two men lifted the ropes and boards with that spear and placed the iron hook (which was not a round one) over the wall. Then they were able to climb up by those wooden steps just as one usually climbs ordinary ladders, and the greater the weight of the climber the more firmly the iron hook clung over the wall. But lest the ropes should lie too close to the wall and hinder the ascent, they had made fenders round every third step which thrust the ropes off the wall. When, therefore, they had placed two ladders upon the wall, the dog betrayed them as I have said, and they left the ladders there which our people next day hung upon a pillory to put them to shame.' These were used in a failed attempt to capture Berwick. The design may have been improved as suggested in the main text which suggests only one hook, the hole being in the centre of the top rung, means it is balanced.

[5] The truce was definitely a year. See BR p115-128. Duncan thought it was 3 months. He was mistaken: in a letter dated 17.11.1313, King Edward II made clear that he knew already about the deadline on midsummer day 1314. That makes the truce at least 9 months for certain. More if the time for the news to get to London was allowed for. A year in effect, as both Scalacronica, Barbour and Bridlington agree.

[6] This spring is on the slope up to Milton farm beside the Ford (north side) on the left of the road, sometimes known nowadays as Beaton's Well, because it was a known drinking place with some mortar to aid water collection, one of only three springs at the edge of the Dryfield. The others are SW of St Ninians also on the left of the road where a tannery was operating in 1860, shown by the first OS map surveyed then by Capt Pratt RE. This is the source of the rivulet which goes down the brae SE of St Ninians, known as P1 in BR, a foot wide and a yard down, so hardly to be seen. This joined the Pelstream just before where the railway is now, as the ground elevations reveal on close inspection. The only other spring at the edge of the Dryfield was very short and joined P1 on its south side. It has disappeared due to drainage and building in modern times. This spring was close to what used to be Broomridge where there once was a farm building.

[7] Though there is no mention of the use of rags in this way in the written sources, it is an obvious solution to the problem of learning to make one's way down through a wood on a slope in the half dark just before dawn. The rags need to be seen in the gloom, so they have to be white or some other bright colour. Grey would do, if the white needed washing. In time, they would become used to walking the sloping path in the dark.

Since Bruce had a whole year to prepare for the battle, he can be expected to have used it sensibly. His problems, after defending the road onto the Dryfield were how to get his men from the top of what is today Balquhiderock Wood down into the Carse, how to get them arranged there in about 30 rows with the best at the front; and when he had marched them right up to the English cavalry lines, how best to deal with the cavalry charge against his army that was then inevitable when the English recovered from their over-confident, drink-induced sleep. This is the only way to accomplish this move and be sure of success. It is the key move in the entire victory. Unless it could be executed correctly without much noise victory could not be guaranteed. Because of the extent of English unpreparedness, it turned out that the Scots could have moved at the first light of dawn and taken 5 minutes or more to marshal in the Carse before setting off. Another five minutes could put them within yards of the English cavalry lines. But Bruce would have wanted to move in darkness if it were possible and without noise. It meant his army would not be seen by the English picket line of archers until they were well into the Carse. Even had he marched out of the wood after dawn, he would still have wanted to have the choice of going before dawn. This is the way to achieve that. Thus it is likely that this move with rags was practised as described for success is very much more likely then.

[8] The strategy for using the pikemen is explained in GB p295-305

[9] The bounding streams of the Carse taper from nearly 1000 yards at the entry to the Carse of the streams, to 830 yards just before the pond is reached.

[10] **The number of Scots.** There is no question that the Scottish army was both hand-picked and very large. Vita p52 tells of 40,000 Scots. Trokelowe (Annales, p84; BR p 192, top) says the Scots were hand-picked and Barbour (p418 line 17: 30,000 fighting men; and p426 line 9: 20,000 Small Folk: this means hand-picked men; BR p229,230) agree on this and when the latter is confirmed he is correct. Baston who was present at the battle, tells of 'the multitude' of Scots in their army (Scotichronicon BkXII p371 line 110; BRp207). The best confirmation is the Charisma-Population Argument: if there are 400,000 in the population of Scotland {Barrow's figure}, there are about 200,000 males, of whom about half are fighting age. This means there are 100,000 fighting men who are Scots. If, as many historians think (even yet) the Scots had only 6,000 on the battlefield [Eg Barrow 4th edition, 2005, p273], where were the other 94,000 Scots? Hiding? Impossible. With a charismatic, successful leader as king defending his country, a decent fraction had to turn up to help him. 40,000 is the bare minimum possible and that only if the population is reduced by warfare, famine and disease to 320,000. See GB p316-322; BR ch 13 esp p158 and p265-270. Of the 40,000, at least 10,000 were surplus to requirements, called Small Folk as a face saving device. Barbour's figures fit the Charisma-Population Argument and the reduced national population found by this research. ie There were 320,000 in the country, after 18 years of warfare and of these, 80,000 men of fighting age, 40,000 of whom turned up at Bannockburn and at least 10,000 were sent off because they were not good enough. ie hand-picked. That means the Scottish army numbered between 20,000 and 30,000 on the field. Barbour has them divided evenly into four divisions. Every English source saw only three divisions approach them in the Carse. Nor are the divisions equal. The Bruce divisions should have been larger because self-important islesmen would not agree to be commanded by anyone but the king. 15,000 in the centre is more sensible with 5,000 on each wing. This is still only 30 rows of pikemen stretched across the Carse, something that is easy to visualise. Originally, there would have been 4 divisions. Because Bruce decided to lead the whole army, his own and his brother's were taken together as one, led by Edward Bruce, probably. If this be so, original divisions of size 5,000 are likely, making a total of 20,000, to which must be added the islesmen, 3000 to 5000, is possible, folk memory in Clan MacDonald favouring the latter figure (conveyed to me by Roger Graham). In that case the army would be 23,000 to 25,000, 5,000 on each wing and 13,000 to 15,000 in the centre. This would produce wings with 25 rows each if these are 200 yards wide and the centre with 32 to 37 rows each 400 in length.

Though this number of Scots would be disliked by historians whose long held prejudice is for small Scottish numbers, despite the figures given by Barbour whom they revere, it is still a problem to satisfy the objection of the Charisma-Population Argument: unless many Scots were rejected because unfit in some manner, there are still not enough Scots in the Bannockburn area. In principle, there is little difference between having 30 rows of Scots and 37. The problem of management is the same. There are just far more men who are also fresh, not having been engaged so far, to pursue and kill fleeing Englishmen in the rout which Bruce probably foresaw. His plan is so brilliant he must have known it would succeed. He really did know his enemy and could play out the entire matter like a film in his mind beforehand. Notice that because the Scots chose to have 3 divisions (as the English who were looking at them approaching make clear: 4 sources tell us this Vita, Lanercost, Scalacronica and Trokelowe, BR p212) it is inevitable that Bruce led the whole army from the front: that is why there are 3 divisions. And his brother's and his own colours would be similar enough for confusion in those who reported. Only had 4 divisions of Scots been seen by all these Englishmen, could Bruce have led his own division and not been leading the whole army. However, Vita, Lanercost, Scalacronica, Baker and Baston all tell of Bruce leading, which was a thing few kings did. All the more powerful this conclusion, then.

Note: If Moray has 5,000 in his division and half is left to defend the slope up to St Ninians, this means 2,500 are available to defend the circle at Randolphfield or thereby (Police HQ). Suppose the circumference of the circle is $\pi r d$ =2,500, and d=100yards, then r, the number of ranks = 2,500/314, approx. = 8 approx. ie 8 ranks of pikes. This would make good sense for the Skirmish between Clifford and Beaumont's knights and half Moray's division. However, the two standing stones still seen at Police HQ are about 50 yards apart. If these stones define the circle (assuming it was roughly a circle) then there would have been 16 ranks of pikemen. Both these calculations fit the facts very well. It may be that the Scots formed a 100 yard circle or that the standing stones merely give the position but not the size of the circle. It may even be that that it was not a circle at all but an ellipse with two foci at the 50 yard separation, ie a 'diameter' of 60 or 70 yards, when the number of ranks would be reduced to 10 or 12. In any event, it is clear that a figure of 5,000 for Moray's division is quite likely, for he would have had to leave half his force in place to defend the Scottish rear and take the other half to fight the English knights. Further, by the time the stones were erected it is very likely to have been long after the battle, after the return of King David from capture in England. If so, the size of the schiltrom may have been forgotten. After the death of Bruce, the Balliol clan had the run of Scotland for about 4 years. Had the stones been standing then, they might well have been removed and destroyed by the English to cover up the battle. Their presence suggests that they were erected after 1334. That is enough time for the exact size and position to have been forgotten. In twenty years, many Scots at the battle would have died. Only 2,500 knew where it was anyway. How many of them would be left? At a time when the average life expectancy of a male was about 30. Forgetting the position after that length of time would be easy for those still alive who might know. Note: the stones at Randolphfield have been much reduced in size by souvenir hunters over the centuries.

Note: Are the men rejected by Bruce the Small Folk? There were lots of men deemed unfit to serve in comparison to others. They really were hand-picked, as the sources tell us. This means too many men had arrived for them all to be usefully employed. The need was for great discipline and control of the troops. The most important problem was not the fighting which was simple but how to get the troops formed up in the Carse in front of the wood in silence and very quickly. If that could be done just before the light came up, the march of the Scots would be very difficult to detect. And we know it was not detected until far too late by which time the Scots had suddenly arrived in position 75 yards from the pond (the edge of the English camp, just out of bowshot). All the reporters, including King Edward and Umphraville, saw them kneeling, the first they knew of their presence. That means they were very close. So Bruce solved the problem of control and silence. His solution has been given: practice in moving in the dark just before dawn, having the men sleep in their divisions, so they had only to stand up to be ready and the method given for moving: two wings moving as stated and the centre moving down through the wood where it is least steep in two groups which join up. After the battle had become a rout, it is inevitable that the rejected men over on Gillies Hill would have come down through the wood onto the field, partly for loot. They were not the Small Folk Barbour mentions. They had no effect upon the battle whatsoever. No Englishmen saw them because every Englishman was in flight (or dead) by this time. But this event (the rejected men appearing) may have been given a significance by Barbour because he did not understand the battle at all. How could he at a distance of 63 years?

[11]The Ordnance Survey maps of 1913, 1923, 1931 etc available to Rev Thomas Miller in his papers where sections of them are printed, show the full extent of Livilands Bog then: a huge rectangle. See BR p390; GB p96, where the bog is estimated as it would be in 1314, a conservative estimate. Shown herein on p176.

[12] The Carse was a sheet of water in May 1985, reported by the farmer Billy Oswald to this author in 1999. Stirling Observer has had photographs which show this.

[13] Only one spring out of Gillies Hill does not go into the Pelstream: the one heading out of the back of the Hill to the south west at Wallstale. The Disappearing Stream, the one that used to go down a hole on Gillies Hill in Roy's time and therefore at the time of the battle, reached the Pelstream underground. The other at Wallstale also falls down a hole on its way to join the Bannock burn. Note: Gillies Hill has been much reduced during the last twelve years by a quarry company which had gouged out a huge area even by 2004.

[14] Wind it around your head under your hat: the origin, it is said, of the admonition: 'keep it under your hat.' Keep it dry for use later as necessary.

[15] There are many photos of the pools that form in the Carse in BR (plate 14a-19b), BP(33-37, 61), GB(6-9,130,136-140) and even GS. That these are an invariant feature of that ground right back to 1314 is easy to show. The road across the Carse, Millhall Road, has been a zigzag road for all time, shown on all the maps back to the first, Roy's, (c1750) because the pools formed there. See GB (p141-143) where some are printed, including Roy's. The road was built in a Zigzag to get around the pools that regularly form there, at extra expense. The Zigzag shows on all the maps right back to and including Roy's c 1750, the OS maps and GB battle area section 2 three pages on from stages in the battle in an aerial photo. Here are some of the pools:

This is part of the 100yard pool and the Knoll (Hillock) seen looking NE in the South Carse. They are all in GB, BR and BP. **Coloured versions are herein on p165-166.**

Below: a pool in the North Carse looking west to St Ninians. The road (Millhall Road) has had to zigzag to get around this pool, at extra expense, confirmed on every map. So the pools are of great antiquity, a factor in 1314 as the reports such as Barbour's Bruce and the Brut y Tywysogyon confirm they were present at the time of the battle. See colour version p165.

Another pool in the North Carse, causing the zigzag in the road (beside the telephone poles). After wet weather there is always a pool here and in the other places in the Carse where the undulation in the ground allows it. Looking NE. See Colour version p165.

Another part of the 100 yard pool in the South Carse with the Knoll off picture right, Balquhiderock Wood in the distance, left and St Ninians in the centre far off.

The South Carse viewed from the pond, looking south to the Bannock burn. The fence above is the same fence in the foreground, taken on another occasion. The white car is on the bypass to St Andrews. The Knoll is on the left and slightly behind the camera.

[16] The Knoll in the Carse can be seen on GB p76 in Thomas Jefferys' map of 1746, and GB p142 where it can also be seen on Roy's map of c1754 where kinks in the mill lade are necessary to get around it. There are numerous photos of the Knoll in BR, BP, GB.

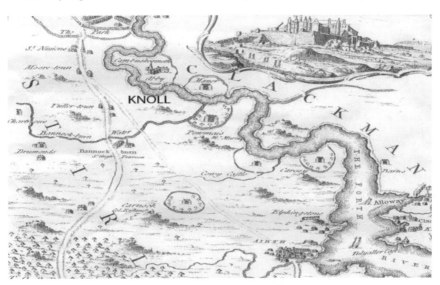

[17] Towards the end of his life Bruce lived at Cardross and employed himself in ship building. The Geilston burn is in a sheltered spot and a perfect place to build and launch ships.

[18] The answer to this is omitted in the text. It is that there are a couple of pools, one permanent at South Cockspow, the other semi-permanent at Drypow. Why the difference? Because South Cockspow is 911 yds from the R. Forth which means it is so far from the river surface that there is no space under the pool to absorb water: the level of water saturation is high, close to the ground. So that pool is permanent exceptionally. Drypow is only 264 yds from the river surface (on the latest OS map) so it is too close to the river surface 30 ft below ground. So there is a lot of space there for absorbing water and that is why it is only semi-permanent. Often it dries out and does so quickly because the water is easily absorbed.   There was another permanent pool at North Cockspow and that is because it is just far enough away from the River 330yds. That extra 66 yds (330-264) makes all the difference. In very wet weather only, a couple of other very shallow pools have been seen about the level of the Great Bend in the Carse of Skeoch but these have no depth and do not last: not pools proper then. This level of precision (among other things) has taken this history subject into the realm of science.

[19] GB p146 is a diagram explaining this fully. Here it is below:
The carses on either side of the Carse of Balquhiderock [spelt with two d's in modern maps; for consistency in this research one is used] the Carse of Stirling and the Carse of Skeoch stretch all the way from the escarpment to the River Forth. Since the water table in these carses falls all the way to the river surface which is 30ft below the ground surface, there is plenty of space for the absorption of rainwater falling directly on these carses, no matter that water is travelling underground from the escarpment. So pools do not form on these carses. The Carse of Balquhiderock is different. It is an enclosed carse. So the water table is uniformly near the surface there. This means that there is no room for the absorption of rainwater directly falling on this carse. That is why pools form there in the undulations. See colour version herein on p168.

WHY THE CARSE OF BALQUHIDEROCK IS UNIQUE IN SHOWING POOLS OF WATER REGULARLY AFTER PROLONGED HEAVY RAIN.

1. The Carses of Stirling, Balquhiderock and Skeoch in 1314 (same as 1750, Roy's maps)

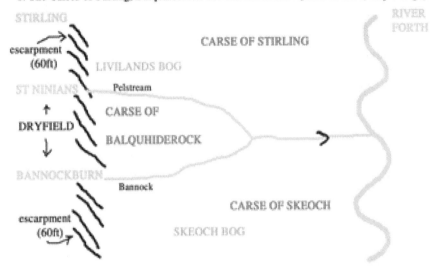

2. <u>The Carses of Stirling and Skeoch only</u>. Section showing the water table (level of saturation) which falls uniformly towards the River Forth, 30 ft below the ground surface. Rainwater falling on the carse is easily absorbed because the water table is low.

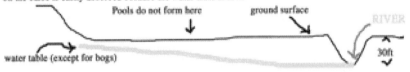

3. This is not true of the Carse of Balquhiderock which is an ENCLOSED carse, ending at the confluence of the Pelstream and Bannock which means the water table is uniformly near the ground surface. Prolonged rain brings the water table to the ground surface which means rain falling on this Carse cannot be absorbed. It lies within the natural undulations, forming pools which do not drain until after the water table has fallen again. The pools are the last things to drain.

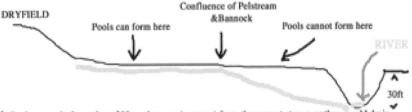

4. Pools can only form about 200 yards away (or more) from the nearest stream or they would drain into it as soon as the water level in the stream falls below ground level. 34 pools some 100yds long and a yard deep have been seen in Balquhiderock Carse. Cockspow (pool), a permanent pool, was 911yds from the Forth. Drypow, a semi permanent pool, was only 264 yds from the Forth, with a water table often too low to support the pool which was absorbed. Rain falling on half the Dryfield is absorbed and comes down under the Carse from all along the escarpment, raising the water table to ground level but only in Balquhiderock Carse, because it is enclosed.   WWC Scott, 14.1.2009

[20] One is at South Cockspow, which is at the level of the confluence, so with a high water table, the other at North Cockspow, both of which have undulations and are so far from the River Forth which is 30ft down, that the water table is high and pools form there exceptionally.

[21] Bruce was born in 1274. Thus, by the time warfare broke out circa 1296, his education was complete, some of it probably at Cambridge, like his brother Alexander. By 1314, Bruce was 40 years of age. Moray and Douglas were younger men, in the next generation: Douglas was born in 1294 [R. McNair Scott, p 111] which means he was only 20 at the battle of Bannockburn. So, growing up in war as he did, his education was necessarily scanty: he had better things to do just staying alive. Thomas Randolph, Earl of Moray was old enough to be captured by the English at Methven in 1306 meaning he would probably be at least 16 then, born about 1290 or a little earlier:1285-90. So from about the age of 5-10 Randolph would have been in a country continually at war. About 24 at the battle of Bannockburn then. This implies that their education had not proceeded beyond the age of 5-10 in one case and never began in another; and could not have involved university training at Oxford or Cambridge. So both Bruce's best commanders, commanders of his divisions on the wings at the great battle, were virtually illiterate and untutored men, at least at the time of the battle. This might have been corrected to some extent afterwards, though both were heavily engaged in warfare even then.

[22] **Three schiltroms.** This is precisely what the sources tell us Bruce did. Four sources, the best four: Vita, 1314, (p52), Lanercost, 1314, (p207), Scalacronica 1314,(p55) and Trokelowe, 1314,(BR p192) all tell us that the Scots had three divisions. This means that these Englishmen saw three separated divisions. BR p254. The only source who says different is Barbour(1377) who gives four divisions. He was mistaken. All the others were Englishmen: they could see, far better than any Scotsman, how many schiltroms (divisions) were approaching. Trokelowe is adamant that Bruce lead the entire Scottish army on foot, could not be clearer:BR p192; Annales p84. For that to be possible he had to combine his division and his brother's into one, leaving his brother in charge of it while he looked after the army as a whole.

[23] **Why is this version of the advance by the Scots into the Carse correct?** Since four sources Vita, Lanercost, Scalacronica and Trokelowe, all tell us there were three Scottish divisions, these had to be separated sufficiently to be distinguished. That means there were gaps between them for certain. The question is how far apart were they? The other question is: were there gaps at the edges? That Bruce moved his army twice: once to set his pikes (pray) and then again after a short time tells us he did not know in advance how close he could get. He could not just have the edge divisions march along the edge of the streams, for in Douglas's case, there is a Great Bend which adds 100 yards to the battle line that the Scots must defend if they do not reach the bend. Thus, although it might seem best to have the divisions formed up fully as a front line of about 800 men with other ranks (up to 37) behind them that was not what Bruce chose to do. He kept his divisions separate and filled the gaps in the middle between them from the rear ranks of the centre and the gaps at the edges from the rear ranks of the divisions at the edge. Because he was in front of the whole army, he was able to decide where to finally set his pikes. English confusion and unpreparedness enabled him to take the decision to move his men closer, right up to the English cavalry lines. Q Would the gaps be filled at the first halt? Yes. When the pikes were reset, then and only then, did the gap filling ranks move a second time. Q why did Bruce not have the divisions in a single line? Answer: This is how it was: 4 sources tell of 3 divisions [Vita, Scalacronica, Lanercost and Trokelowe]. That's that. They had to be

separated to be seen as three distinct divisions. But why? Keeping the divisions separate made control easier? Yes, partly: a section falling like dominoes, which could happen, would at least be limited to one division. With him controlling the army? In a tapering carse, how did this help? The shape of the edge is the shape of the stream. That can only be filled by rear gap filling ranks moving into position. No other solution is viable. This was especially problematic in the case of Douglas, on the right with about an extra 100 yards to defend if he did not reach the Great Bend. Douglas might have to move to the right but, if he did, a gap would form on his left, even had there been no gap there to start with. It was deemed best to start with a gap there which would have to be filled from the rear of the central division (not Douglas's). That meant he had to proceed straight ahead but was free to fill the gap on his right as necessary. He was under pressure to get into the Carse as far as the Great Bend, for then he would have 100 yards fewer to defend. Q Do the edge divisions go along the stream side as an edge? Definitely not! The rest of the division cannot move to accommodate the shape of the stream. The edge divisions must move into the Carse as far as possible and then fill the gaps. Nor can they move outward having got there. Too difficult. Especially true of Douglas. He has to move as far in as possible and then fill his gap. Q Does that mean that there should be no gaps in the middle then? Q Why are gaps necessary there too? Because three divisions were observed by four sources. That tells us there were three. This means there were two gaps in the centre that had to be filled. We have seen why this is desirable.

[24] Bruce (like his brother Alexander, known as the best student there of his generation) almost certainly attended Cambridge University. At that time, there were but two in these islands. Cambridge became the second c1209 after a student had shot a townswoman of Oxford with an arrow, accidentally or not. Unable to find the scholar, with the consent of King John, three other students were hung outside the town walls (the origin of the enmity between town and gown), whereupon that university was dispersed in fear of further reprisals by the townsfolk. Some of the staff happened to live at Cambridge and, having gone there to escape, began teaching there instead. [p17,18 A History of the University of Cambridge, Vol1 by Leader, D.R.] The universities were dispersed at various times. In 1665-1667, the University of Cambridge was closed twice because of the presence of plague in the town. The year between was Newton's annus mirabilis: when he discovered many unusual things such as the binomial theorem and the law of gravitation, having been sent home to Woolsthorpe where the descendants of the apple trees can still be seen.

[25] Four sources mention pottes: Baston, Baker, Barbour and Fordun, See GB p360 where they are quoted. The assumption is that they were used at the entry to the New Park and Dryfield: Milton Ford. If they were, why did Bruce not damage his horse when attacking de Bohun? Why did de Bohun not suffer damage as soon as he arrived on the north bank? This is the answer; there were pottes but they were not at the Ford. They were on the left of the road before the Ford to dissuade travel upstream. Even pottes right in front of the pikemen would be a mistake: they would have made it more difficult for the pikemen killing the knights after being pulled down. That ground needed to be free of pottes to ensure freedom of movement for the hatchet-men who had to move quickly, unimpeded.

[26] Barbour places Bruce at the entry to the New Park, ie the Ford, Moray at St Ninians defending the Scottish left flank and Douglas is to help any who need help: in the centre of the Dryfield, then. The natural position for Edward Bruce, being brother of the King and a famous warrior, was defending Robert Bruce's right flank. BK XI 440-460.

[27] Barbour BK XI line 447-460. Barbour is mistaken of course. How could two commanders be left to decide for themselves where they should be? Impossible that they were not ordered as stated. Commanders of Bruce's stature leave nothing to chance, that is why they are successful.

[28] Because of the detailed account by Barbour about Douglas's reaction to the intensity of the fighting around Moray's schiltrom, his position is very likely to have been in the centre of the Dryfield on the highest ground there. From that point, (200 ft above sea level) Douglas could see the fighting, for the ground dips all the way to St Ninians Main Street and even the flat ground beyond can be seen for the elevation there is only 124ft. See Area Map GB; Barbour BK XII lines 87-107. Notice that the sources, (Vita 52,53, BRp175 and Trokelowe 85, BRp193) eg agree that Douglas's men killed Gloucester. Since Moray is on the Scottish left on day 2, Douglas must be on the Scottish right on day 2. This means Gloucester camped on the south Carse. Coming from the King's tent he headed for the Scottish right wing because he expected his men who were encamped opposite would ride to assist him. As the leader at the Ford, Gloucester would have been one of the first to reach the south Carse and naturally chose it for his camp.

[29] **How do we know that Bruce defended the road at the Ford**? This has been dealt with earlier in the narrative. However, the facts are:

1.There were no bridges across the burn at this time. The first bridge was erected a mile downstream from Milton Ford in 1516, by Robert Spitall, tailor to King James V (1513-1542). The second was at Chartershall in 1696 GB p428; BP p38. As Thomas Jefferys' map of 1746 shows (see it on GB p 74. Shown herein p192) Milton Ford was still the preferred route at that time, confirmed by General Roy's map c1750 (see it on GB no 25, p70, no 203). How can we certain that the road is crossing at the Ford? Because the road has, exceptionally, been required to curve to the Ford to cross the burn. It is nearly dead straight to St Ninians Main Street, from Pirnhall. Further, as Jefferys' map shows, the route across the Ford is very much shorter and quicker than any other at that time. The crossing of the burn at the Ford can also be seen on GB p209 in OS 1923. The burn tallies with Roy's rendering in 1750. The next bridge to be erected was Telford's Bridge (1819) which is about 80 yards downstream from The King James Bridge which was not much used because of the steep slopes on either side of the burn which a horse and cart often could not manage easily (see the steep slopes on GB 49, 50, p113; to locate these quickly, see pxi GB)). Telford's Bridge spanned the two escarpments on either side of the burn and made the crossing easier. Milton Bridge which today carries Glasgow Road was not built until the 19th century, exact date unknown (archive lost in fire, it is reported). This bridge has been gradually straightened out over the years as shown by OS 1860 (see it on GB p211) and Harvey's map (GB p210).

2.The Kirk at St Ninians was erected in 1242 on the site of an earlier kirk on Main Street. The Kirk before 1750, was right beside St Ninians Main Street which was until c1930 still the only street north and south through St Ninians. In 1746, the Kirk, used as a gunpowder store for Jacobites, was blown up during the retreat to Culloden. The remains of the old Kirk can still be seen. Originally, it extended to the street itself. That the Kirk was built in 1242 on Main Street, means that this was the main road of 1314. Since there was no bridge at that time across the burn until 1516, this means that the road crossed Milton Ford in 1314. Had the road of 1314 been anywhere else, the Kirk would have been erected beside it. See P174 herein: the Kirk tower [the church stretched as far as the street, the tower, all that remains, was on the extreme NE side.] GB p198-222, especially p211-212, p220-222.

3.Finally, Milton Ford is a bottleneck, the only place where only a few knights can cross at one time: the burn elsewhere is impassable for a mile up and downstream. The road of 1314 is the road we still see there. By depriving the English of the Dryfield which is a natural fortress, even today, but then, with far more trees on the escarpment slopes, even more impenetrable, the English were compelled to retreat to move to their right, NE, into the Carse, where they made camp, as Barbour (BK XII line 391-395);BR p241 says: 'they camped in the Carse because in the Carse there were pools of water'. Vita, p52, BRp174 says they had arranged to camp there, probably because their King, when Prince of Wales, had camped there before during the earlier invasion with his father. Besides, as the narrative makes clear, they had always camped there because it was an excellent camp site, there being no comparable campsite for miles around. See the maps at the front of GB. These maps which are the first to be fully justified in a volume of book length in BR, BP and GB, took three years full time to make.

4.Two reporters say that Bruce defended the Ford:

I. **Barbour[1377]:** 'The king ordered them to make ready, for he knew for a certainty that his foes lay all night at Falkirk and since they were aiming straight for him with many mighty warriors, therefore he ordered his nephew, the Earl of Moray, to defend the way beside the Kirk (St Ninians Kirk), so that no man should get through that way to relieve the Castle. And he said that **he himself would defend the entry** (of the New Park).' The entry of the New Park was Milton Ford. BKXI 447-460

These are the critical lines in the original Scots.

' **And he said himself suld weill**
Kepe the entre with his bataill' See GB p244

II. **Sir Thomas Gray in Scalacronica [1314]: 'The said constable Philip (of Stirling Castle) met him (the King of England) three leagues from the Castle, on Sunday, the vigil of Saint John, and told him..how the enemy had blocked the narrow roads in the forest. [But] the young troops would by no means stop, but held their way. The advanced guard, whereof the earl of Gloucester had command, entered the road within the Park, where they were immediately received roughly by the Scots who had occupied the passage. (The Bottleneck!)** Here Peris de Mountforth, knight, was slain with an axe by the hand of Robert de Brus.'

Note: there was no sign saying: 'New Park'. The English would take the New Park to begin where the trees (defended by the Scots) began, at Milton Ford. Effectively, the New Park was all the ground from the Bannock burn at the ford to the Pelstream, including Halbert's and Milton bogs. Also, a mistake in the name was made: not Mountforth but de Bohun. And there are not roads plural, only one. Since he never did get into the forest he was not to know that. He went off to the Carse and attacked and was captured near St Ninians. Note further: Sir Philip Mowbray, Constable of the Castle for the English, should not have been able to get out of it to communicate with King Edward. If this is correct and it might not be, he may have had a secret escape route, such as existed at Edinburgh Castle and was the cause of its capture by Moray, the year before the battle.

[30]**De Bohun.** This is exactly what **Vita describes: [1314]:** 'The Earl of Gloucester and the Earl of Hereford commanded the first line. On Sunday, which was the vigil of St John's day, as they passed a certain wood and were approaching Stirling Castle, **the Scots were seen straggling under the trees as if in flight,** and a certain knight, Henry de Boun, (sic) pursued them with the Welsh to the entrance of the wood (Milton Ford). For he had in mind that if he found Robert Bruce there he would either kill or carry him off captive. But when he had come hither, Robert came suddenly out of his hiding-place in the wood and the said Henry seeing that he could not resist the multitude of Scots, turned his horse with the intention of regaining his companions; but Robert opposed him and struck him on the head with an axe that he carried in his hand.' Denholm-Young's trans, p51; BR p174

Sir Thomas Gray describes when de Bohun (whom he incorrectly names Pieris Mountforth) is slain by Bruce in Scalacronica [1314]:
'The said constable Philip (of Stirling Castle) met him (the King of England) three leagues from the Castle, on Sunday, the vigil of Saint John, and told him...how the enemy had blocked the narrow roads in the forest. [But] the young troops would by no means stop, but held their way. The advanced guard, whereof the earl of Gloucester had command, entered the road within the Park, where they were immediately received roughly by the Scots who had occupied the passage. (The Bottleneck!) Here Peris de Mountforth, knight, <u>was slain with an axe by the hand of Robert de Brus.</u>'

[31] **De Bohun.** There are two detailed versions of this famous event. The one by Archdeacon John Barbour written in 1377 and the other by the author of Vita Edwardi Secundi {The Life of Edward II} ('Vita', for short) written in the year of the battle within days of it, as proved in BR p58,59. Vita is an excellent source, probably by a lawyer or escheator, John Walwayne, who had attended Oxford and therefore likely to be more accurate. An escheator was someone employed to deal with the inheritance of a dead person, in this case Gloucester, usually a lawyer. Barbour's version is romanticised and, written 63 years later, is definitely less accurate. Therein, Bruce is unprepared and on a small palfrey. Not possible. Bruce had been preparing for this all his life and, especially for a year before the battle. This is the one thing above all he would be prepared for. Not being prepared in his first battle at Methven which he lost, and lost many good men's lives, he was never unprepared again, winning battle after battle, partly because of his careful preparation. The description by Vita is given in the previous endnote.

[32] **How Bruce got his men to believe they could win.** Sir Thomas Gray senior was captured on the first day at St Ninians. This is the scene described by Gray's son in Scalacronica where Seaton tells the Scots that he has come from the English army and reports that they are demoralised. In an analysis of statements in *Bannockburn Revealed p254*, every source reports repeatedly that the English were overconfident, except one: Scalacronica, whose father had been captured by the Scots on the first day and overheard the story that Seaton told. The essential fact is that the English were definitely confident of victory, their morale was high as every other source confirms repeatedly. See BR p254. Thus Seaton is telling a lie. Why is he doing that? Because he fell into Bruce's hands and Bruce got him to do so. This was Bruce's solution to the problem any Scot must confront when fighting Englishmen (or even playing them at rugby): how to get the Scotsmen to believe they can win. Without that self-belief, victory is very much harder and may even be impossible. GB p235-237; BR p188; Scalacronica, Maxwell's trans.p55. Notice that according to Gray, Seaton came late in the day, having crossed over from the Carse. If the

Scots really intended to fight a token battle, as Gray said, they should have been long gone into the wilderness to give them time to disperse and evade capture from pursuing Englishmen. Bruce had no intention of fleeing or he would have been somewhere else than at Bannockburn putting his infantry army at a disadvantage to chasing cavalry. It is also inconceivable that Seaton was able to cross the empty Carse under the eyes of the English camped there. Thus, he did not come from the English camp at all. Seaton's story was a lie and Bruce must have engineered it. Once this is realised every source agrees that the English were overconfident: all six, in that case.

[33] **Date Scalacronica counts from.** This is in full accord with what Sir Thomas Gray senior told his son, the author of Scalacronica, the Ladder Chronicle, which he wrote in Edinburgh Castle in 1355-57. Note: that when Gray senior was ransomed he would have discussed the battle and this very scene with his son who would have known his version of events from an early age. What counts in a primary source like this is not when it was first published or even when it seems to have been written down for the first time (it may have been written down in note form years previously because it was perceived to be important to make a record) but when the information was first available to the writer. In this case, that is likely to have been in 1314, for the detail about the battle and the vividness of the description could not apply to a time years later. The one thing that any delay causes is loss of all details of this kind. See BR Ch 6; BR p61,62; GB p56-58;GB p235-23. Sir Thomas Gray junior was the son of a first marriage of a man old enough to be present at Lanark in 1297 [Maxwell, Early Chronicles.,,,p227, 1912] when Wallace slew Heselrig and was almost certainly old enough to discuss the battle with his father as soon as he arrived home in 1314.

[34] **Proof of battlesite, that the Scots were all on foot and that they took the English by surprise.** The idea that the battle took place anywhere else is easily seen to be false. Anyone who knows the ground or who has seen the maps of 1314 (there are 3 versions, the first in BR, 2000; the next in BP, 2005; the latest and best in GB, 2012) knows it took place in the Carse. The Dryfield is an impossible site because of the ridges and depressions which cover it. The latter are 75 ft deep and 54ft deep. A cavalry charge of English in that ground is impossible; and there is no water there. So where are the pools of water in which the battle took place? All the other suggested places are impossible because of the bogs in or beside them.

There is not the space. Why has this not been accepted more widely, when the matter is simple and the evidence overwhelming? Of course you must have all the evidence and be able to use it together, simultaneously. You need to have an open mind. You need to have common sense and a range of disciplines outside the narrow one of history. Being able to perform calculations is helpful, to make maps, to translate sources which may be in Scots or Latin or French and when there is a difficulty, to be able to use all this knowledge to resolve discontinuities in translation and even go all over the country surveying streams and pools to understand fully the nature of the errors handed down from the past, unexamined, because they carried authority but were nothing better than pure speculation. An important factor, often neglected in the past is the reliability of the written sources. That is crucial and the research which needs to be studied and understood is in the realm of psychology, Professor Bartlett's work at Cambridge. Once this is absorbed, the actual dates of writing the reports on the battle are very easily understood and where there are mistakes in the sources, they are easily spotted from all the others and just as easily dated correctly. The idea that a mistake in a source should be noticed, corrected and shown to be corrected accurately, is itself an original aspect of this research. A source like

Scalacronica is easily seen to be 1314 because of the huge amount of detail which could not have been remembered had it not been written immediately, at least for the first time. To see the force of this, imagine an event you saw last year: a rugby match, a concert, a picnic, a walk. How much can you remember a year later? Very little. Details of conversations are lost, who was present is now largely forgotten, the ebb and flow of change during the experience. And so much more. The aim of this research has been the formulation of a decisive result in every case and to communicate it as a proof. This takes training in philosophy, mathematics and science, as well as psychology, history, hydrology and cartography. Here then is a proof of (1) the site of battle and (2) that the Scots, <u>every one of them on foot</u>, moved their position to the Carse close to the English cavalry lines and (3) surprised them there, so that they mounted in great alarm.

I The English crossed the burn before the battle

1. **Lanercost [1314]:** 'Another calamity which befel (sic) <u>the English was that, whereas they had shortly before</u> **crossed a great ditch called Bannockburn,** <u>into which the tide flows, and now wanted to recross it in confusion,</u> many nobles and others fell into it with their horses in the crush, while others escaped with much difficulty, and many were never able to extricate themselves from the ditch.' p208, BR p185.

2. **Scalacronica [1314]:** 'Some of whom [the English] fled to the castle, others to the king's army, <u>which having already left the road through the wood had debouched upon a plain near the water of Forth</u> **beyond Bannockburn,** an evil, deep, wet marsh, where the said English army unharnessed and remained all night.' p54, BR p188.

This plain is the Carse of Balquhiderock.

3. **The Brut or the Chronicles of England [1333]:** 'Allas þe sorw and losse þat þere was done! for þere was slayn, þe noble Erl of Clare, Sire Robert of Clifford, a baroun, and meny opere; & of opere peple þat no man coup nombre; and þere Kyng Edward was scomfitede. And Sir Edmund of Maule, þe kynges stiward, for drede went and drenched him-self in a fresshe ryuer þat is callede Bannokesbourn; þerfore þe Scottes saide, in reproofe and despite of Kyng Edward, foralsemiche as he louede forto to go by watere, and also for he was discomfitede at Bannokesbour[n]e, þefore maidenes made a songe þerof, in þat contre, of Kyng Edward of Engeland and þis maner þai songe:-

    Maydenes of Engelande, sare may ze morne,
    For tynt ze haue [lost] zoure lemmans at Bannokesborn.' p208, BR p94

Replace 'þ' by 'th' and this makes good sense. { Alas the sorrow and loss that there was done! For there was slain, the noble Earl of Clare, Sir Robert of Clifford, a baron, and many others; and of other people that no man could number; and there King Edward was discomfited. And Sir Edward of Maule, the king's steward, for dread went and <u>drenched himself in a fresh river that is called Bannock burn</u>; therefore the Scots said, in reproof and despite King Edward, for as much as he loved to travel by water, and also because he was discomfited at Bannock burn, therefore the maidens made a song thereof in that country, about King Edward of England and this manner they sang:

    Maidens of England, sore may ye mourn,
    For you have lost your loved ones at Bannock burn.

To have perished in the Bannock burn means that they first crossed the burn before the battle and were drowned fleeing, as other sources here confirm.

4. **Bower, Scotichronicon, XII c, 21. Author Unknown [1314]:** 'In 1314, on the day when the Baptist was born, this new favour was granted, that the king of Scots with part of <u>his foot-soldiers</u> defeated the English and their cavalry along with their king. <u>It happened near a stream called the Bannock and those who fled drowned in it.</u>' p357, BR p202

To drown in the Bannockburn means that the English crossed it beforehand and were seeking to flee back across. [A few Scots, with the Earl of Atholl, defected and attacked Cambuskenneth Abbey before the main battle]

5. **Bower**: 'The <u>muddy Bannock</u> holds the nameless whose people at home will wonder at the resting place of the missing.' p 357, BR p203

Since the Scots are defending the Castle and the English coming from the south, for the English to drown in the Bannockburn means they crossed it before the battle.

<u>It is already clear that the English crossed the Bannock burn.</u>

6. **Barbour [1377]**: 'Tharfor thai heberyd thaim that nycht
        Doune in the Kers, and gert all dycht
        And maid redy thar aparaill
        Agayne the morne for the bataill,
        And for in the Kers pulis war.' BkXII line 391-395, BR p240/241

i.e. 'Therefore they camped down in the Carse that night, cleaned and got everything ready for the battle in the morning. And <u>because there were pools of water in the Carse</u>.'

This means that the English crossed the Bannockburn so that they could camp north of it in the Carse.

Note: Because of the two previous quotes we know this is the Carse of Balquhiderock for sure. It is the only Carse where pools of water regularly form and it is north of the burn. See p168, p194 herein. See photos of the pools herein: p164-166;190-192 and BR, BP and GB where there are far more photos on different occasions.

There is of course nowhere else north of the Bannock burn where the English could camp. Livilands Bog lay between this Carse and Stirling Castle; after heavy rain, it was far worse than usual. The English could not afford to camp far away from the Scots who, fearing a pitched battle against a superior force, were expected to flee when the full English army assembled, as the Scots (their cavalry anyway) had done at Falkirk. The Carse of Balquhiderock is the only place within close contact of the Scots up on the Dryfield above Balquhiderock Wood which they had defended so easily on the first day.

Barbour's statement tells us not only that the English crossed the Bannock burn into the Carse but that they camped there.

7. **Brut y Tywysogyon [1314]**: 'Llywelyn, bishop of St. Asaph, died, and Dafyyd ap Belddyn was elected in his place on the eve of the feast of John at Midsummer. And on that day occurred **the encounter in the Pools,** and Gilbert the Younger, earl of Clare (Gloucester), and many of the men of England besides, were slain by the Scots. And the king of England ignominiously fled from that encounter.' [Peniarth MS 20 294b 25-296a. 15 page 123 translated by Prof Thomas Jones, of the University of Wales, published 1952] See p169

So this is a battle fought between English and Scots in 1314 at which Gloucester and many Englishmen were slain and the King of England fled the field. This is Bannockburn. <u>And the battle occurs among pools of water.</u>

Note: the translation is correct. Jones was an expert in medieval Welsh. But the reasons given by him for this are nothing like as powerful as those given in GB Ch VI esp p158-193. These are utterly compelling.

So we already have a proof of the site of battle: 1. The English camped the night before in the Carse <u>because of the pools of water</u> [Barbour]. And 2. the battle took place the next morning <u>among the pools of water</u> [Brut y Tywysogyon]

The 3rd element of this proof is the one we had before: **this Carse is <u>uniquely</u> a place where, after prolonged heavy rain pools are wont to form. No other Carse is like this.** Many pools have been counted in this Carse, some 100 yards long and a yard deep. Many have been photographed on different occasions and can be seen herein and in BR, BP, and GB. The sign that <u>this property of pools of water is invariant</u> right back to 1314 is in the fact that the road across this Carse has had to zigzag to avoid them, as shown on every map proper, right back to Roy's 1750, the first there is. This carse is unique because it alone is enclosed by bounding streams which keep the water table high, near the surface. When rain falls it cannot be absorbed by the ground because of underground water coming off the Dryfield from the escarpment. The pools remain for days until the underground water from the high ground behind escapes to the River Forth a mile away. Only then can the water in the pools be absorbed. The adjoining carses are different. In them, the water table falls all the way to the level of the surface of the River Forth about 30 ft below the ground surface. This space leaves ample room for rainwater falling directly to be absorbed, so that pools cannot form there.

II **It is already clear that the battle was fought in the Carse among the pools of water that regularly form there.**

BUT THIS IS NOT ALL.

Scalacronica [1314]: 'Some of whom [the English] fled to the castle, others to the king's army, <u>which having already left the road through the wood had debouched upon a plain near the water of Forth</u> **beyond Bannockburn**, an evil, deep, wet marsh, where the said English army unharnessed and remained all night.' p54, BR p188. This is Maxwell's translation of the words of Sir Thomas Gray junior. Is it correct?

The important fact is that Sir Thomas Gray senior (who told his son about it in 1314) was not present at the battle because he had been captured on the first day at the Skirmish near St Ninians. All Gray senior saw of the battle field was the Carse as he crossed it on horseback out of his right eye. He would have seen the pools of water reported by Barbour to be present and reported by the Brut y Tywysogyon as the place in which the battle took place. How would he describe such a place? One he had not seen properly at all. He saw pools of water and called it a marsh. It was not a bad description except for this. It was not a marsh. It never is a marsh. It is hard ground with undulations in which pools of water form. They often cannot be seen until you walk into them! It is clear water above grass. You see only the grass unless you are close. It is not the translator who is mistaken but Gray himself. Had he been involved in the battle of day 2 he would have known it was not a marsh. How could the King of England and all his wealthy nobles agree to camp in a marsh? Impossible. They camped there because of the pools of water as Barbour tells us they did. So Scalacronica has fully supported the idea of them camping in this Carse. A better translation is: **4. '[The English] debouched upon a plain with pools of water in the undulations.'** For that is what it is and has always been.

BUT MORE: **Scalacronica [1314]:** At sunrise [The Scots] **marched** out of the wood in three divisions of <u>infantry</u>. They directed their course boldly upon the English army which had been under arms all night, with their horses bitted. They [The English] **mounted in great alarm**, for they were not accustomed to dismount <u>to fight on foot</u>; whereas the Scots had taken a lesson from the Flemings, who before that had at Courtrai defeated on foot the power of France.' Maxwell p55, BP p189

That is: **5.** the Scots marched out of the wood (Balquhiderock Wood) and **SURPRISED** the English who **mounted in great alarm.**

Vita [1314]: 'Meanwhile Robert Bruce... **led his whole army out from the wood**. About forty thousand men he brought with him, and split them into three divisions; and <u>not one of them was on horseback</u>.' Denholm-Young p52, BR p175

The same wood: Balquhiderock Wood, as it is known today.

Baston [1314]: 'Black Monday renews the deadly plague, which by force of fortune Scotland makes grievous for the English...The English fighters look expectantly for Scots whom they may do to death—**Scots no longer remote but close at hand**.' Scotichronicon Bk XII p373 lines 156-162; BR p208

Again: **6. the Scots have moved their position close to the English and taken them by surprise.**

Baston [1314]: '**Rushing down** (the slope of Balquhiderock Wood), **the raging Scottish fighters advance on foot**. Scotichronicon BKXII p373, line 169; BR p209

The Unknown in Scotichronicon [1314]: 'The muddy Bannock holds the names of those we do not know...'**Between the stony stream and the obstruction of their camp the treacherous English people come to grief as a result of their own dishonest conduct**.' Vol VI BKXII p359 lines 61-75 BR p202

That is: **7. the English are mainly killed between the English camp around the Knoll in the Carse and the Bannock Burn.**

These matters are settled. Eight sources here are conclusive proof of the site of battle. There are no contrary sources.

Here are three others:

Trokelowe [1314]: 'Emboldened they [the Scots] awaited the arrival of the English...On their side [the Scots] were all on foot: picked men, very courageous, proper;y armed with sharp axes and other weapons of war, with their shields tightly locked in front of them, forming an impenetrable formation. They completely abandoned their horses, avoiding the danger which had once befallen them at Falkirk where the Scottish cavalry... fled and left the footsoldiers to die in the field. Robert the Bruce, who claimed to be king of Scotland, on foot with his whole entourage, **went ahead of his whole army**...so that no one would think of running away.' [Annales p84; BR p191,192]

Baker [c1329]:'To that place the proud host of the English who were accustomed to fight on horseback brought up great quantities of ...warhorses and polished armour....On that night you might have seen the English race...sodden with wine, vomiting up their drink and crying "Wassail and Drinkhail"... The next day, the Scots, having obtained a field (position) best suited to victory, the King their leader, **having forbidden any to mount a warhorse**...' Galfridus Le Baker, Chronica p 7; BR p196.

Lanercost [1314]: 'When the two armies had approached very near each other, **all the Scots fell on their knees** to repeat *Pater Noster* commending themselves to God and seeking help from heaven; after which they advanced boldly against the English.' Maxwell's trans p207; BR p183.

If all the Scots fell on their knees, they had to be all on foot. You could not dismount, fall on your knees and then remount when so close to the English that they can see you very easily. Lanercost is telling us that the Scots are all on foot, like everybody else. Notice that Lanercost is not quite correct: the Scots fell on their knees but it was not to pray but to set their pikes and kneel beside them. We also have a mild conflation: an exact description is very difficult for anyone: both armies did not approach each other at the same time: the Scots moved their position close to the English; the English were unready and the Scots moved again because they were free to do so. The English could do nothing about it. Some time elapsed before the English charged the Scots. By then, the Scots were so close that the English had little space to get up speed for their charge.

III We now have six sources that tell us the Scots were all on foot: Baston, Vita, Lanercost, Scalacronica, Trokelowe and Baker. All of them Englishmen who would have seen the Scottish approach or heard of it from other Englishmen. Only Barbour disagrees:

he wrote 63 years too late to know this. It had been forgotten by then. Besides, no Scotsman was positioned to see it happen. We have ten sources all contributing to the results found and there are no other sources which have anything of any value to offer. That the Scots took the English by surprise is obvious. That is what all the sources are telling us: the Scots moved a long way!

Note: No reports of the battle say that the battle was fought south of the burn. It could not have been fought there since so many Englishmen were drowned in the Bannock burn.

Since Stirling castle was never relieved by the English, it follows that the battle took place somewhere between the Bannock burn and the Castle. The Carse of Balquhiderock is the place.

Note further: The Unknown in Bower is saying that the English died in the ground between the stony stream (the Bannock burn, already referred to by him) and their camp in the Carse. This is the south Carse of Balquhiderock. What he is describing is the rout, once the knights have been killed just beyond their camp, when every Englishman left alive is fleeing for home.

What follows is a copy of the page from the Brut y Tywysogyon translated by Professor Thomas Jones published by the University of Wales Press, 1952: See colour version herein p169.

[1306–1306]. Anno. vj. There was a breach between the men of Scotland and the king of England.

[1307–1307]. Anno. vij. Edward, king of England, went to subdue Scotland. And coming thence, at the town called Burgh-on-Sands the eminent king died on the seventh day of July.

    In the same year, on the feast-day of Matthew the Apostle, the sixth day from the Calends of March, Edward Caernarvon, his son, was crowned.

[1308–1308]. Anno. viij. Piers Gaveston began to govern the realm at his pleasure. And the other leaders took that ill.

[1309–]. Anno. ix.†

[1310–]. Anno dm̄. m. cccx.

[1311–1312]. Anno. j. Edward the Third was born.†

[1312–1312]. Anno. ij. Piers Gaveston was slain on the feast-day of Stt. Gervasius and Protasius,† near Warwick, after he had been lured out of the castle.

[1313–1314]. Anno. iij. Llywelyn, bishop of St. Asaph, died, and Dafydd ap Bleddyn was elected in his place on the eve of the feast of John at Midsummer. And on that day occurred the encounter in the Pools,† and Gilbert the Younger, earl of Clare, and many of the men of England besides, were slain by the Scots. And the king of England ignominiously fled from that encounter.

[1314–1315]. Anno. iiij. Dafydd,† bishop of St. Asaph, was consecrated.

[1315–]. Anno. v.

[1316–]. Anno. vi.

[1317–1315]. Anno. vij. The war of Llywelyn Bren took place.

[1318–1316]. Anno. viij. Llywelyn Bren was seized.†

[1319–1317]. Anno. ix. There was discord between the king and the barons.

[1320–1320]. Anno dm̄. m̄. ccc°. xix°. The barons came fully armed to the council at London, and they wanted to seize the king and Sir Hugh the Younger, unless he placed his seal to the letters of the barons. And he wept and did their will.

The footnote gives futher explanation of Jones's translation. Ch VI GB completely demolishes any alternative translation. Jones was correct! This next page is from the translation of Barbour's Bruce by W.W.Skeat, Professor of Anglo Saxon in the University of Cambridge dated 1878. This ms is the C ms. There are two. The E in Edinburgh, the C at Cambridge. Duncan used the E. This shows that 'pollis' = 'pools.' In the E ms we find 'pulis'. Both words mean 'pools'. Other compelling reasons are given for this translation in GB Ch VI. This translation was first published in 1870.

Fecht [or] the morñe, bot he var socht.

The English rest all night down in the Carse of Stirling.

Thair thai herbryit thañe that nycht

Douñe in the kerβ, and gert all dicht,   392

And mak reddy ther apparale

Agañe the morñe for the Battale.

Because the Carse was full of pools, they bridged these with boards and pieces of thatch.

For in the kerβ <u>pollis</u> ther war,

Howsis and thak thai brak, and bar   396

To mak bryggis quhar thai mycht paβ.

And sum sais ʒeit, the folk that wes

Iñ the castell, quhen nycht can fall,

For at thai knew thair myscheiff all,   400

Thai went furth neir all at thai war,

The people from the castle brought them doors and windows,

And durys and vyndowis with thaim bar,

Swa that thai had befor [the] day

Briggit the <u>pollis</u>, swa that thai   404

[Fol. 94. C.] and thus all the pools were bridged over.

War passit our euir-ilkañe,

*And the [hard] feld on horβ has tañe,

*All reddy for till gif battale,

Arayit in-to thair apparale.

The battale of Bannokburne.

At daybreak, the Scotch hear mass, take a sup, and array themselves.

The scottis men, quhen it wes day,

Thair meβ deuotly herd thai say,   408

Syne tuk a sop, and maid thame ʒar.

And quhen [thai] all assemblit war,

And in thair battalis all purvait,

390. [or E] on C ; while H. *bot*] that. but H ; that E.
391. *Thair*] Tharfor EH.
392. *kerss*] kers E ; Kersse H.
393. *mak*] make H ; maid E. *ther*] all ther C ; *but* EH *omit* all.
395. *For*] And for. *kerss*] kers E ; Kersse H. *pollis*] pulis E ; Puilles H. *ther*] EH *om.*
396. H *as* C. *and—and*] thai brak, and thak E.
400. *at*] that EH. *thair*] the E ; their H.
401. *furth*] foorth H ; full E. *at*]

403. [*the* EH] that C.
404. *pollis*] pulis E ; Pooles H.
405. Were passed ouer them euerilk- ane H ; War passyt our ilkane all hale E.
406*, 407*. *Not in* E ; H *has—* And the hard field on horse hes tane, All readie for to giue battell. [*hard* H] herll C ; *but see* l. 447.
406. *in-to*] in-till.
408. *herd*] gert. *herd—say*] heard haue thay H.
410. *thai all* E] that thai H ; all C.

[35] **How do we know that Bruce led, on foot, in front, the entire Scottish army?** **Because the sources tell us he did.**
Four sources Vita, Trokelowe, Baker and Lanercost tell us. GB 254-264. BR p214, line 23 et seq Briefly,
1. The tactics demand it. [When understood: Bruce led 3 divisions to block off the Carse, he set his pikes twice (as Lanercost, Barbour and Bridlington tell us: the Scots attack after praying: ie they kneel once and then go forward and then kneel again before the cavalry charge happens) ie as the English are unready, he can put his men right alongside the cavalry, depriving them of space to get up speed, saving lives. He has to be in front to control this. Someone has to go first. Who but him? Everybody would follow him, no one else. Because he is on foot he cannot run away, unlike Falkirk, and everyone can see it. Every Scot is on foot. Trokelowe confirms this.]
2. Trokelowe: 'Robert the Bruce..on foot with his entourage, went ahead of his whole army..' Annales 84, BR 192
3. Vita: 'Robert Bruce... led his whole army out from the wood (Balquhiderock Wood)...and not one was on horseback.' Denholm-Young's trans. 52, BR 175.
4. Baker: '...the King, their leader, having forbidden any to mount a warhorse..' Chronica...8, BR 196 [It was very unusual for the King to be the leader. That is why this is remarkable.]
5. Lanercost: 'They [the Scots] had so arranged their army that two columns were abreast in advance of the third, so that neither should be in advance of the other and the third followed in which was Robert.' Maxwell's trans. 207,208 BR 184
Why is Lanercost not quite right? Because he was not present. Trokelowe was there, saw it for himself. His is the most vivid and detailed account of them all. All five propositions amount to the conclusion reached. Bruce himself is leading. Who else should lead? Bruce could not order and execute that second move without being ahead of everyone from the start. Edward Bruce might have led the centre. But Robert Bruce was out in front. They would have similar colours. Where was the reporter to Lanercost? (Unable to see Robert Bruce who was closest to the English lines, because of the tents and wagons in the way, yards away when he set his pikes for the second time [There was nothing the English could do about it! He took them very close to cut down the speed of the cavalry charge to save Scottish lives]). Probably, at the side of the Knoll, hidden by tents and wagons. [Note: no historian has ever put these quotes down in this fashion before (or anything remotely like this). The procedure is matchless, especially when there is space to print the whole thing (as in GB), unlike here.
Inspiration: the achievements of Bruce and his men are inspirational. The plan is so brilliant that no historian has ever understood it before and all would have lost the battle had they been in control, for they do not understand the ground as Bruce did. Because he marched on foot at the head of his men against the greatest army ever assembled in these islands till then, an army full of experience and success in other wars.
[36] Lanercost [1314]: 'Another calamity which befel (sic) the English was that, whereas they had shortly before crossed a great ditch called Bannockburn into which the tide flows and now wanted to recross it in confusion...' (p208, Maxwell's trans, 1913; BR p185)
[37] **What were the English saying on seeing the Scots approach?**
Barbour [1377]: "And when the King of England saw the Scotsmen dare to take the field thus so openly and on foot, he was astonished, and he said, 'What are yon Scots going to fight?' 'Yes, indeed, Sir,' said a knight called Sir Ingram Umphraville, who continued, 'Forsooth, Sir, now I see quite the most astonishing sight that I ever saw, when, in order to

fight, the Scotsmen have undertaken to give battle against the might of England on <u>open hard ground</u>. But, if you listen to my advice, you will easily beat them. Pull back suddenly from here, with divisions and pennons, until we pass our tents and you will see quite quickly that they will break ranks, despite their lords and scatter to take our equipment. And when we see them scattered like that, gallop on them fiercely and we will have them quite easily, for then none will be closely arrayed to fight who could withstand your great impact. The king said, 'Indeed, I will not do that. For nobody is going to say that I shall avoid battle, or that I withdrew from such a rabble.' When what I've just reported was said, the Scotsmen all together knelt down to pray to God. They made a short prayer there to help them in that fight. And when the English king had sight of them kneeling, he said at once, 'Yon folk are kneeling to ask for mercy'. Sir Ingram said, 'You are right this time; they ask mercy, but not from you. They ask God for mercy for their sins. I'll tell you something for a fact, that yon men will win all, or die; none will flee for fear of death.' Then the king said, 'So be it.' And then without further delay, they had the bugle call for the attack." [Barbour, BkXII, 447; BR p243]

Vita [1314]: 'The Earl of Gloucester counselled the king not to go forth to battle that day, but to rest on account of the feast, and let his army recuperate as much as possible. But the king spurned the earl's advice, and, growing very heated with him, charged him with treachery and deceit. 'Today,' said the earl, 'it will be clear that I am neither a traitor nor a liar,' and at once prepared himself for battle.' This conversation takes place before the Scots have arrived before the English lines, before they have even been seen, probably in the king's tent. Outside the tent, Gloucester sees the Scots approach and rushes to stop them.

'[The Scots] advanced like a thick-set hedge, and such a phalanx could not easily be broken. When the situation was such that the two sides must meet (i.e. the Scots had closed up on the English and dug their pike-butts in: the English are too stupefied to move) James Douglas, who commanded the first phalanx of the Scots (the right wing) vigorously attacked the Earl of Gloucester's line. (In fact, Douglas's men are merely running in to close off the Carse on the east side, for if he can get really close, the Scots will save a great distance near the Great bend and they will close off the Carse where it is the minimum distance across of 830 yards. So the Scots are not attacking. They are trying to reach a specific position from which they can far better withstand an English cavalry charge. Of course Vita does not realise this, for he does not understand the tactics.) The earl withstood him manfully, once and again penetrated their wedge, and would have been victorious if he had had faithful companions. But look! At a sudden rush of Scots, the earl's horse is killed and the earl rolls to the ground. Lacking defenders, and borne easily down by the weight of his body armour he could not easily arise, and of the five hundred cavalry whom he had led to battle at his own expense, he almost alone was killed. For when they saw their lord unhorsed, they stood astonished and brought him no aid. Accursed be the chivalry whose courage fails in the hour of greatest need! (It is not lack of courage. They are merely surprised and too slow to react. Of course they are all courageous men. Most do not realise it is Gloucester, for he has not stopped to put on the surplice bearing his colours. There was not time for that: the Scots were closing down the space for the cavalry charge: he had to prevent it.)

'Alas! Twenty armed knights could have saved the earl, but among some five hundred, there was not found one. May the lord confound them! Some said that the Earl of Gloucester had perished suddenly by reason of his rash attack. For there was rivalry between him and the Earl of Hereford, who should take precedence in the line, and the Earl of Hereford said that this was lawfully his, because he was Constable of England. Gloucester replied that his forebears had always led the van, and therefore this pertained to him by custom. **While they disputed in this fashion, and the Scottish forces were approaching rapidly, the Earl of Gloucester dashed forward in disorder, seeking the glory of the first encounter**; but see! The earl is met by the onrushing Scots and his horse immediately killed; because when thrown from his horse there was no one to defend him, he was pierced by many wounds and shamefully killed.' [Vita, Denholm-Young's trans. p52,53; BR p175, 176]

In fact, Vita and Trokelowe are incorrect: Gloucester alone understood the danger of the Scots pikemen positioned so close to the cavalry that they could not get up speed to behave like cavalry.

[38] **The Scots Kneeling to receive the English cavalry charge; the double move. This is established below:**

I **Lanercost[1314]: When the armies were near each other, 'all the Scots fell on their knees to repeat** Pater Noster (The Our Father prayer), **commending themselves to God and seeking help from heaven; after which they advanced boldly against the English.'** [Maxwell, p207; BR p183,184]
So the Scots kneel down and then get up again and move forward.
Notice the crucial elements:
1. ALL the Scots kneel down.
2. They are not kneeling to pray. To do so, so close to the English on the day of battle, would be madness. They are kneeling to set their pikes.
3. After the pikes are set, they rise and move boldly forward. Why? because Bruce has noticed that the English are so surprised and so unprepared that he has plenty of time to do so: to steal some more space and deprive their cavalry of even more space to get up speed. That is, the English are unable to prevent him getting closer.
4. What happened next? When the Scots got as close as Bruce wanted: 10 yards, maybe less! Bruce ordered them to kneel again and set the pikes for the last time. Then they were ready. That is what this means, as the others, who follow, confirm.

The monk who wrote this could not conceive that the Scots might have had another motive for kneeling. This was not a time for communal prayers. Under the very eye of The King of England and his huge army.
Communal prayers were unnecessary. Every man would be praying on his own account, as men do in battle. As a clergyman, of course the monk would presume that kneeling men meant men kneeling to pray. We now know that he was wrong.

II Barbour[1377]: "When what I've just reported was said, <u>the Scotsmen all together knelt down to pray</u> to God; they made a short prayer there to God to help them in that fight. And when the English king had sight of them kneeling, he said at once, 'Yon folk are kneeling to ask for mercy.' Sir Ingram said, 'You are right this time; they ask mercy, but not from you. They ask God (for mercy) for their sins. I'll tell you something for a fact, that yon men will win all or die; none will flee for fear of death.' Then the king said, 'So be it.' And then without further ado they had the bugle-call for the attack." [Bk XII Duncan's trans. p472; BR p243,244]

Note the crucial elements:
1. The Scots kneel down.
2. The English king thinks they are begging for mercy.
3. Umphraville thinks they are praying to God.
4. Why does Barbour not report that the Scots rose after praying and marched boldly closer to the English? Two reasons. (i) Barbour wrote in 1377 and this detail would have been forgotten by those he talked to. (ii) This may have been the second time the Scots knelt to pray. The English king might not have been informed about the Scottish advance until that moment. If it was the first time, the English would be making ready and may not have seen the next Scottish move which was to get really close, so close that they could not be seen at all over the heads of those English in front. It should be the first time. Note: Since the King of England can see them and see that they are kneeling, it follows that they are very close.

III Bernard de Linton (Abbot of Arbroath) [1314]: 'Maurice abbot of Inchaffray [later the bishop of Dunblane], who heard the king's confession on that day and celebrated mass for the Scots on a prominent spot, put forward a short and effective statement on freedom and the defence of their right..... Barefooted then and wearing his canonicals, the said abbot went before them bearing a crucifix like a commander, and before the battle was engaged he told them <u>all to kneel and pray to God</u> as suppliants. Seeing this, the English, buoyed up with a baseless light-heartedness, began to shout: 'Look! all those Scots have surrendered to us with trembling hearts.' An older English knight, Ingram de Umphraville, formed a sounder understanding and replied to them saying: 'You are right that they are surrendering, but to God, not to you. I hope therefore that that no greater spirit of enthusiasm is vainly aroused than consideration of the circumstances will require for action.' <u>At this the Scots rose eagerly and attacked their enemies.</u> On the English side two hundred knights were killed, besides the [earl] of Gloucester and innumerable others. On the Scottish side two knights fell, namely William de Vieuxpoint and Walter de Ros.' [Bower, Scotichronicon Vol 6, Bk XII p365]

Note the crucial elements:

1. **The Scots kneel to pray.** This is after the abbot leads them forward to engage the English. This is nonsense: Bruce is in command of these men, all of them. Other reporters, the best of them have told us this repeatedly: Vita, Scalacronica, Trokelowe and Baker—Englishmen who saw the Scots approach or knew those who did. They are kneeling to set their pikes, not kneeling to pray.

2. The English [king] thinks that in kneeling they are surrendering. {Remember Barbour's account, above}. Umphraville says they are surrendering to God. i.e. praying.

3. After this, the Scots rise and attack their enemies.

4. What this means is that the Scots rise to get closer to the English cavalry lines. Because the Scots get really close, they are not seen kneeling again for they cannot be seen because they are so close to the English. That they rise after kneeling tells us they are getting closer and will kneel again closer still to the English cavalry lines.

5. The presumption is that Bernard is not in the battle and therefore back in Balquhiderock Wood.

6. Why is abbot Maurice stated to be leading the Scots? He may have been leading a small group (a company commander); there would be very many small groups: 100 groups of 200 just to get down into the Carse. His might have been at one side. Bernard may actually have been unaware that Bruce was leading the entire army in the centre. When the men kneel, it might seem as if Maurice does what he is said to do to some. But this is not so. The tactics do not allow for communal prayers under the eye of the King of England with his great army in front of him, an imminent threat. The likeliest explanation for this discontinuity is that while the groups were arriving in the Carse, Maurice led his group in prayer and Bernard was a member of it. The latter was not aware of the bigger picture. Even that Maurice's actions took place on the Dryfield before the marshaling and the advance took place. The text merely says 'before' it does not say when before. Time and again, reporters of the battle omit vital actions and telescope others, remembering only what seems to them, from their limited point of view, to be relevant. Having all the reports, we can see what he means, what his errors of memory are.

7. That this kneeling takes place close to the English who can see them easily. That means they are in the Carse at the time. The English are on the Knoll.

8. NB After kneeling, the Scots get up and attack their enemies; ie the Scots march even closer to the English cavalry lines. When they get really close they will kneel again, for that is the best way to receive the cavalry charge.

IV The Canon of Bridlington. [1330's]

'And therefore, as a true Catholic who trusted in the Lord, he [Robert the Bruce] made all his men take thought before going into battle through the agency of the ecclesiastics so that each one received the Eucharist well-confessed and contrite; in order that they should go to war thus armed with the arms of God, all having first heard mass and **knelt in most devoted fashion** in the Lord's presence, humbly beseeching grace and praying God for the liberation of the kingdom [Scotland]. When the English saw this they smiled and said: 'Look the Scots have yielded themselves to us asking our pardon'; but a certain knight, old in years but sounder in his wits than they, said to them in answer: 'It is true that they yield themselves; but it is not to you but to Almighty God; in whom they place their hope and have their trust.' And who indeed [in the event] granted them the victory.' Gesta Edwardi Caernarvon, p48

Note the crucial elements:

1. The Scots knelt down.

2. The English saw them kneel which means that they are kneeling close to the English cavalry lines.

3. The English think they are asking pardon.

4. A knight (Umphraville) says they are praying to God.

This is like the words of Bernard de Linton, quoted by Bower. Nothing is said about what the Scots do next. But we know anyway from the others: they get up and get even closer and then kneel again.

Thus, four clergymen have seen (or been told that) the Scots kneel and assumed they were praying. Indeed, the King of England and Ingram de Umphraville both see the Scots kneeling and the former thinks they are surrendering, the latter that they are praying. But they are not praying. They are setting their pikes, preparing to receive the cavalry charge. Six people, then (at least), saw the Scots kneel.

The very fact that the Scots have risen after praying and then attacked the English (Lanercost and Bernard de Linton) tells us that they will stop and set the pikes a second time before the charge is made. That is inevitable. The Scots will not fight the English while standing up with pikes. They have to fight them by setting the pikes in the ground and then let the English run onto the pikes, which is what the reports tell us took place. That is why Scottish casualties were so light: just 2 Scottish knights (Ross and Vieuxpont {Oldbridge}) killed as against hundreds of English knights and why there is much splintering of pikes.

Lanercost [1314]: 'When both armies engaged each other, and the great horses of the English charged the pikes of the Scots, as it were into a dense forest, there arose a great and terrible crash of spears broken and of destriers wounded to the death.' [Maxwell's trans. p208] [spears should be translated pikes: they are not for throwing or even prodding]

The English are bound to charge but only when they are ready. Bruce has got his pikemen up to move a second time and set the pikes again nearer the English lines because he sees he has plenty of time to do so, as they are unprepared.

Here then is an important advance: the Scots were seen kneeling to pray but the 4 reporters were all clergymen who expected this and interpreted kneeling in this way. They were all mistaken. The Scots were kneeling to set their pikes in the ground, in the best formation to receive the inevitable cavalry charge which was also best defended by kneeling. Why is that best? Because the pikes all have their butts in the ground and point up at an angle over the shoulders of the man in front. So the energy of the horse and rider is taken, not by the man, but the ground. Packed together, 14 pikes will strike the horse and rider before his lance hits anyone. Thus, despite the passage of so much time, it has been possible to correct the mistaken interpretation of events at the battle itself. GB 260-270.

There is something more we can deduce: the fact that Bruce set his pikes twice tells us that he knew it would work. That means he had full control. That means he had trained them. How awful if having got the pikes set, his move closer to the English had caused everything to go wrong when he tried to do so a second time. Why did Bruce take this decision? Because he knew it would work. Had there been any doubt, he would never have chanced it. The Scottish army that day was no militia of farm hands, they were highly trained soldiers. GB ChXII

[39]Gloucester:

Vita [1314]: 'The Earl of Gloucester counselled the king not to go forth to battle that day, but to rest on account of the feast, and let his army recuperate as much as possible. But the king spurned the earl's advice, and, growing very heated with him, charged him with treachery and deceit. 'Today,' said the earl, 'it will be clear that I am neither a traitor nor a liar,' and at once prepared himself for battle.' This conversation takes place before the Scots have arrived before the English lines, before they have even been seen, probably in the king's tent.

'[The Scots] advanced like a thick-set hedge, and such a phalanx could not easily be broken. When the situation was such that the two sides must meet (i.e. the Scots had closed up on the English and dug their pike-butts in: the English are too stupefied to move) James Douglas, who commanded the first phalanx of the Scots (the right wing) vigorously attacked the Earl of Gloucester's line. (In fact, Douglas's men are merely running in to close off the Carse on the east side, for if he can get really close, the Scots will save a great distance near the Great bend and they will close off the Carse where it is the minimum distance across of 830 yards. So the Scots are not attacking. They are trying to reach a specific position from which they can far better withstand an English cavalry charge. Of course Vita does not realise this, for he does not understand the tactics.) The earl withstood him manfully, once and again penetrated their wedge, and would have been victorious if he had had faithful companions. But look! At a sudden rush of Scots, the earl's horse is killed and the earl rolls to the ground. Lacking defenders, and borne easily down by the weight of his body armour he could not easily arise, and of the five hundred cavalry whom he had led to battle at his own expense, he almost alone was killed. For when they saw their lord unhorsed, they stood astonished and brought him no aid. Accursed be the chivalry whose courage fails in the hour of greatest need! (It is not lack of courage. They are merely surprised and too slow to react. Of course they are all courageous men. Most do not realise it is Gloucester, for he has not stopped to put on the surplice bearing his colours.)

'Alas! Twenty armed knights could have saved the earl, but among some five hundred, there was not found one. May the lord confound them! Some said that the Earl of Gloucester had perished suddenly by reason of his rash attack. For there was rivalry between him and the Earl of Hereford, who should take precedence in the line, and the Earl of Hereford said that this was lawfully his, because he was Constable of England. Gloucester replied that his forebears had always led the van, and therefore this pertained to him by custom. **While they disputed in this fashion, and the Scottish forces were approaching rapidly, the Earl of Gloucester dashed forward in disorder, seeking the glory of the first encounter;** but see! The earl is met by the onrushing Scots and his horse immediately killed; because when thrown from his horse there was no one to defend him, he was pierced by many wounds and shamefully killed.' [Vita, Denholm-Young's trans. 52,53; BR p175,176]

The key to the meaning is that the Scottish forces were approaching rapidly. Gloucester is on the Knoll at the King's tent, surveying the surprising sight of the Scots attacking them, something never anticipated. So this attack by Gloucester takes place at the very start of the battle. Gloucester argues with Hereford, before the King, about the precedence of either to lead the van. But, the argument still unresolved, Gloucester sees the advancing Scots, the forest of pikes and understands the extent of the danger the English are in. The Scots, he realises, are about to get so close to the English that they will deprive the English cavalry of space to get up speed. This means, at a stroke, the cavalry will be unable to act as cavalry. They will be halted and hemmed in between the streams. Gloucester sees the urgent need to keep the Scots at bay, jumps on a horse and rushes toward the advancing Scots, heading for their left wing which is opposite his own encamped forces. Note: Gloucester (Gilbert, Earl of Clare) was Bruce's nephew: he would have understood better than anyone Bruce's audacity.

Trokelowe[1314]: 'For quite some time the fighting went on with swords ringing loudly about their heads; as both sides strove manfully against one another, very many fell mortally wounded. When Gilbert, earl of Gloucester, saw this, he was very angry at their savagery. He urged his fellow soldiers to rush ferociously against these effeminate Scots, who were not used to facing English attacks; and, wanting to acquire a military reputation for himself, setting himself up as an example to his men, like a warlike boar he rushed in his blazing anger into the ranks of the enemy **making his sword drunk on their blood. Whoever he touched with his blade**, he cut his head or a limb off. Eventually, the weight of the whole battle concentrated itself on him as he so thirsted for their slaughter, to such an extent that, with the points of spears driven into every part of his body and thrust from different directions, he was laid low and his head was hammered on all sides with the enemies clubs until he breathed out his soul with his life-blood under the horses' hooves. All the rest of the army, seeing that he had fallen in this way, were terror-struck and fled, leaving their lord slain – oh woe! – on the battlefield.' Annales p85, BR p193

Gloucester should have been armed with a lance. But no! All he has is a sword. The version in Vita is correct: Gloucester has seen the danger presented by the advancing Scots and has acted with great speed to lead his own men to repel the Scots before they get close. That is why he is armed only with a sword. But his own men, too surprised, like every other Englishmen, do nothing. This is the start of the battle, not as Trokelowe has implied, the middle of it. This kind of error: transposition of events we have seen before in Trokelowe: He described the Scots awaiting the English cavalry charge and only later described them marching boldly into the position they wanted to be in to meet the charge. Vita is the superior source on the issue of when in the battle Gloucester was killed. Vita is quite certain it was at the very beginning. Trokelowe is just the kind of person who takes little interest in the sequence of events.

Notice this: Trokelowe or his reporter had to be stationed on the Knoll and on its south side to be able to see Gloucester's sudden attack upon the advancing forces of Douglas, for Douglas must be leading the Scottish right wing, Randolph being on the Scottish left, having come out of Pelstream Woods after defending St Ninians the day before. This tells us that Gloucester's men are encamped on the English left in the south Carse, along the sides of the burn, an ideal place for a leading commander and his retinue. Gloucester attacked the advancing Scots on his left because he had every reason to expect that his men would follow him there. Because he was unprepared, had no colours etc, perhaps they were largely unaware who it was that set off against the Scots.

Le Baker [1341-]: 'There died at that time Gilbert Earl of Gloucester whom the Scots would gladly have kept for ransom if they had recognised him by his personal coat of arms; but he was not wearing it at the time.' Chronica p7,8; BR p198

Confirmation: Gloucester had not taken the time either to arm himself with a lance or even to show his coat of arms. He just had to lead the attack on the advancing Scots to keep them away from the cavalry lines so that they would have room to charge properly. An inspired move just the same. Quoted from GB p231-232

[40] Scalacronica and Lanercost act as if the English cavalry, acting as one unit, all charged at the same time. Impossible. This is a conflation, a telescoping of many events into one. Where there was no control and no possibility of a command to charge which could never have been heard amid such a confusion in a camp, everyone at sixes and sevens horses, wagons, tents, campfires, hangers-on, knights and their attendants and infantry all mixed up together, a concerted cavalry charge by all the cavalry at the same time was inconceivable. They had to charge when they were ready; not wait for everyone to be ready. Had they waited, what then? Since there was no control, there would have been no command to charge. How would the knights who were ready, mounted and anxious to charge, sit their horses and wait for the rest to mount? In that set of circumstances under the eye of the King, when everyone had seen the slaying of Gloucester, waiting was not an option. It would have looked like cowardice. Plainly, the king demanded attack. Honour demanded attack, revenge. Chivalry had been affronted. The very fact that the English cavalry was split into two halves by the Knoll which lay between them, shows clearly that a uniform cavalry charge was impossible.

[41] Baker p8/9, BR p198

[42] '[King Edward] gathered a large army both of men in armour and of foot-soldiers with cross-bows and archers well-experienced in the art of fighting... from every part of the kingdoms of England Scotland, France and Germany, Wales and Ireland, Flanders and Gascony, Boulogne and Brittany, Guelders and Bohemia, Holland, Zealand and Brabant, and from every region round about, consisting of every kind of mercenary to the number of 300,000 armed fighting men on horseback, not counting the countless attendants on foot and the common throng of either sex.' Scotichronicon Vol VI, BKXII, p351, lines 30-42.

[43] Sir Giles d'Argentin, a famous tournament knight of legendary prowess. Having led King Edward to safety near the Castle, he is reported to have declared that he had a duty to see that the King was safe but, never having fled from a fight before, he did not intend to begin now. He rode back towards the battle, recrossed the Pelstream and was soon slain by the same methods as all his colleagues. The King himself was probably most reluctant to leave and, according to Trokelowe, did not otherwise dishonour himself. It was not really his fault that he lost. His father would have fared no better against such a master general at the summit of his powers as Robert the Bruce.

[44] Most of the killing of Englishmen was done by the first few rows of Scots. Only during the rout when the English were fleeing did the rest of the Scots play a part. Of course some Scots in the front rows were slain or wounded and others came from behind to replace them.

[45] **How long did main battle last?**

Vita[1314]: 'Oh day of vengeance and disaster, day of utter loss and shame, evil and accursed day, not to be reckoned in our calendar; that blemished the reputation of the English, despoiled them and enriched the Scots, in which our costly belongings were ravished to the value of £200,000! So many fine noblemen and valiant youth, so many noble horses, so much military equipment, costly garments and gold plate—all lost in one unfortunate day, **one fleeting hour**.

Vita is one of the very earliest and best sources. This should be believed, then.

[46] **Kill Knowe**: In some of the older maps, such as those used by Rev Thomas Miller, there is such a place in the adjoining Carse of Skeoch to the east called 'Kill Knowe'. See plate 32 BR, for example. It is about the level of the Great Bend in the burn and about 250 yards south of Redhall.

Proof that Bruce led all his men on foot

Vita [1314]: 'Robert Bruce...led his whole army out from the wood. About forty thousand men he brought with him and **not one of them was on horseback** but each was furnished with light armour, not easily penetrable by a sword. They had axes at their sides and carried lances (pikes) in their hands. They advanced like a thick-set hedge and such a phalanx could not easily be broken.' [Denholm-Young's trans p52; BR p175]

Vita [1314]: 'Oh famous race unconquered through the ages, why do you, who used to conquer knights, **flee from mere footmen**? At Berwick, Dunbar and Falkirk you carried off the victory, and *now you flee from the infantry of the Scots*... Thus was Ben-Hadad, a most powerful King of Syria, put to flight by the footmen of Samaria.' [ibid, p 54; BR p177]

Trokelowe [1314]: 'Robert Bruce, who claimed to be king of Scotland, **on foot** with his entourage, went ahead of his whole army, so that in this way, with the danger shared equally by greater and smaller, no one would think of running away...**The Scots were all on foot**: picked men, very courageous, properly armed with very sharp axes and other weapons of war with their shields tightly locked in front of them forming an impenetrable formation. **They completely abandoned their horses**, avoiding the danger which had befallen them in the battle of Falkirk, where the Scottish cavalry, seeing the large numbers of English advancing in such good order, fled the field and left the foot soldiers to die.' [Annales, p84; BR p192]

Scalacronica [1314]: 'They (the Scots) at sunrise on the morrow **marched out of the wood** in three divisions of infantry. They directed their course boldly upon the English army, which had been under arms all night, with their horses bitted (but unharnessed). They (the English) mounted in great alarm, **for they were not accustomed to dismount to fight on foot;** whereas the Scots had taken a lesson from the Flemings, who before that had at Courtrai defeated **on foot** the power of France.' [Maxwell's translation, 1913, p55; BR p189]

Why did the English mount in great alarm? Because the Scots had got really close before their presence was noticed generally.

Lanercost [1314]: 'When the two armies approached very near each other, **all the Scots fell on their knees** to repeat *Pater noster* (the 'Our Father' prayer), commending themselves to God and seeking help from heaven; **after which they advanced boldly against the English**.

They had so arranged their army that two columns went abreast in advance of the third (a pincer formation), so that neither should be in advance of the other; and the third followed in which was Robert. Of a truth, when both armies engaged each other and the great horses of the English charged the pikes of the Scots, as it were into a dense forest, there arose a great and terrible clash of spears broken and of destriers wounded to the death; and so they remained without movement for a while. Now the English rear could not reach the Scots because the leading division was in the way, nor could they do anything to help themselves, wherefore there was nothing for it but to take to flight.' [Maxwell's trans. 1913; BR p183,184]

Because the Scots knelt down apparently in prayer (but actually to receive the cavalry charge), they all had to be on foot. Remounting could not be guaranteed when under the eyes of the English who were so close.

Le Baker [1330-]: 'To that place (Stirling) the proud host of the English who were accustomed to fight on horseback brought up great quantities of coursers, warhorses and polished armour. In a spirit of self-flattery they promised themselves the victory...and they were so confident in their own security that besides the military necessities of horses, arms and supplies in abundance, they got together to bring with them vessels of gold and silver such as men of rank are used to indulge themselves with in times of peace. Never up to that time nor later has been seen so much nobility so nobly equipped nor swelled with such arrogance. On that night you might have seen the English race, not in the manner of living angels but sodden with wine, vomiting up their drink and crying "Wassail and Drinkhail". The next day, having obtained a field best suited to victory, **the King (of Scots), their leader, having forbidden any to mount a warhorse.**' Chronica p8; BR p196

The Unknown in Scotichronicon [1314]: 'The king of Scots with part of **his foot soldiers** defeated the English and their cavalry along with their king. It happened near a stream called the Bannock.' XII, 21, p357, line 3; BR p202. [Why part? Because some were led by the Earl of Atholl to change sides and attack the monks of Cambuskenneth Abbey]

Baston [1314]: '**Rushing down the raging Scottish fighters advance on foot**', XII p373, line 168; BR p209

It is quite clear that every Scotsman is on foot. You could not take the risk of dismounting from a horse to kneel and pray and then remount when so close to the English just before a battle. Lanercost's report confirms the others. Seven reporters, many of them present at the battle tell us the Scots were all on foot. QED.

[Notice an important principle which we will see again: sometimes a reporter gives an insufficiently detailed report about some particular fact. The other reporters can tell us what the missing detail is. Here, *Lanercost* omits to tell us directly that the Scots are all on foot but he says enough for us to work it out and the result is confirmed by so many others that it is plainly correct. That is, because Lanercost has the Scots kneel to pray (very close to the English) we know that the Scots are all on foot. In fact, they were kneeling not to pray but to set their pikes and remain kneeling because that was the best way to receive a cavalry charge. Another is in the *Vita* which tells us of very many Englishmen being killed in a great ditch. Everyone else tells us the name of the ditch. It is the Bannock burn which Barbour half a century later says was so full of dead bodies you could walk over dry shod. The author of the *Vita* simply did not know the name of the burn and why should he? In a land without maps, a land foreign to him, how could he be expected to know that kind of thing? Vita was written in the year of the battle, probably within days of it. See BR p58-59. This is definite because the next section of Vita is about the inheritance of Gloucester's 5 earldoms which is then an unsolved problem within six months of his death.

Notice that the sources agree that Robert Bruce leads the Scots. Only Lanercost suggests that Bruce is not actually out in front whereas *Vita* and Trokelowe and Baker and Scalacronica say that he is leading. The two wings of the Scots (led by Randolph on the left and Douglas on the right) said by Lanercost to be ahead of the centre are probably not much ahead. But ahead they must be for the detail is significant and must be believed because it is stated: you do not make up that kind of thing. The reporter to the monk of Lanercost probably saw the colours of Edward Bruce leading the centre division and took them to be Robert's, because Robert was hidden from view being so close to the English cavalry lines that he could not be seen from where the reporter stood on the edge of the Knoll. Note: if Bruce were to have been killed in the approach (by a lucky shot from an archer, say), his brother would then have led the whole army.

Either *Vita* and Trokelowe do not think this significant or they were not so placed as to be able to notice it. The small contradiction is resolved if, though Bruce's schiltrom is in the centre, Bruce himself is leading the whole force farther out than the wings. Even if Bruce is within the centre at its front, as the translation has given, he is still seen as leading by *Vita*, Trokelowe and Baker. To marshal his men into their final position to dig in before the expected charge, the best place for Bruce to be was out in front of everyone, yet still leading his division, the greatest, in the centre. Only out in front could he see both wings fully and be seen by their leaders. That, then, is what the totality of information on this point provides. Bruce would decide when the Scots would start their march and when they were close enough to the English. He really had to be out in front to be able to control the two wings, each (excluding the centre) about 200 yards long. He controlled them by providing a focus, for they could see him in the centre. Signalling was unnecessary. Bugle calls would have alerted the English from their sleep after their carouse. Arm waving was a waste of time. The three divisions lined up at the foot of Balquhiderock Wood in orderly ranks, each commander walking along their front eyeing everyone, but silent. Then Bruce marched out to the front, turned and surveyed them and, satisfied, then, with his standard fluttering in the breeze, he marched off. The two wings set off, because their commanders followed Bruce in marching into the Carse. The centre division set off after Bruce, commanded by his brother, behind Robert, leading the whole army. That was the critical point of the battle. Would the men follow their commanders into the Carse? A lot of brave men would be in the front row. They would march off. How could those behind remain? Unthinkable. These men were mainly warriors come to defend their country. But Bruce would cover this possibility with a back row, carefully chosen for courage. [See the marshalling in the Pikemen's formation Chapter XII GB.]

Probably, where Bruce stood still finally, was the point in the Carse where the lines were to stand fast. He would not have to signal anything or even say anything. The central division would come right up to where Bruce stood (arms outstretched perhaps, his standard held by a squire flying high would be seen right across the field) and the others would dress their ranks on the same line. Once that line was formed, the battle was as good as over, as Bruce would realise. The very suddenness of the move as well as the fact that the English had no unified overall command or way of transmitting orders effectively, would ensure that there was plenty of time for forming the lines across the Carse. What could the English do about it, with their cavalry in front? Nothing, except saddle up and mount and charge, all of which took time.

NB **Unless Bruce was out in front he could not make the decision to get his men up and march them closer and then reset his pikes. There is no question that this is what happened**.

Notice that Vita [1314], Lanercost [1314], Scalacronica [1314], Trokelowe [1314] and Baker [1341-] and Baston [1314] all agree that the Scots were all on foot. These are all English. If anyone should have seen Scottish cavalry, it was them. They saw no Scottish cavalry. The Unknown in Scotichronicon [1314] was Scottish. He saw all the Scots on foot. [That this is only part of Bruce's foot soldiers may refer to the fact that the Earl of Atholl changed sides and attacked the Scots at Cambuskenneth.]

The only source which disagrees that the Scots were all on foot is Barbour [1377] who wrote 63 years too late to know and had to invent a Scottish cavalry charge to explain a victory he did not understand. It is obvious that Barbour was mistaken. Twenty statements in seven independent sources, several written in the year of the battle, all affirming that the Scots were all on foot is a decisive weight of evidence. The map of 1314 and the tactics made this clear a fortiori. See BR p254

Note That Bruce led the whole Scottish army on foot is shown first in *Bannockburn Revealed* on p214, published in the year 2000. The argument has just become far more powerful over the years. The site of the battle and the site of Bruce's killing of de Bohun were also shown in BR. Plate 25a and 25b, after p408; p410-417; p137-138; p338-339 eg.

Bruce's masterstrokes are these:

I The Dryfield of Balquhiderock is a natural fortress whose wooded, mostly steep, slopes needed no defence. The entry to the Dryfield from the south is at Milton Ford where alone the Bannock burn, which is impassable up and downstream for a mile, is crossed by the main road, the only road from Falkirk to St Ninians at that time.

II The defence of the road (Day 1) was at Milton Ford, where there is a natural bottleneck at which only a few knights can cross at one time. A semi-circle of pikemen on the north bank would attract glory-hungry knights across into a space which was soon filled and they could not manoeuvre; and were easily repulsed.

III The English could not go left (west) because of the bogs (which they would know about from previous visits). The route to the Carse (NE) was inevitable, the only way forward to relieve the Castle (first, retreating back along the road). The English were bound to camp in the Carse, the best campsite for miles, out of bowshot of Balquhiderock Wood. Their cavalry were bound to take the best places for the expected fox-hunt of Scottish rebels, closest to these rebels. This camp was probably customary to the English who had been there often before because of its advantages.

IV Bruce moved his men off the Dryfield early in the morning of the 24th (Day 2) marshalled them at the foot of Balquhiderock Wood and marched quickly into the Carse to close it off and put the English in a sheep pen from which they could not escape because of the bounding streams.

V Bruce dismounted all his men. Mounted, they could not reach the Carse through Balquhiderock Wood which is mainly on steep slopes. They needed, above all, to reach the position closing off the Carse and then stand fast and halt the English cavalry charge. Once halted, they ceased to behave as cavalry and were easily pulled down and killed.

VI Bruce took his men as close as possible to the English cavalry lines to deprive them of space to get up speed to minimise their momentum and impact. Lanercost, Barbour, Bridlington and Abbot Bernard definitely tell us the Scots attacked (moved forward) after kneeling to pray: ie they moved twice and set the pikes twice; and they had plenty of time for the English were surprised.

VII The 830 yard stretch across the Carse in front of the pond is a second bottleneck. Only 830 knights can get into the battle at one time. All the rest of the English are kept out of it until it is too late and general flight by them occurs. Other knights charging behind the first 830 do no damage to the Scots. Once halted, all are easily pulled down and killed.

VIII The greatest of all masterstrokes is the pikemen's formation. Each man behind each other, a couple of feet apart to enable the pike to be manoeuvred in the gap. The pike to have its butt in the ground, so that the pressure of the attacking knight is taken not by the man but the ground. The men kneel down. Then they can manoeuvre the pike far more easily and they present less of a target to cavalry and archers both. Unless they do kneel down, the pikes cannot project ahead of the first rank to anything like the same extent. Also to make the pikes effective, the butt would have to be taken on the chest. If they kneel, 14 pikes (7 from each side) will hit the knight before his lance hits the front rank which it may never do, because the cavalry have been deprived of space to get up speed. Few knights would reach the front rank of Scots.

IX A further masterstroke (found herein) is the method for getting the entire Scottish army off the Dryfield and lined up ready to march in their divisions in the Carse at the edge of Balquiderock Wood. All the divisions slept where they would form up off the Carse, the centre in the Dryfield. Each wing of the army about 5,000 men (200 x 25 wide) marched quietly onto the Carse from their assembly points close to the bounding streams and turned, in the case of the right wing, to the left (Douglas) along the side of the front of the wood; the other (Moray) turned right and moved along the front of the wood. They stopped at markers. Douglas's right column and Moray's left formed part of the front row. The entire centre division moved down the centre of the wood (which is a lot less steep and free of trees because these are big there with glades between). Half went to the left and the other half to the right, nearly but not quite joining the wings. Because of the practice in moving in the dark and the use of rags and the hand on the shoulder of the man in front this was easy because it was midsummer day, when it never gets fully dark. The Scots were very quiet about this and marched a long way into the Carse, hidden by the dark background of Balquhiderock Wood on its slope. They were not noticed by the picket line of English archers until they were about 75 yards from the pond. Their silent approach took the English completely by surprise. Because of it, their unreadiness, a second move right up to the English cavalry lines was easy. There was nothing the English could do to prevent it. What is the evidence for this method of marshalling and Scots? The fact that when first noticed by the King of England and Umphraville on the Knoll, the Scots were in plain sight, kneeling close by. Others: Bernard de Linton, Barbour, Lanercost and Bridlington, knew about this too (GB p297-299). Trokelowe supports this (BR 192,193; Annales p84) for Gloucester is close to the Scots when he attacks, seen by the King and his other commanders. Vita also supports this for the same reason (BR p176, 177). That the English 'mounted in great alarm' (Scalacronica, BR p189, Max p55) shows that Sir Thomas Gray supports this. It means that the Scots got very close before being seen. Baston who was definitely present says the Scots having been far away were suddenly very close (Scotichronicon Vol VI XII p373 line 162: 'no longer remote but close at hand.' Vita also supports this (BR p175; Denholm-Young p53): Gloucester is watched by the English commanders when he attacks the advancing Scottish lines led on that side by Douglas. The evidence is therefore overwhelming.

NB The first seven of these masterstrokes were first revealed in BR published in the year 2000 (one of them in the Topography chapter).

Four reporters, some of them at the battle, all thought the Scots were kneeling to pray. Not so! They were kneeling because that was the best way to resist the cavalry charge.

They made the mistake because they were all clergymen. A mistake was made by them all, corrected now at a distance of eight centuries.

King Edward II made a similar mistake: he thought the Scots were kneeling to ask for mercy. Umphraville corrected him.

Question: Why was the Carse not a peat bog in 1314 as many people think?

Answer: Because Roy shows this Carse as flat ground without a bog in 1750. Since Roy shows all the other bogs in the area in magnificent detail: Halbert's, Milton and Skeoch bog and even mentions Livilands, though the map was unfinished at that place, we can be sure Roy is right about this. Roy's map is brilliant as to details. But clearing peat bogs did not begin until after 1767 [Hansom & Evans, The Carse of Stirling, p 71, Scottish Geographical Journal 116 (1)]. This clearing began at Flanders Moss, west of Stirling, several miles north of the battle area. How could this Carse have been a bog in 1314 when no bogs anywhere had been cleared until 17 years after Roy in 1750 made his map showing no bog there?

But there is an even better answer. This Carse could never have been a bog at any time in the past because of the two ridges in the Dryfield and the great crater 75 ft lower to the west of them. This means a stream in the direction of the Carse was impossible: there is no higher ground to the west to provide the pressure for a stream in the north easterly direction; only lower ground. Therefore a bog in the Carse was impossible.

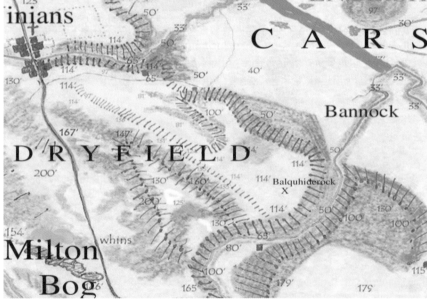

This map is a detail from the map of 1314 showing this area in GB p192. There could not even have been a stream at any time coming out of the Dryfield from any direction because of these ridges. Without a stream there would have been no water to enable the formation of a bog in the Carse. The thick line shown, is the battle line. Bannock, refers to the Bannock burn. The meaning of Balquhidderock is explained in GB and this spelling with 2d's eventually preferred because of it. There is a connection between this Carse and Balquhidder.

Question: Why is the line of the Pelstream in 1314 as shown on the maps?
Here below is a detail from OS 1923, used by Rev Thomas Miller, quoted from GB p96. The blue and red lines have been added. The blue line is the line of the Pelstream in 1314, the line on the ground determined by the sides of the deep wedge cut out of the land by the stream originally. To confirm this you must go and look, as many have since it was pointed out in this research. The part of it (not blue) to the NE is called by locals, the Pelstream and is so called on good maps. Today, the blue bit is underground in a culvert. It can be seen on Roy's map c1750. The diversion of the stream to Stirling in the Town Burn began about that time, signs of which remain in the woodland. The red area is an estimate of Livilands Bog in 1314. See Swimming Pond near Kersepatrick. In fact this is a conservative estimate of the size of Livilands Bog after the amount of prolonged heavy rain which preceded the battle. On such occasions, the very flat ground of the Carse of Stirling would have allowed the bog to proceed even closer to the River Forth. See the coloured version of the B&W below on p176 herein.

Question: Why are the written sources dated as given?

There are many reasons. How many details of a cricket match or other event can you remember after a week? A month? Six months? A year? 5 years? Very few, even after a week! After the Battle of Alamein those present remember little, even with films, tapes, records and maps. How much worse in the 14th century when none of these aides to memory were available? The key to understanding the reliability of historical sources is Prof Bartlett's work on serial transmission of a story, some of it experiments performed on Cambridge undergraduates. BR Ch 6,7. When a story is told or an event described, mistakes occur in the transcription. Bartlett found that after just one telling of a story even by the brightest people in the land, there were invariably mistakes. After a few repetitions, these multiply with every telling and after only seven, the story told was unrecognisable. The writer does not fully understand what the speaker is saying and gives his own interpretation. If some fact is not picked up correctly, the writer will often 'work out' what was meant and that is a source of error: inventions being made by him to make the tale intelligible and make sense. His experience, some of it very different, may colour the account that he thinks will be correct. The errors in the telling of the story not only increase with the number of tellings but also with the delay in the telling. The sign of a source writing close to the battle is high emotion, great grief at the loss of admired participants, even a writer repeating himself because he is so deeply affected by it as well as the presence of many details. For many details are soon forgotten. In a single week or a month, many are lost. As time goes on all details are lost. Within a few years this is so. This is why a source like John of Fordun, writing c 1380, can only remember a short paragraph whereas, a source like Vita, written within days of the battle has several pages of valuable information. Commonly, events are telescoped. Thus in:

Baker's Chronicle, a source that was not begun until 1328, the two days of the battle have become a single day; the pottes (the holes dug by the Scots on day 1) become conflated with the great ditch into which the English were driven on day 2 and drowned. Even so this source does contain some very useful statements. We know its value because these are confirmed by other sources written much closer to the event. Occasionally, a singular fact appears and this is often invaluable for it answers questions no other source does and should be believed because it does provide another piece of the puzzle which fits exactly. Baker was interested in archery and his statements about the failure of the English archers are like this: invaluable. We can believe them because they make sense, are consistent with all the other things we know from other reports and they tell us things that answer questions arising in the developing picture from them. Baker tells us why the English archers failed. They were positioned behind the cavalry who wanted the best places for themselves when the foxhunt of rebels began the next day. Behind the knights seated six feet high, and themselves presenting an obstacle nine feet high, the archers could not see the Scots at all. Worse, the Scots were all kneeling, impossible to aim, let alone to hit. Shooting had to be in a high parabola and arrows bounced off Scottish helmets. Soon, in frustration, a whole regiment of archers fired in the usual way and shot many of their own knights in the back. Of course they were told to stop shooting from those knights suffering from it at the front. The other thing that impeded the archers was that they were not on high ground and could not see. Worse, their shooting was impeded by other infantry and hangers on running into the space vacated by the cavalry so the space to shoot was not available. Does Baker actually say that the English archers were told to stop shooting? No. He does not need to. When a lot of knights high on horses have been shot and they and others are screaming, an order to stop shooting was unnecessary. Of course they stopped shooting. It is what anyone would do. BRp63-65; p195-199; GB Ch3 p60,61. How could you go on shooting when your arrows were killing your own men? Nothing you could do would enable you to hit Scots you could not see over the heads of your own men in front and very close to you. What else could you do but stop shooting?

Trokelowe's Annales ends shortly after the death of Edward II. However, what matters is not the date the book was finished but the date the words about Bannockburn were written. Of course it was written at different times, soon after the event. The source itself tells us they were written close to the battle. The unusual amount of excellent detail would otherwise be impossible. There is excellent confirmed detail about the Scottish approach. But one especially telling sentence: Trokelowe was angry with Gloucester for dashing into the Scots and thought him thirsting for blood. Not so! Gloucester was trying to prevent the Scottish infantry getting so close to the English cavalry that these would be unable to charge. It is Trokelowe's emotion that tells us this is written soon after the event. This source is definitely in 1314, within a few days of the battle. A year later, six months later, it would have been impossible to remember so much and the emotion would have disappeared by then. Trokelowe may have been unaware that Gloucester was the nephew of Robert the Bruce. That was partly why he alone dashed forward: knowing his uncle's audacity, he was quicker to see what the surprise move meant. BR p62,63; p191-195;GB Ch3 p58-60.

Vita Edwardi Secundi (The Life of Edward II) is likewise an excellent source who is likely to have known Gloucester, so grieving is he at his death. He even repeats himself, a sure sign of what it meant to him. Three times he refers to it, each time with grief and astonishment [p52,53]. In this case, the words are provably 1314, for the next tranche refers to the problems of resolving the inheritance following Gloucester's death, problems unsolved at the time of writing. See BR p58,59; p171-179; GB Ch3 p54,55. The very idea that this might have been written down years later is ridiculous. There is far too much detail and too much emotion. The sceptic should ask himself: how much he can remember of a rugby match (or some other event that lasts about an hour) after a few years. Very little! The author of Vita is steamed up about the matter when writing. That is, he has not even had time to absorb the catastrophe.

Scalacronica, though written down in 1355-7 by Sir Thomas Gray Junior, would have been first known to the author as soon as Sir Thomas Gray senior returned to Yorkshire when he would have related what he knew to his son. That is the reason for the great amount of detail, confirmable elsewhere. This would have been before October 1314, probably, for the most important Scottish hostages were returned by then. This battle would have been discussed endlessly by father and son thereafter, which is why so much of it is clearly correct. But we do have one man telling another. That is what Prof Bartlett was investigating. So it is no surprise that de Bohun's name is incorrectly given as Mountforth. Gray senior may never have known who it was. Why should he? He was captured a mile away and kept in captivity thereafter. Here there were not a reporter and a writer but a reporter and a listener and a writer: at least two repetitions of this fragment of the story. See BR p6,62; p186-191; GB Ch 3 p56-58. Here again the source is excellent and close to the battle because of the huge amount of detail. Sir Thomas Gray's reaction to being accused of cowardice [BR p188] and King Edward's brave conduct [BR p190] (which was reported to Gray since he was a prisoner at the time, probably while awaiting ransom) would not have been remembered by his son 40 years later without these words having been recorded very close to the battle after conversations with his father after release. Grey had to have written this down that same year to have remembered so much. That is why, closeted in Edinburgh Castle in 1355, he can still remember so much about the event in which his father was captured.

Lanercost (a priory near Carlisle) was probably written down by a monk at either the priory of that name or a collegiate one at Berwick or elsewhere not far off. Probably the story was told by an English or Welsh soldier who stopped there on his way home after the defeat. Who would have known that the Bannock burn is tidal? Sir Ingram Umphraville, for one: he had lands at Dunipace only 8 miles from the battle site. But it might be a number of people. The words in this case date from a few days after the battle, that is the most probable time. 1314, then. It is quite certain that English and Welsh troops from the battle would call in at monasteries during their retreat. The information definitely would be relayed to a monk at that time. It is likely to have been added to the document in the scriptorium soon afterwards. That the burn is tidal is a fact unknown to almost everyone else. That is the kind of thing that would ordinarily be lost very quickly with a delay in writing. BR p179,186; GB Ch 3 p55,56

Brut y Tywysogyon. This is 1314 because the document says it is. It is printed in GB p159 and in the book of the title by Prof Thomas Jones, Univ of Wales Press, 1952. GB p62, p159: copy of the text. It is quite unlikely that these words were written down even a month after the battle. The first person to reach Wales after the battle would have informed the monks and one of them would have recorded what he knew. Why must we believe this source? Because it is confirmed by John Barbour: he too mentions the pools as an important factor in the English decision to camp there, a valuable asset to have pools of fresh water available for men and horses to drink on a midsummer day. But the best reason is that this Carse and this Carse, uniquely, regularly has many pools of water after prolonged heavy rain. The source is confirmed by the place itself. There is only one such place in that entire neighbourhood. See it here on p226, p169 (colour).

Baston is 1314 because he was present at the battle and had already written a poem before it started which was derided by the Scots who forced him to rewrite it, a task he would have done within a few days. There is little detail precisely because he wrote most of it beforehand, despite the Scots. What does stand out is his terrible grief at so much loss to the English and the dishonourable reasons for it. That grief confirms his writing in 1314. This source is printed in Scotichronicon. BKXII 23 p367-376, BR p205-210

The two other sources in **Scotichronicon, the Unknown** and **Abbot Bernard**, are both 1314, as given by the editor, Professor Watt in the preface pxvi, xvii and other considerations such as the fervour expressed, the significant details and with Professor Bartlett's findings in serial transmission in mind. BR p66,68,69; GB p61,62.

Barbour's Bruce was written between 1375-78. The signs are that Barbour died in 1395 because a pension he had been awarded by the King which was transferable was then transferred to Aberdeen Cathedral where he had been Archdeacon. Since the average length of a life in those days was about 35, it is very likely that he had not been born at the time of the battle. He was forced to rely on the fading memories of a few very old men; and when things had been forgotten, he was compelled to imagine what happened, a source of important errors explained in BR,BP,GB. But in referring to the pools in the Carse as the reason why the English camped there, he performed an invaluable service for, with the Brut y Tywysogyon alone, the battle site is determined and, with a knowledge of the map of 1314 and the other sources, the tactics that were successful. His main errors are the invention of a Scottish cavalry charge that none of the half dozen English sources (who should have seen it) saw or reported. And the Small Folk; the same. No Englishmen saw anything of the kind. These were inventions by Barbour to explain what he could not understand. Neither is possible, for many reasons, already gone into in depth herein and elsewhere. Barbour knew there was a cavalry force and a cavalry commander. It never occurred to him that the Scots would all dismount because the ground, the plan, the tactics demanded it. A Scottish cavalry charge was impossible: the horses could not have got down the wooded slopes of the escarpment in the dark, would have made too much noise, would have awakened the English camp and spoiled the element of surprise. The idea of enclosing the English between the two streams would have been impossible with Scottish cavalry involved. Had they been seen charging, they were very easy to hit with a blizzard of arrows which the pikemen were not, especially when kneeling: these could not be seen by English archers because of this. The invention of the Small Folk was the Scottish socialist romance: the people get the credit. Bruce has to get the credit, most of it.

Making the Maps in *The Genius of Bannockburn.* [As in each of BR and BP, there is an area map: a map of the battle area, and 12 maps showing the different stages of the battle. These maps are justified: the reasons for everything in the map is explained and established as well as confirmed by independents. The maps and their justification show a development and improvement over the years from 1999 to 2013, due to further research. In each book there are many photographs and details from old and new maps such as Roy's (c1750) and the Ordnance Survey map of 1860 (pub 1865) as well as all the revisions of the OS maps and others like Thomson's, Edgar's, Jefferys' and Pont's. These explanations with photos and details from other maps are important in the justification. Thus the justification goes far beyond the topography chapter in BR. A great deal of BP is about this and in GB there is a full couple of chapters which reveal very deep and powerful arguments which explain the meaning of words like 'pulis' and 'polles' which are important and show that, for example, the Carse could never have been a bog at any time because a stream from the Dryfield to provide it was impossible because of the crater 75 ft deep in the centre and the ridges which prevent it. A stream could not flow uphill out of that crater. The two ridges close together at the NE side mean that there never could have been a stream at any time into the Carse, for there was no backing of ground to send water forth from it. For this reason, the amount of justification of the map is 100 pages in BR (50,000 words) 27,000 words in BP and 80 pages in GB (40,000 words): a total of about 117,000 words.

These maps took over three years full time to make. The first version in *Bannockburn Revealed* [BR] took a year. Roy's maps of Stirlingshire which in 1998 existed only in 2 maps that overlapped, only recently taken from the Queen's Library to the British library, had to be combined into a single map, known by this author as RMJ: Roy Maps Joined. This was an A2. Because Roy's maps were untriangulated [he was the first to promote triangulated Ordnance Survey Maps, and the first to make them possible by providing a standard starting line on Hounslow Heath (for which he was awarded the Copley Medal of the Royal Society)] a perfect join of the two overlapping maps was impossible. It is mathematically impossible to join sections of an untriangulated map. [To this day, the Roy maps in the National Library are shown unjoined because of this, which makes RMJ such a valuable map (available from the author). It is also much larger]. Nevertheless, the outcome is very good, the work of many trials. The two maps by Roy were made c1750, probably 1754, because they are unfinished, the last maps made before they were given to the Duke of Cumberland and afterwards stored in what is now the Queen's Library [now in the British Library since about 1997]. The problem was to make a map that applied in 1314. The first thing to recognise is that though Roy's maps are untriangulated, they are brilliant as to details. Indeed, it is a miracle that the maps are as good even geometrically as they are.

These perceptions have been obvious over the many years of study of the maps in connection to the ground and all the other available maps of the area; a study that has been confirmed by another enthusiast who has also spent years at this task.

To make the estimated map of 1314 from RMJ, everything that had been added between 1314 and 1750 was excised from the map of 1750 [RMJ]. The work of Rev Thomas Miller with charters was useful in this as was the ground as we see it today and all the other maps, especially the Ordnance Survey Map of 1860 and the several editions thereafter, such as 1896, 1913, 1923, etc and many books and papers of diverse kinds, such as the Statistical Surveys and the Surveys of Ancient Monuments. In that first two and half a year period, there would have been over 100 visits each lasting a day to the battle area just to understand the particular changes that had taken place. For example: what was the original line of the Pelstream? This took many visits to determine: it is clear from the wedge cut out of the ground by the stream: it goes directly into the Carse. Only in later centuries was it diverted to make The Town Burn, a stream that went to Stirling. That it originated (as seen in 1998) in a dozen springs on Gillies Hill (which has been changed by quarrying since then) was a sign that the Pelstream in 1314 would have been a powerful stream after rain which remained open even when crossing the main road, St Ninians Main Street, in 1945, being culverted soon after, a culvert that was too narrow for the purpose to begin with, for there was a water spout 40 ft high close to Mr Borek's garden, a Polish man who had lived there at the time and spoke to the author in 1999. BR Ch22 p322-417. The line of the Pelstream was important because it provided one arm of the enclosure of the Carse and one important obstacle to English cavalry trying to escape from Bruce's surprise move just before the main battle.[Plate 29a BR shows this line]

An important question was: what was the road in 1314? Since the first bridge was not built until 1516, it had to be across Milton Ford. Indeed, the line from Pirnhall to Stirling Castle is almost a straight line which goes along St Ninians Main Street, only diverging to cross the Ford, the only Ford, at Milton. The clinching fact is that right beside St Ninians Main street in 1242, the Kirk was built just 20 yards uphill from the Pelstream. Had it been anywhere else, the Kirk would have been built beside it to obviate the need to carry materials from the road to the new building, materials that would come along the road from many places.

Another vital discovery was that the hillock in the Carse centre, The Knoll, so called by this author, was not the pit bing supposed but the same hillock shown on Roy's map by his parallel lines, but mostly by the fact that the mill lade that crossed the Carse then had to have kinks to get around it. This was soon confirmed by Jefferys's map of 1746 which shows the Knoll in the right position and the right sort of orientation: it is a quarter mile by an eighth, approx. and 60 ft high.

Great efforts were made to understand what the woodland of the battle area would have been in 1314, a task that has continued for the 13 years since. As every detail was understood the reasons why the estimated map of 1314 had to be that way and no other were written down carefully like a lab experiment which could be studied and, if an error found, changed. This process has been continued. Thousands of significant details have been discovered; no errors have ever been pointed out by other people; two changes of little consequence have been found and corrected by this author in late books. This record was all the more important because the accelerating rate at which the battle area was being built upon at the permission and even encouragement of the Council was making the task of making a good map of the battle area in 1314 increasingly difficult. It is believed that the matter was caught just in time.

Why was it necessary to use Roy's untriangulated map as the basis for the estimated map of 1314 and not an OS map which is more accurate geometrically? Because Roy shows the bogs in such brilliant detail: Halbert's and Milton, especially. These drawings are brilliant, too detailed to be anything but an accurate rendition. They constitute an important defence for the Scots and deserved to be kept and recorded as Roy drew them, especially since no historian had ever shown them this way before. BR was published in the year 2000. The oldest OS map was surveyed in 1860 by which time the bogs had been drained.

After much more research, involving hundreds more visits to the battle area, the problem of getting Roy's rendering of the bogs onto a triangulated map was largely solved and so by 2004/5 a further book, **Bannockburn Proved** [BP] had been published. The reason for it is:-

One important move in BR was to find all the written reports of the battle and all other relevant material and get it translated and printed in one book. There every report could be analysed for reliability and examined simultaneously for each issue. Eg Was there a Scottish cavalry charge? It soon emerged that 7 sources, half of them written in the year of the battle, days afterwards, had 20 statements stating categorically that every Scotsman was on foot and that only one, Barbour, written after all these, 63 years later, thought there was a Scottish cavalry charge. [BR p254]. The truth was obvious: no cavalry charge of Scots, no Scottish cavalry at all that day, everyone was dismounted, for the tactics required it. It was also realised therein on BR p214 that Bruce led the whole army on foot.

Every question can be answered in this way and the procedure is matchless. Eg Did the English have high morale, or not? Every source but one repeatedly stressed the high morale. The reason for the difference has now been explained: they really did have high morale and that mistaken other source tells us how Bruce got his men to believe they could win. The chief motive for BP was to provide proofs of the important results, such as the place of battle and the tactics and reasons for the victory. Half a dozen proofs were produced, from a single sentence proof with a page of quotation and two others one of about eight pages of quotation from every relevant source, a new advance in this subject: when did a historian ever produce anything resembling a formal proof of anything? To this mathematician it was an obvious ambition.

However, the problem of making even better maps was addressed and the maps in BP were triangulated at the outset from an OS map in such a way that Roy's beautiful drawings of the bogs could be got onto the map. In addition, very many ground elevations were included, an important advance and, best of all, the ridging in the Dryfield was very carefully plotted. This showed, all by itself, how impossible was a battle on the Dryfield (Barrow's and Watson's opinion of the site). Other uses have been seen: the Carse was never a bog because there never could have been a stream crossing the Dryfield from west to NE because of the 75 ft depression in the centre and the pair of ridges which made a stream in that direction impossible. A stream in the past would have been necessary to provide the bog with water. No map has ever shown a stream; recent work has proved that a stream would have been impossible because of the depression and the ridging in the Carse. In 2012, a further book became necessary to include some important new research which took the matter far beyond the competence of the historians of the past. This was GB. The mistakes in translating two words [pulis and polles] in written sources by contemporary historians, words which had been correctly translated a hundred years before, in one case, by another historian, long dead, were explained and proved. 'pulis' = 'polles' = pools. [The mistake was to translate them as 'streams', an elementary error, based on nothing but speculation, which any native born Scotsman should have seen: how could 'pulis' in 14th century Scots mean 'streams'? Impossible! When the mistakes were corrected, this made a very simple proof of the battle site possible, another advance: this proof became just two short paragraphs in length.

SHORT PROOF OF BATTLE SITE:

1.The English camped in the Carse because of pools of water there (Barbour: Bk XII 391-395; BR 241). And,

2.The battle took place among pools of water (Brut y Tywysogyon Peniarth MS 20 version, p123 trans Jones, Univ of Wales Press, 1952). Problem solved.

In addition,

3.This Carse is <u>unique</u> in having pools of water regularly (GB p146, herein p142). And

4. Further, the English 'mounted in great alarm' (Scalacronica 55: BR 189) when the Scots advanced upon them in the Carse. So they were in their camp. And finally,

5. Most of the English were killed in the Carse <u>between their camp and the Bannock burn</u> (Scotichronicon; The Unknown p361 Bk XII 21; BR 203). QED.

The proofs in *Bannockburn Proved* (BP) were the first examples of their kind and made in 2004/5. These were greatly improved in GB published in 2012: lengthened and strengthened in several ways, even stylistically different. The aim was to include every relevant source in combination and the deeper research into the meanings of words in sources was an advance but nothing to compare with the structure of these new proofs which are paradigms of proof in history. Of course, working at the greatest depth, other insights could be included in these deeper proofs adding to their compulsive force. Three very valuable fresh insights were achieved in GB:

1. The work on the pikemen's formation was first done in GB; and that the Scots knelt not to pray but because that was the best way to deal with a cavalry charge and why this was so, backed up by quotations from the four relevant sources.

2. Showing how Bruce got his men to believe they could win: the resolution of the one discontinuity [See it in BR p254] in the sources: alone of six sources, Gray had believed the English were demoralised: not so. It was all explained in GB p235-237; 343-344.

3. That Bruce led the whole Scottish army on foot was shown with greater force: there are several powerful reasons, most of them sources. [This was first shown in BR p214 published (2000).]

A study of Halbert's and Milton Bog was made and it was soon shown that the top half of Halbert's Bog, after heavy rain ended up in the Pelstream, making it an even more powerful obstacle at the battle than ever realised before. The detailed work in Ch VI GB on polles, pulis, pows, pols and pals meant that the maps could be drawn with even more confidence, now that these things had been completely understood. In effect, very few changes in the maps of BP were necessary in the maps of GB. <u>By then</u>, the justification of the estimated map of 1314 had reached a volume of book length; about 80,000 words in all, in three books and it had all been confirmed independently by other able people.

The maps in GB are the best available and unlikely to be bettered because of the depth of research and the sheer quantity of insight and explanation carefully recorded and confirmed independently. Roy's rendering of the bogs is a very accurate rendition of his drawing and the triangulation is very good, as shown by the fact that several important measurements taken across the map are either exact or very close to what they should be. Of course the actions shown in the 12 stages of the battle are completely backed up by the investigation of sources and the proofs obtained in the several books of this work. Even the position of houses on the map of 1314 has been a matter of intense study, requiring an investigation of the population of the battle area. Since several independent calculations have provided identical or nearly identical results and since these have been confirmed by the various maps such as Roy's and the Ordnance Survey map of 1860, these maps are additionally valuable. Everything confirmed by able men. The idea of a justified map of the battle area first seen in this research is original and important. The justification occupies a volume of book length: 100 pages (50,000 words) in BR, an extra 27,000 words in BP and an update of a few extras in GB where the work of BP on maps and population is repeated and extended. Ch VI GB I also vital topographically. Another 20,000 words making about 150,000 all told. No map of a medieval battle should ever be printed in a work of history without such a justification; and no battle can be understood without such a map of the area at that time.

It should be realised that never before have the important results been proved in this subject, Bannockburn, at all. Many historians do not believe that proof is possible, even yet, 14 years after it was first available in BR. It has occurred because of the use of so many written sources quoted (some of them never seen before or because never translated or, worse, translated incorrectly), together with the finest maps of the battle area at the time, which have been both fully justified in every detail and confirmed by several people, all of them very able. The very idea of proof in an event in medieval history is a novel feature of this research which has been developed over 15 years. Everything about this research is exhaustive: every relevant source has been examined, rated and used along with every other; every feature of the ground has been understood and written up like a lab experiment. These characteristics will be found in all the books of this research: BR, BP, GB and The Summary of GB as well as herein. In effect, a whole range of disciplines: mathematics, science, psychology, cartography, hydrology, geography, Latin, Greek, Scots, French, philosophy as well as history, have been deployed together to solve the Bannockburn Problems. New procedures have been devised which are matchless:

1. Printing every source in one volume, translated, where they can be compared simultaneously. Settling every issue by comparing every statement, pro and con, in every relevant source and tabulating results. Many results are immediately clear with this. That the Scots fought on foot, for example. See BR p254 The ratio is 6 to one and that one was the latest source of all: 63 years later; the others were mostly written in the year of the battle.
2. Making a justified map, the work of years, every detail explained and confirmed by others.
3. Rating all the arguments.
4. Investigating every source for reliability, explaining and resolving discrepancies between them where they occur (rare) and dating them accurately.
5. Computing the population of the battle area and villages in it using the Statistical Accounts and Webster's. When independent calculations give the same result they are clearly accurate.
6. Testing extrapolations with the oldest and best maps, such as Roy's and the first Ordnance Survey map. The fact that there are only 64 houses in St Ninians in 1750 by counting them tells us there were about half that in 1314: a population of about 150; It cannot be much greater because a village on a main road between Stirling and the Capital must have experienced a gradual increase in housing as time goes on. So it must decrease as we go

back in time. This small population tells us that the woodland of 1314 was extensive because there were not the people to cut it down and use it: the New Park was still under wood after 1369 [Miller 1923, p61; Miller 1933, p35]. So it would seed everywhere.

7. The focus upon arguments throughout is a technique from philosophy and utterly compelling to anyone with a normal grasp of logic.

This is why laymen are far better at this than historians of the battle. Laymen usually have open minds, do not come to the issues with a baggage of fixed ideas they are reluctant to re-examine, have a range of skills; numerical, scientific, use reason in their work. Best of all, the layman has nothing to lose by it: his job, promotion, grants, awards and honours do not depend on it. So his ambition to discover the truth and promote it is untrammelled by self-interest: how will this affect me?

This research has:

i. Taken over two decades on one event, half of it full time.

ii Exhaustively investigated the entire battle area, writing up the explanations for all the important changes over time like a lab experiment using all the the maps and the ground: 150,000 words.

iii The most accurate maps ever produced: streams, elevations, ridges and depressions as well as escarpments, bogs and woodland, accurately and painstakingly shown.

iv These have been confirmed independently, the work of years, by others.

v The first fully justified and confirmed maps of the event and the battle, ever seen.

vi Every relevant source— letters, maps and reports— has been translated and printed within the books.

vii Every relevant report has been exhaustively analysed, issue for issue. The conclusions are overwhelming, the technique persuasive.

viii Every conclusion has been proved, often in several different ways, confirmed by several able people skilled in proof, such as Advocates, Sheriffs, QC's, Crown Prosecutors, Theologians and Historians as well as decorated Military experts.

ix What a proof in history should be and how conveyed has been a constant study, with improvements made in this novel technique.

x The technique of using quotations from primary sources like batteries of cannon is an important advance on the usual historical narrative with a few references. Here, every relevant reference is lined up like a cannon.

xi Every conclusion of interest has been rated for its compulsive force.

xii Every effort made from within to try and falsify this research has failed. It is difficult to see how it could be falsified.

What all these features reveal is that this research should count as science. Its conclusions are not a matter of opinion, though some historians do not believe anything else is possible, which is why they decline to read it with the necessary care.

The history community has never seen most of these maps before and some of the reports of the battle, none of which they have spent any time getting to know. They did not believe it was possible to understand the changes in the ground or to prove anything with the reports of the battle [See GB p 198 line 15 where Michael Brown is quoted saying this in 2008]. But even if they had known them, they would never have known how to put them together to prove things, that, too, is new. Up to now, historians have aimed to make an engaging narrative which proves nothing, leaving out all the maps and lengthy quotations that would help, giving only a list of references nobody bothers to check. Since they believed it was a matter of opinion, precision, depth and proof were never an ambition. So they have all been left behind, cannot even usefully comment because they do not know enough and are, some at least, actually terrified by mathematics even if it is only arithmetic. The idea that the difference between a pow and a dry pow in this Carse is that the first is 66 yards further from the river, is a precision which the unscientific historian will struggle with. The scientifically minded layman sees the point instantly and marvels.

The independent scholar, especially when he has gone beyond every academic whose light would be cast in the shade by it were he to approve, is in difficulty. Everyone expects historians to be the experts, even when their work is full of mistakes because they have spent little time on the problems. So the independent does not get read and his work is buried by the academics who see quite well that their errors will be exposed if it is ever noticed. But the essential problem is that ordinary people expect 'historians' to be able to judge best based solely on the belief that they should know what the independent, no matter the quality of his confirmation, is taken to know. Historians are not specialists, have many things to do, lectures to prepare, classes to teach, papers on many things to write, jobs to do, money to earn. The independent is different: he can devote himself for years to the task and achieve the deepest understanding of it. That is what has happened here. But the historian does not want to read a book like this for he sees instantly that it is very different, uses maps, photos and quoted sources galore in ways that can only produce conclusions that are unarguable, as many very able people have already confirmed. And because he is not a specialist it will take a very long time to plumb its depths. The most telling point is that for half a century there have been in the literature of the battle, by the best known historians, errors in translation which had been correctly translated a century before. And no historian ever noticed! And the books were on everyone's shelves. However, it is clear that historians are not reading this research; have not read it up to now. Why not? Because to do so is to lose control of the subject. They care more about their status as experts than anything. From this comes rewards, jobs, promotions, money, tv appearances. They prefer to act as if this research of two decades and all its confirmations does not exist. Any of the able laymen who have read it know far more than any of the historians of this battle who would fail very badly an examination set by any of us. A situation that is likely to continue, to the embarrassment of them all.

Bibliography (selected: see BR, BP, GB for more)
Baker, Geoffrey Le, *Chronica Galfridi le Baker de Swynebroke* (Geoffrey le Baker's Chronicle) Ed, E. Maunde Thomson, Oxford 1889.
Barbour, Archdeacon John, *The Bruce*, trans. Duncan, Canongate, 1997, revised 'corrected' 2005.
Barbour, Archdeacon John, The Bruce, trans Walter.W.Skeat, **1870** Early English Text Society, 1889, the 1968 reprint, OUP,1968 vol 2
Bower, *Scotichronicon*, Ed D.E.R. Watt Vol 6 Aberdeen Univ Press, 1991 for Baston BKXII, 23, p367-376; Bernard, Abbot of Arbroath BKXII, 22, p361-366; The Unknown BKXII, 21,357-361
Bridlington, *Gesta Edwardi Carnarvan*, Chronicles II Rolls Series 1882 [also trans in BR]
Brut y Tywysogyon, (Chronicle of the Welsh Princes) Peniarth MS 20 version, trans Prof Thomas Jones, with notes, Univ of Wales Press, 1952
Brut (Chronicles of England), Ed FWD Brie (Oxford Early English Text Society) 1, 1906
Gray, Sir Thomas, *Scalacronica*, trans Sir H Maxwell, Glasgow, 1907
Lanercost: *The Chronicle of Lanercost*, trans Sir Herbert Maxwell, 1913, facsimile reprint, 2001, LLanerch Press, Vol 2.

Scalacronica: Sir Thomas Gray of Heton, ed and trans by Sir Herbert Maxwell, Glasgow 1907.

Scalacronica: Sir Thomas Gray of Heton, Maitland Club, 1836.

Scott, W. *Why did we win at Bannockburn?* Article in *Quill*, 1993, 0952191008

Scott, W. *The Bannockburn Years*, (BY) 1998, Luath, Edinburgh.

Scott, W. *Bannockburn Revealed*, (BR) 2000, Elenkus. 0952191016

Scott, W. *Bannockburn Solved* (BS1) 2003 0952191013

Scott, W. *Bannockburn Proved*, (BP) 2005, Elenkus. 9780952191094

Scott, W. Bannockburn Settled (BS2) 2008, pub D Morrison

Scott, W. *The Genius of Bannockburn*, (GB) 2012, Elenkus. 9780952191087

Scott, W. *The Genius Summary*: Summary of the Genius of Bannockburn, (GS) May, 2012, Elenkus

Skeat, Barbour, Archdeacon John, The Bruce, trans Walter.W.Skeat, **1870** Early English Text Society, 1889, the 1968 reprint, OUP,1968 vol 2

Trokelowe, Johannis de, et Henrici de Blaneforde Chronica et *Annales*, Ed HT Riley, Rolls Series 1865

Vita (*Vita Edwardi Secundi*) : The Life of Edward II) translated by N.Denholm-Young, 1957, pub Nelson.

Maps: (selected)

The Battle Area map of Stirlingshire in 1314. In GB (The Genius of Bannockburn)

The 12 maps showing the stages of the battle in GB.

Jefferys, Thomas: Scottish Battles Folder-Falkirk, 1746-JEFFERYS, Thomas. A plan of the battle of Falkirk Muir..by an Officer in Batteraus, EMS.s.161 National Library of Scotland. This map shows the Knoll in 1746 and the roads then, one crossing at Milton Ford, the other at the King James Bridge (1516).

Roy, General William Roy: maps of Stirlingshire [c1750] National Library of Scotland. This shows the kinks in the Mill lade in the Carse which were necessary to get around the Knoll and the Zigzag Road across the Carse because of the pools that always form there after heavy rain.

Ordnance Survey Map of Stirlingshire surveyed in 1860 by Capt Pratt, R.E. published 1865 and revisions of 1896, 1899, 1913, 1923, 1931 etc.

Ordnance Survey Explorer 366 2001, 2007; Landranger 57 2004.

Harvey's Map of Stirlingshire shows the Knoll and the Zigzag Road.

The Status of this work

Some historians (and far more laymen who know nothing about it) will write off this work as a mere narrative, a work of imagination with no value as scholarship. The kind of stock response because they have not read it carefully and are too arrogant to think it important enough to deserve their time. For they are the experts, so they prefer to think.

Not so! When every account in a history book of this battle outside this research has been of the site in the wrong place (most), the tactics never explained, the fabled English archers (in their thousands) chased off by a Scottish cavalry charge of 500 light horse (which is impossible), Bruce on horseback (of course: when did kings ever attack an enemy on foot?-the truth!) and 4 Scottish divisions (Barbour) with Bruce's entering the fray last —of 6,000 men who defeat 20,000! A ridiculous idea demolished 14 years ago in BR p158, p302-318—of course this work is miles better than any of them! For this work is the conclusion of 23 years of scholarship, half of it full time, which has proved every material factor in the victory: Bruce killed de Bohun at Milton Ford (BR, pub 2000), led the Scottish army on foot (ahead of it **on foot**!) BR p214. There were 3 divisions of Scots. No Scottish cavalry were deployed because they would have been no use for the tactics: to leave the natural fortress they had defended and march to within yards of the English cavalry, who, overconfident and taken by surprise, could do nothing about it. The Pelstream and Bannock burn were essential factors in hemming-in the English within their camp BRp426, para 2, 3 and 4. None of this is opinion. It has all been proved many times, within the 5 previous books of this research in every one of which there are important advances of our knowledge of the event: longer and more powerful proofs using every relevant source, better and better maps which show, finally, the pools and the ridging with greater accuracy and show that the Carse then in 1314 was similar to today: no peat bog, no streams. The pikemen's formation which explains why there were so few Scottish casualties (GB Ch12) and how Bruce got his men to believe they would win (GB p270, p343). And the correction, at a distance of 8 centuries! of the 4 sources (some of the authors present) who say that during their march the Scots knelt to pray. Not so! They knelt because that was the best way to deal with a cavalry charge; and they got really close to deprive that cavalry of space to get up speed. Only the very stupid or those with much to lose by the dissemination of this will attempt to assert that these discoveries are untrue. Since this current book **has them all within it and even proofs of them in the endnotes**, of course it is a far better history than any of these by academics who understood nothing of value about the battle. **That it is presented as a narrative is an advantage, not a defect**. The exercise of imagination has led to further discoveries: how the Scots prepared, marshalled, formed up and how they got onto the Carse just before dawn in good order. And also, what no one ever considered before: how did Bruce communicate with the whole army and get them fired up? These could only have come from the effort of reconstruction. The answer, in both cases, had a lot to do with the ground. The ground that Robert Bruce in 1314 and the present writer, 8 centuries later, (despite the abominable building everywhere by the Council!) understand better than anyone else. The narrative is far better in other ways: it is easier to read. Anyone can read this and see how the various arrangements developed. Nigel Tranter would have loved it.

EPILOGUE

It is a particular pleasure to present this last book on the subject to my countrymen, the Scots. The first was *The Bannockburn Years*, published by Luath in 1998, the year after it won the Constable Trophy. That was a reconstruction of the events of the battle based on my knowledge at the time. One I remain proud of, for it has many original things.

This last book, my sixth on the subject, is another reconstruction based on a knowledge of the subject which, I am entitled to say, is phenomenal, a consequence of 23 years acquaintance with the subject, more than half of it full time work. My first book was dismissed because historians assumed I had not read their work. I had, and rejected it. My second book, *Bannockburn Revealed* (BR) was a very scholarly investigation with many original achievements: the first appearance of all the many sources, translated in one volume where they could be analysed—a procedure that was matchless: the conclusions compelling and wonderful; the first well-justified maps of the area and the battle: the justification took 100 pages. Above all, gathering insights and arguments to make and rate the conclusions. What made that certain of a quiet reception was my discovery, inevitable in an investigation of greater depth than ever before, of the errors of historians taken to be the experts. They wanted it buried. That was the point at which I decided that the only way forward was to fashion proofs of the main results. As a mathematician (as well as a philosopher, psychologist and scientist) this was natural. *Bannockburn Proved*, (BP) published 2004/5, was the outcome. There were half a dozen proofs ranging from a sentence backed up by a page of quotation to one of eight pages with quotations firing like batteries of cannon. This too was ignored by historians: even refused free by a university library because the person asked to vet it saw that it was inconvenient to his own less important work which he was about to publish.

My research continued: could other things be proved? Yes, it turned out that they could. The outcome was *The Genius of Bannockburn*, (GB) 2012. Even more errors by historians were discovered and established beyond doubt, some of them catastrophes. *The Genius Summary* (GS) was published soon after. The effort of burying my work by academics with something to lose by it, continued with greater force in 2012, 2013. About 1,000 new copies of my various books were donated to Oxfam (300 of GB and 320 GS). One of the historians who made the mistakes expressed his unhappiness in an Oxfam shop: tried to get them withdrawn; another, involved in Historic Scotland, the same. These actions are a measure, if one were needed, of just how important this research is. The latest ruse is that a company: 'Bookdonors', on Amazon (10.9.13) has offered 12 copies of GB for sale at a penny each. Since this says it exists to help the community, we must ask: how could it do so selling books at a penny each? Why is this being done? To obstruct the sale of books inconvenient to some people. Who would buy a book for £20 when it is on sale for a penny? Charity has nothing to do with it because it has nothing to gain. Where could the copies come from? Oxfam. A condition of my donation was that copies be sold only to individuals. Not hard to see what happened. Oxfam took the money…. Oxfam has since withdrawn all my new books from sale. I bought 2 from Amazon for a penny and had to pay the postage. They had Oxfam stickers on them. I keep them carefully and the packing. Most of them never reached a shop. They were bought as a group, paid for, probably by historians with something to lose, despite my pre condition of donation that they be sold in Oxfam shops to individuals. So much for the integrity of Oxfam and the History Community. I was buying back for a penny new books I had gifted to Oxfam for nothing, books that cost thousands to research and to print, the work done at huge personal cost for no other reason than that no one else had done it or could do it. Note: efforts were made for years to get the books of this research listed in the bibliography of the Battle of Bannockburn in Wikipedia, in vain. All the books that achieve nothing were listed. About a year or two ago, one book of this research appeared on the Wikipedia bibliography list: 'Bannockburn Proved.' Why? Because it was out of print: it was no threat. The historians in control are not gentlemen. They care far more for their reputations than the truth, in this case, the inspiring truth, the truth that would set Scotland alight if it were known for every future generation.

The idea then, among academics that an author should have only one book in the subject is shown to be false. Each advance here was partly the result of the obstruction of the history community to the previous book. It had to be proved and the proofs had to be developed so that they became very clear even to the most ossified historian, anxious to protect the cherished nonsense of his life's work of speculation. However, the ambition to answer deeper questions and discover more was basic. It had become clear at an early stage that if I did not solve these problems, no one ever would, because of the rate at which the battle-area is being eroded by building, partly caused by the refusal of arrogant historians to recognise my work and partly through the self interest within sections of Stirling Council. In this reconstruction, months after the second draft, an idea that is marvellous came to mind, just two days ago. A publisher and a friend who is a publisher, acting as agent, decided that the reconstruction needed to be jazzed up at the start to increase its readability and saleability. Some little thing that was exciting was wanted. A chunk from the bit that really is exciting near the end, was suggested. I tried this but gave it up. You have no business to try and create excitement at the beginning of a reconstruction: what you seek is reality, as near as you can get to it with knowledge and imagination.

Thus, I asked myself what Bruce would have done about the terrified Scots who answered his call to assemble at Torwood, a month before the battle? What would he say to them and how would he manage it? The outcome is marvellous! Not just what he would say but how he would be able to communicate with the whole army at one time. That, you see, is crucial. If Bruce were to speak to the army in small groups of 100, it would take him days just to get round 20,000 and he would have been worn out by it. Worst of all, he would have been unable to inspire anybody after a few efforts, would lose all his freshness and enthusiasm. That is the key to inspiring people: they need to be collected together in large numbers. Then, the ones who are inspired affect the inspiration of the rest who, left to themselves in a small group, would never manage it.

Then arose the question: was it possible for Bruce to speak to the whole army at once? And it is! What ecstasy to realise that there are three places in the Scottish position at the battle area, that are tailor-made for such a speech. One is in the Dryfield between the ridges. The best is in the depression 54 ft deep at the north east of the Dryfield where there is a natural amphitheatre. Bruce could stand at the centre and address all his men arrayed above him on the slopes which are not too steep. And though he would be only three quarters of a mile from the edge of the English camp, nothing would be heard or seen because of the great earthen slopes and the trees on them which lie between.

Did Bruce do this? Did he make use of this geographical feature so peculiarly advantageous to the Scots? There is nothing to tell us in the sources. But Bruce was a genius and a genius, confronted with the problem of communication, would have seen this. It would have been possible for him to fire up the entire army and send them confidently into the attack the next morning. Without this, the task would have been more difficult. Was it possible that the amphitheatre was so full of encamped troops, that he would not see it? No. The place is too far from water to be useful as a camp-site which must always be close to water. Bruce could not have avoided seeing it as the solution of the problem. He was there every day for weeks and for many days long before. None of the sources tell us how Bruce communicated with the army and the little they tell us of what he is alleged to have said is rather bland, not what was needed.

ACKNOWLEDGEMENTS

I am proud to acknowledge the help and encouragement of so many supporters who have become my friends, mainly during the years of this work. The aid of Tom McCallum, a friend from 40 years before, was essential, especially at the start, when I had forgotten my Latin. Tom translated many things and was on hand to produce answers quickly. He was also responsible for focusing my attention on the second ms. of Barbour's Bruce. Consideration of both produced treasure: a very short proof which is decisive. Donald Morrison's aid and hundreds of discussions were invaluable, detailed at great length in GB; a phenomenal help to a scholar working alone. Being able to talk to someone as enthusiastic and able as Donald was invaluable, even helped me clarify my explanations as he very occasionally struggled to understand them. He even had advice, as a teacher used to presenting material, on how it might be best presented. For years he devoted himself to these matters, his knowledge of them is exceptional and he has confirmed all the discoveries made to great depth. Iain Macleod, a friend from my days at George Watson's (where Dr Peter Jones, the Newcastle University Classicist, joint author of the Cambridge Classics Texts, also taught) was an invaluable textual critic, being a superlative poet and translator of drama. Though I completed two university courses in Classics and attended Peter's summer schools at Durham for several years the pressure to deal with the history was too great for me to acquire the degree of expertise I sought: fluency, of course. You cannot stop doing history to learn Latin. The history was primary. Since the landscape was being eroded all the time, the job had to be done fast, one reason for the haste in publishing and the (mercifully few) typing errors in the texts that arose. Even so, for all but a single year between 1999 and 2012, the work on this history was full time; nothing else was done (except Classics courses, summer schools and 3 novels that took little more than a month each). Rev Jock Stein, publisher and theologian, has been a vital force in this work, always encouraging, often criticising and occasionally falling out with my determination to produce full proofs (especially full justifications of the maps) and therefore knowledge, when it was thought impossible by every historian. I am quite certain I have succeeded, no matter what historians may think. Even so, a criticism of a proof in BP by Jock forced me to think again and the much better proof in GB was the result. Jock once settled a bill for me at the National Library and got commissions for two articles by me in the Scottish Independent, when no other newspaper would pay attention and he offered to try to find a publisher for this, always going to be difficult, for what historian given it to read and seeing the catalogue of errors exposed by it would want to yield his status to an outsider? The one they really hate is the idea that someone else has solved the problems they believe impossible of solution. They do not like the idea of someone stealing their thunder and will do anything to prevent it, even if it means burying the truth. David Torrie, an editor, has been a constant encouragement and proof-reader, even offering to pay for an artist to make the first map in 1999. Because the artist thought he knew better, he had to be fired and I spent years learning to make maps myself. Roger Graham (editor, journalist and author) has been a very encouraging presence, occasionally taking me to lunch to raise my spirits at the difficulties of getting this important work into the public domain and even writing and getting published two valuable articles about this work in Greenock Telegraph and Scottish Field the latter of which, alas, was mangled by the editor who thought he knew better. The traditional rubbish firmly lodged in any person of power always has an effect, despite so much effort at discovery, insight and proof which completely demolishes it. This fact in this case explains why original work like this is so badly received: every silly clot thinks he knows the answers already, because he believed all the rubbish he was fed at school. Angus MacCrury has been a remarkable encouragement: sending, me over the years, around £800 to help pay for my work, knowing my unaffordable expenses. John Dick has supplied much advice over the years and kept me on my mettle at times for he believed that there was a way of presenting this work whereby it would be accepted. Alas, he was never aware of the raft of meanness and downright lying that went on to protect a few elderly vanities. Col Bruce Niven, MBE, MA, SAS in his eerie on Everest or a Singapore high-rise, has also been an encourager who volunteered from afar a glowing tribute which convinced a few and may convince more yet. Dr David Simpson, Stirling, the late Patrick Cadell, historian, (ex Keeper of the Records of Scotland), Chris Jackson, English Crown Prosecutor, Sheriff DB Smith, advocate and historian, and Gordon McConnell, mathematician, have confirmed the value of the work and been very encouraging. Irvine